MODERN
TECHNICAL
WRITING

PRENTICE-HALL INTERNATIONAL, INC., *London*
PRENTICE-HALL OF AUSTRALIA, PTY. LTD., *Sydney*
PRENTICE-HALL OF CANADA, LTD., *Toronto*
PRENTICE-HALL OF INDIA (PRIVATE) LTD., *New Delhi*
PRENTICE-HALL OF JAPAN, INC., *Tokyo*

THEODORE A. SHERMAN

Professor of English
University of Idaho

MODERN
TECHNICAL
WRITING

SECOND EDITION

PRENTICE-HALL, INC.   *Englewood Cliffs, New Jersey*

Library of Congress Catalog Card Number:
66–15399

Printed in the United States of America
C–59877

PREFACE

The second edition of Modern Technical Writing consists of four parts: *Technical Writing in General, Reports and Proposals, Business Correspondence,* and a *Handbook of Fundamentals.* This is the same over-all plan that was used in the first edition except that the material on Proposals is entirely new.

The logic of such an arrangement is that the various skills which, combined, comprise skill in technical writing can best be acquired if first studied separately and then put together in the writing of reports or other longer pieces. The parts are so presented, however, that an instructor who wishes to take them up in a different order may do so.

In Part One the only change of pattern consists of the chapter on style being placed before rather than after the chapter on organization. This change was made because the skill or lack of skill in style affects the quality of many a piece of writing that is so brief as to present no serious problem in organization.

The most important new material in the first part consists of new sections in Chapter 5, *Special Problems*, dealing with *Analysis* and *Instructions*. Chapter 5, it should be pointed out, serves a dual function: It provides assignments calling for original writing that can be used while the study of style, organization, and mechanics is under way, and it develops ability to handle certain problems that arise during the writing of such major forms as reports and proposals.

In Part Two one major change has been made in the organization of the material on reports. In the first edition the special elements that occur in reports were covered in the chapter on *Formal Reports*. In the second edition these elements are covered in a separate chapter. This treatment is an improvement because either on the job or in the classroom a writer may need to use some or all of them before he is called upon to write formal reports, even though he may not use all of them in a single piece of work.

The addition of a chapter on *Proposals* in Part Two is the largest and most significant addition in the book, just as the concern with proposals has been the major new development in technical writing for government and industry in recent years. It shows the nature and importance of the major proposals on which the welfare of many a corporation depends, and it provides an opportunity to write simple proposals —thus giving valuable experience and pointing up the fact that at every level, proposals perform a key function in industry, government, and education.

In Part Three the major change is a revision of the chapter on *The Letter of Application*. Under its new title, *Letters Concerning Employment*, the discussion is better geared to a day and age when potential employers send representatives to the colleges and universities to interview potential employees.

In all parts of the book, new ideas have been added and miscellaneous changes have been made wherever it appeared possible to make the book better. The specimens are new, the exercises are new, and most of the subjects suggested for writing assignments are new except where the assignment was broad enough to allow the student considerable freedom in choosing his own subject.

Though the general approach to the subject of technical writing has not been changed, the effort to make the new edition as useful as possible has not been superficial. Since the first edition was published, the writer has traveled from coast to coast—a total of about 14,000 miles— to discuss the subject of technical writing with scores of corporations and governmental bodies in order to determine what skills in technical writing are likely to be demanded of the man on the job. He also consulted faculty members in numerous colleges and universities to see what kind of a book would best serve their needs. If this thorough-going study had revealed additional opportunities to improve the quality of the book, the changes would have been more extensive.

The number of people who have been of service while revision was under way is so great that it would be impractical to list them all, but a particular debt of gratitude is owed to the following: James Souther of the University of Washington; J. E. Buchanan, President of the Asphalt Institute; P. E. Haggerty, President of Texas Instruments Incorporated and Kenneth Brasted, formerly with Texas Instruments; G. A. Riedesel of the Washington State University Institute of Technology; Dr. Lynn Stauffer of General Electric; Robert Betts of Western Electric; Victor S. Casebolt of Washington Water Power Company; and three people among many others at Boeing Company—R. W. Jensen, C. W. Duffy, and W. W. McKissick.

The corporations and governmental agencies listed below were extremely cooperative. Most of them were visited in person, and the representatives interviewed gave generously of their time and provided valuable specimens. The list includes: The Allis-Chalmers Manufacturing Company, The Asphalt Institute, Boeing Company, The Bonneville Power Administration, California Packing Corporation, Carrier Corporation, Cornell Aeronautical Laboratory, Inc., General Electric Company, General Motors Corporation, Hewlett-Packard Company, Hughes Aircraft Company, Leeds and Northrop Company, Los Angeles County Civil Service Commission, Linfield Research Laboratories, North American Aviation, The Oregon Wood Products Laboratory, Pacific Gas and Electric Company, Pacific Telephone and Telegraph Company, Philco Corporation, Potlatch Forests, Inc., Space Technology Laboratories, Standard Oil Company of California, Texaco Incorporated, Texas Instruments Incorporated, Thompson Ramo Wooldridge, Inc., Tidewater Oil Company, Union Carbide Corporation, The United States Wood Products Laboratory at Madison, Wisconsin, Western Precipitation Corporation, Western Electric Company, Inc., The Weyerhaeuser Company, Washington Water Power Company, the Washington State University Technical Research Institute, and W. P. Fuller and Company.

The faculties of the University of Idaho Colleges of Agriculture, Engineering, Forestry, and Mines have given encouragement and cooperation at all times.

The exchange of ideas with faculty members at the following colleges and universities has also been stimulating and profitable: Los Angeles State College, Milwaukee School of Engineering, Montana State College, Montana School of Mines, San Fernando State College, Texas Technical College, Syracuse University, University of Michigan, and University of Washington.

T. A. S.

CONTENTS

Part One
TECHNICAL WRITING IN GENERAL

Part Two
REPORTS AND PROPOSALS

Part Three
BUSINESS CORRESPONDENCE

Part Four
HANDBOOK OF FUNDAMENTALS

APPENDIX

MODERN
TECHNICAL
WRITING

Part One

TECHNICAL
WRITING
IN
GENERAL

1

INTRODUCTION

In order to profit by a study of technical writing you will find it necessary to recognize one fact at the outset: Writing will be part of your work in the jobs that can do most to advance your career. Skill in writing must therefore be regarded as a professional tool, to be ranked on a par with the other knowledge and skills that will comprise your professional qualifications. If you can think of writing as something you will do on the job rather than only in the classroom—something you will use to convey information for practical use by an employer or client rather than just to demonstrate academic proficiency— you will have a motivation for improvement. And if you are motivated to make a genuine effort to profit from a technical writing course, you have every reason to expect that the time you devote to the course will contribute to a successful career.

No one who has been exposed to the comments of your future employers can doubt that the preceding statements are justified. In articles, public addresses, and personal remarks, high-ranking executives in industry and government have long been stressing the value of good writing in the technical professions. For example, in a personal letter one industrial executive has said, "To rise to an executive position one must be able to present his ideas effectively, first on paper and then orally. If the ideas are not presented well on paper, the chances are that he will never get a chance to present them orally." Another executive wrote, "Unless an engineer can write a good report, he might as well reconcile himself to something a little better than a drafting job for the rest of his life." And the chief engineer of a nationwide company has commented that if its field engineers could write more clearly, the company's long distance telephone bills would be reduced by about 25 per cent.

Why do men in positions of authority consider skill in writing so important? The reason is clear to anyone familiar with the postgraduation demands made on a worker with technical training. In engineering, agriculture, forestry, bacteriology, mining, metallurgy, public health, or any other technical field, writing is essential in almost every stage of every important project. Before work is started, the possibilities of a project must be stated and evaluated, and plans must be made in writing. When the work is under way, memoranda and letters must be exchanged as problems arise, and written reports must be made so that those in authority can learn how the work is progressing. When the project has been completed, the results must be recorded. Often, indeed, the only tangible result of a long and expensive project will be a written report; and if that report is ineffective, the benefits of all the time and energy expended may be jeopardized.

Since your writing will be important to your employers, it will also be important to you. Certainly it is one part of your work that is sure to reach the attention of your superiors on every level. If you write badly, not only will your weakness in writing be recorded against you, but your ability in other aspects of your work may be obscured. On the other hand, if you write effectively, you will not only receive credit for being a good writer, but will also find it easier to gain recognition for your other abilities. Many a person first catches the attention of those upon whom promotion depends by means of well-written reports; and unfortunately, many a person entering a technical profession finds progress more difficult because he had not realized the necessity of learning to use language correctly and effectively.

So much for the reasons that technical writing is important. Another question that may come to mind concerns the relationship of technical writing to writing in general.

Certainly the qualities cultivated in general writing are important in technical writing also. As a technical writer you will continue to work toward correctness in grammar, punctuation, and spelling; and whatever skill you have acquired in making your sentences and paragraphs effective will improve your technical writing. Sound organization, desirable in writing of any sort, is a matter of special concern; and the same might be said of clearness, simplicity, and directness of style. All in all, skillful, effective technical writing is built upon the foundation of skill in writing in general.

Still, general writing ability does not in itself guarantee that your technical writing will be satisfactory. Technical writing is governed by a sense of values that other writing does not usually emphasize so strongly; it often calls for the use of special forms, and it requires familiarity with some special techniques.

Dealing as it so often does with the sciences, regular or applied, technical writing sets an unusually high value on objectivity, meticulous accuracy, and restraint. It is directed to the reader's mind and makes little effort to appeal to his emotions. Its purposes are utilitarian, and it is usually intended for readers who already have, to some degree, a special interest in the subject matter. Consequently, though it places a high value on interest, it does not try to be so colorful and entertaining that it runs the risk of becoming flashy and superficial.

Some of the forms in which technical writing appears are the bulletins and pamphlets issued by experiment stations and government bureaus, and the technical or semitechnical papers and articles read at meetings or published in technical periodicals. Many of these forms do not have to be studied as separate types, but there is one form of technical writing —the report—that is particularly important and calls for special study. Though not every technical writer is called upon to produce all of the other forms listed, almost anyone who does any technical writing at all must write reports. Because of this fact and because reports vary so widely on different occasions, they are given special emphasis in this book. Special attention is also given to proposals, which industry and government have come to regard as immensely important in recent years.

As you work in any of the forms of technical writing, you will at various times need to give instructions, write a definition, explain a process, describe an object, or analyze a condition or problem. The problems that arise on each of these occasions will receive individual attention in this book.

You will also find it necessary, in technical writing, to know how to use numbered lists, tables, and figures. You will need unusual familiarity with the conventions that govern abbreviations and the use of figures or words for numbers, especially in cases when the conventions of technical writing differ from those that govern writing in general. You will need to acquire skill in the use of topical headings so that the reader can easily grasp the organization of your work and find what he is looking for. And further, since the soundness of technical writing must bear up under critical appraisal, you will need to master the process of documentation.

The treatment of technical writing in this book is divided into three parts. The first is devoted to matters that concern all forms of technical writing. Style is discussed first, because a writer's style can affect the quality of whatever he writes, even a memorandum of two or three sentences. Next, suggestions are made about organization. Succeeding chapters cover mechanical form, special problems, and the use of tables and figures.

The second part of the book is devoted to reports and proposals, which deserve special emphasis for reasons already mentioned.

The third section of the text proper deals with business correspondence. Though letters do not always have to do with technical subjects, they assuredly comprise a substantial portion of the writing demanded of almost anyone in a technical profession, and therefore merit attention.

The three main parts of the book are followed by a Handbook of Fundamentals so that if your general ability in writing is weak, you will have access to the information you are most likely to need in overcoming that weakness.

All in all, the material in this book should provide the help you will need in acquiring a reasonable degree of skill in technical writing. To be sure, neither a book nor a course can rapidly develop your full writing potential. Only long experience and extensive practice can do that. But study of the subject can at least do these things for you:

1. It can make you aware of the standards your future employers will expect you to meet—standards of accuracy and compliance with instructions as well as standards of writing;

2. It can familiarize you with practical, tested writing procedures;

3. It can give you a clearer picture of the manner in which writing fits into the total pattern of professional activity;

4. It can reduce the likelihood that at the beginning of your professional work you will form undesirable habits which will harden until they become difficult to break;

5. It can leave you a better writer than you were before; but even more important,

6. It can lay a foundation for self-improvement in the future, so that your skill in technical writing, like your other professional skills, will steadily increase as your career continues.

One final comment is in order. In the present day and age, characterized as it is by rapid change, questions are constantly raised about whether various time-honored courses justify retention in one or another college curriculum. Authorities tell us that in some fields what is learned now will be out of date in ten years. Yet no one has been heard to say that *writing* will cease to be an essential skill; and though language is not static, you may take comfort in the fact that skill in writing acquired today will not become outdated.

Thus the ability to write effectively is well worth the time you will spend in acquiring it. Long after some of the things you are learning have ceased to be useful, you will still be using whatever ability you have acquired in using the English language. It would be an overstatement, perhaps, to say that a career in a technical profession will be impossible if you cannot write effectively. It is no overstatement, however, to say that weakness in writing is a handicap that will weaken your qualifications for many desirable positions, and that skill in writing is an asset that can make your professional advancement faster and easier.

2

EFFECTIVE
STYLE

Many an inexperienced writer gives little thought to style, concerning himself only with getting his ideas down on paper without making errors. If you adopt this attitude—if you think of style as merely an ornament—you are neglecting one of the major opportunities to make your writing more effective. Of all the weaknesses that annoy those who read technical writing, ineffective style is one of the most damaging.

What do we mean by style? It is style that makes the difference between the enthusiasm of a patent medicine advertisement and the restraint of an article in a medical journal, or between the fervor of an attorney pleading a case and the analytical impersonality of a judge in his charge to the jury. In short, style concerns not what a writer says but how he says it.

In technical writing you will not need to develop a distinctive personal style. Rather, you can concentrate on such qualities as clearness, directness, conciseness, and readability. Your style should ordinarily be neither so informal as to sound unprofessional nor so excessively formal as to sound stilted. It should lean toward restraint, for though a reasonable degree of enthusiasm is sometimes an asset, an excess suggests bias. It should not be charged with emotional intensity, for it usually deals with questions that are answered by the mind rather than by the emotions.

Yet even in the limited context of technical writing the subject of style is elusive. A long list of desirable qualities compete for attention. This list includes not only those mentioned—clearness, directness, conciseness, and readability—but also simplicity, precision, and specific, concrete, understandable diction. Some of these qualities overlap. Some of them are the result of others. (For example, readability and clearness are the end results of attention to directness and simplicity.) Also, unfortunately, an excessive effort to attain one quality may cause the loss of other qualities equally desirable. (For example, up to a certain point conciseness improves readability, but carrying conciseness too far will make your writing less readable.)

This chapter will concentrate attention on what you can actually *do* in order to make your style more effective. At a working level, you have two major questions to think about as you try to improve your style: *How can I be sure that my choice of words will make my style more effective?* and *How can the construction of sentences make my style more effective?*

The two sections that follow are based on these questions, but the subject of conciseness involves both diction and sentence structure to such an extent that it is discussed separately in a third section.

EFFECT OF DICTION ON STYLE

If your diction is to do its part in making your style effective, you will need to bear in mind the following points until you can apply the right principles automatically:

Avoidance of stiff, pompous language
Avoidance of needlessly technical language
Use of concrete, specific language

Avoidance of Stiff, Pompous Language

One of the main reasons that style in technical writing often becomes ineffective is that writers, perhaps subconsciously, try too hard to be impressive. Consequently they sound stiff and pompous, producing a style that at best is ostentatious and at worst becomes needlessly hard to translate into concrete meaning.

A technical writer's style is pompous when he uses such expressions as *increase the visibility of the incandescent gases* when he might say *make the flame easier to see,* or *has a deleterious effect upon* rather than *harms* or *injures* or *damages.* Some writers cannot resist the temptation to use *optimum* when *best* would convey the idea, or *finalize* when they might use *complete.* A practicing engineer once produced the expression *minimize the expenses to an optimum degree.* (Why not just *hold expenses to a minimum?*) The classic example of a rebuke to such ostentation occurred when President Roosevelt, looking over black-out instructions during World War II, crossed out *terminate the illumination* and substituted *turn out the lights.*

Pompous style also results from the inordinate tendency of many writers to resort to words like *characteristic, property,* and *condition.* The result is such phraseology as "It possesses the quality of malleability" instead of "It is malleable"; or "It lacked the property of hardness" instead of "It was not hard enough" (or "It was too soft"); or again, "It passed into a solid condition" instead of "It solidified."

Avoidance of Needlessly Technical Language

Technical language has come into existence because it is often needed for clear, effective communication. A single technical term will frequently convey an idea that would otherwise call for a long phrase or clause; and there are some subjects that it would be almost impossible to discuss without using technical terminology.

Nevertheless, technical language should not be used when it can be avoided. The purpose of writing is not just to get a message down on paper, but to get it into the mind of the reader; and you cannot safely assume that your reader will always possess your own specialized vocabulary. One of the most common complaints against technical writing is that those who produce it apparently believe that everyone who reads it is a specialist in the subject.

Moreover, the best authorities on writing agree that even when you are writing solely for technically trained readers, it is best to use technical language only when you need it. It is not good style to use *ozostomia* when you might say *bad breath,* or to refer to *imbricate scales* when you might call them *overlapping. Scutellate* could be replaced by *flash* on almost any conceivable occasion. And the writer who wrote *reducing the mean diameter of the spray spectrum* might better have used *making the spray finer*—and saved himself the embarrassment of having his style ridiculed in a technical magazine.

The warning against overly technical language applies not only to words that are formally correct, but also to the technical jargon that specialists in any line of activity use when they talk informally among themselves in a shop or laboratory. Such terms as *woofer* and *tweeter* (common among hi-fi addicts) are examples. *Hardware,* when applied to the intricate mechanisms used in probing outer space, is another. To be sure, such language may lend flavor to a popular article and is entirely natural and unobjectionable in personal conversation or informal memoranda with limited distribution. But it is not suitable when standard English is called for, and you may be sure that the conversational language used by a scientist in the laboratory seldom appears in his technical articles or reports.

Use of Concrete, Specific Language

In any writing, technical or otherwise, concrete and specific language makes a writer's style more vigorous and colorful. In technical writing it is especially desirable because it not only increases liveliness but also gives information more effectively and reduces the likelihood of vagueness.

Concrete and *specific* are not identical in meaning, as you can see when you consider their respective antonyms, *abstract* and *general.* But in a practical effort to improve your style you can try, at the same time, to find words that are both concrete and specific.

The improvement that can result from such an effort can be seen by comparing the following specimens.

ABSTRACT AND GENERAL: We are taking precautions against fire.
CONCRETE AND SPECIFIC: We are installing fire doors and an automatic sprinkler system.

ABSTRACT AND GENERAL: We plan to make the laboratory comfortable and will make provisions for shutting out the noise from the shop.
CONCRETE AND SPECIFIC: We plan to air-condition the laboratory and to soundproof its walls.

ABSTRACT AND GENERAL: We used chemical-control methods to prevent weeds from growing in the tract.
CONCRETE AND SPECIFIC: We sprayed the tract with a mixture containing 2,4-D to kill the weeds.

Technical writers must constantly make this kind of choice. Note the contrast in these additional examples.

Abstract and General	Concrete and Specific
receptacle	jar, beaker, can, box
transfer a liquid	pump, pour, siphon a liquid
poor driving conditions	icy roads
malfunction (of a motor)	loss of power, running hot, vibrating
obtain	buy, rent, requisition

As we will point out later, use of the concrete, specific diction recommended above is not only valuable for its own sake, but also because it contributes to directness.

Vagueness is a serious defect in technical work. Often, to be sure, vagueness is not just a matter of style. You will sometimes be tempted to write vaguely in a conscious or unconscious effort to conceal your lack of specific information. Yet there will probably be times when you have enough information to avoid vagueness but may neglect to use that information. You may tell us, "*Small* samples are taken at *frequent* intervals," when you know the facts well enough to say, "Samples of *100 cc* are taken at *half-hour* intervals"; or you may write, "A *fairly large* piece of steel is placed in the machine," when you might have written, "A *12-inch* piece of steel." Or you might use, "The pouring of concrete is *seriously* behind schedule" when you might have used "*three weeks* behind schedule."

This last example brings up another consideration. The engineer who supplied it commented, "I want my people to tell me the objective facts; I'll draw my own conclusions about whether three weeks is or is not a serious delay." His attitude should not be taken, however, to mean that *interpretation* of specific facts is never desirable. Sometimes interpretation is really needed. Someone might be told that a certain number of pounds of soil per acre had been lost because of erosion, and be unable to judge whether the amount was alarming. Consequently, a writer might do well to add that this loss amounted to half an inch, and that the loss was serious because the topsoil was only ten inches deep. The significant point is that in offering this interpretation a writer would be providing *additional* objective facts rather than omitting them in favor of vague expressions or unsubstantiated interpretation.

EFFECT OF SENTENCE STRUCTURE ON STYLE

In discussing the effect of sentence structure on style we shall not concern ourselves with the damage done by errors in fundamentals of English. It is true, of course, that such errors often affect style—for example, by reducing clearness—but they are covered in the Handbook. In dealing with the question of how to make sentences not only correct but also effective, we will consider sentence length, simplicity and directness, precision, and the choice between active and passive voice.

Sentence Length

Avoidance of Excessive Length. Though some long sentences are clear because of their simple construction, there are many times when the use of shorter sentences could make some piece of writing clearer and easier to read. The following example shows how confusion was created by an effort to jam too much into a single sentence.

> Cold work, proceeding by a complex process of slip, either alone or accompanied by twinning, within the grains or movement between the grains, always results in a distorted or disrupted crystalline structure, a marked increase in both hardness and strength, and a decrease in workability.

Note how clearness is improved by the use of two sentences:

> Cold work always results in a distorted or disrupted crystalline structure, a marked increase in both hardness and strength, and a decrease in workability. This holds true whether the work proceeds only by the complex process of slip within and movement between the grains or whether the process of slip is accompanied by twinning.

Long sentences are not always so involved as the preceding example. Sometimes they are merely stringy. Stringy sentences may not be especially hard to read, but breaking them up will result in more satisfactory style. The following example was taken from a student's paper:

> These figures for the pressure, temperature, and length of cooking time are not hard and fast, never-deviating figures, but are changed slightly from day to day, depending on reports from the testing room, where samplings of the corn are taken for testing to determine the best cooking procedures for the corn then being processed, because the grades change from field to field and the corn is not of the same consistency throughout the canning run. (One sentence, 76 words)

To improve it may necessitate some rearrangement, but the effort of rearranging is justified. One improved version might be:

> These figures for the pressure, temperature, and cooking time are not constant, for the grades of corn change from field to field and the consistency of the corn is not the same throughout the canning run. Consequently, samplings are taken to the testing room, where the best cooking procedures for each particular lot are determined. Thus it is possible to adjust the process of cooking so as to obtain the best results.

Avoidance of Primer Style. In the effort to avoid making your sentences too long you should not go to the other extreme and use "primer style." An excessive number of extremely short, simple sentences causes writing to become jerky and monotonous. Moreover, it does not necessarily result in clearness. Each sentence, it is true, may be clear; but the relationship of the ideas contained in the individual sentences is often hard to perceive. The primer style forces the reader to combine for himself the ideas that the writer should have combined for him. Also, it necessitates the repetition of words and thus destroys conciseness.

Note how, in reading the following examples, you are slowed up by being forced to come to a full stop too often.

Primer Style

1. These bacteria multiply rapidly. Their multiplication causes a pressure to be exerted against the sides of the can. The pressure builds up until it is at last extremely high. Finally it becomes so great that it bursts the can apart at the seam.

2. Various names have been proposed for the disease. Of these, "pole blight" has come to be accepted. This is because the disease is most destructive to pole-size trees. It is trees between the ages of 40 and 100 years that are attacked. These are the age classes that are already deficient when future cuttings are being planned on a sustained-yield basis.

More Mature Style

1. These bacteria multiply rapidly and cause a pressure inside the can that increases until it bursts the can apart at the seam.

2. Various names have been proposed for the disease, but "pole blight" has become accepted because the disease is most destructive to pole-size trees. These trees, which are 40 to 100 years old, are in the age classes that are already deficient when future cuttings are planned on a sustained-yield basis.

To sum up the matter of sentence length: Some sentences should be short, some long, some medium. It is very easy, however, to fall into a habit of making all the sentences similar in length and type, and care is necessary to prevent such a pattern from forming.

Simplicity and Directness

Simplicity and directness are closely related—so closely, in fact, that when a passage is simplified it usually becomes more direct as well. The present discussion will not try to draw a line between the two, but since each of them includes certain ideas not included in the other, they will be discussed separately.

Simplicity. Simplicity is important in diction and in sentence structure. It has already been covered in connection with diction, so here we shall be concerned with sentence structure only.

No one would build a complicated mechanism to do a job that a simple mechanism could do equally well, nor analyze a specimen by a complicated method if a simple method would get the same results. By the same token, no one should express an idea by creating a complicated grammatical construction when a simple form would serve the purpose equally well. When you can substitute a word for a phrase or a phrase for a clause or sentence without sacrificing anything of value, you will usually improve your writing by doing so.

For example, consider the sentence, "The next step consisted of looking for methods by which the losses that occurred in the bearings might be eliminated." This could be simplified to read, "The next step consisted of looking for methods of eliminating the losses in the bearings." Or consider, "A series of continuous runs made under conditions that were identical often yielded results that were different." This might just as well be, ". . . made under identical conditions often yielded different results." In each case the sentence was simplified by cutting out two clauses—clauses that did not make the relationship of ideas one whit clearer than they could be made by a simpler form.

The effort to write simply should not be limited to avoiding needlessly complicated sentences. A passage may consist of relatively simple sentences yet be too elaborate in its general approach. For example, note the following passage: "The process was performed in two steps. The first of these consisted of drying the sample, and the second consisted of weighing it." A simpler style would use only one sentence: "The process consists of two steps—drying the sample and weighing it."

To be sure, if the list of steps were longer and if some or all of the steps could not be expressed briefly and simply, it might be necessary and desirable to introduce the list more elaborately, but for a short list of brief items, a simple approach is adequate.

It is possible, of course, to carry simplicity too far. The writer who substituted *variable elimination* for *elimination of variables* and *concrete information* for *information about concrete* reduced a phrase to a word in each case but in doing so became ambiguous. Similarly, the writer who used *one way of determining system applicability* for *one way of determining the applicability of the system* simplified the grammatical construction but sacrificed readability. Usually, simplifying the structure of a sentence makes it clearer and more readable; but when it produces the opposite effect, it is not desirable.

These examples achieve their simplicity in a manner that calls for additional comment. In each case the sentence was simplified by converting a noun into an adjective. It is true that the English language contains a great many words that can be used as either; but some technical writers go to fantastic extremes and make adjectives out of nouns that are not used in such a manner by the vast majority of literate people. As a result they develop an annoying mannerism that makes it more difficult for them to communicate with the rest of the world and irritates even many of those who understand them.

Directness. Directness, like simplicity, calls for attention to sentence structure. Consider for example the following indirect sentence: "There are parts of the report in which his statements have been influenced by his feelings." The main statement is, "There are parts." The main *fact,* however, is that a writer's feelings have influenced his statements in a report. To make the style direct we might write, "The report contains statements that have been influenced by his feelings," or "He has made statements in the report that have been influenced by his feelings." Each of these direct versions, you will notice, has a meaningful subject and a meaningful verb.

You might take the following suggestion as a formula for directness: Ask yourself, "What do I want to make a statement about?" and let the answer to this question tell you what your main subject should be. Ask yourself, "What do I want to say about it?" and let your answer tell you what your main verb should be.

Consider the result of applying this formula to some additional sentences:

> It must be expected that there will be complaints from people who live in the neighborhood.

> A recent article makes the statement that before 1950 Cuban reserves of manganese had been exploited almost to the point of depletion.

Directness in style would suggest:

> Complaints from people who live in the neighborhood must be expected.

> Before 1950, according to a recent article, Cuban reserves of manganese had been exploited almost to the point of depletion.

You have probably thought of other versions that would be just as direct. The significance of your being able to do so becomes apparent when two more sentences are considered.

> The new alloy is harder than the one we have used in the past.

> The alloy we have used in the past is softer than the new one.

These two sentences give us exactly the same fact, and they are equally direct. They differ, however, in one respect: the first makes a direct statement about the new alloy and incidentally gives information about the old. The second makes a direct statement about the old alloy and incidentally gives information about the new. As sentences, they are equally direct; *but they are not equally direct about the same thing.* A writer's choice between them should depend on which alloy he is primarily attempting to discuss. In other words, directness is more than just a matter of sentence structure without regard to purpose. It is also a matter of presenting the facts as they bear upon our purpose in writing and the reader's probable reason for reading.

Differences like the one illustrated may seem trivial when we look at only one or two sentences, but many an article or report has extended passages in which the writer seems to have gone off on a tangent because the facts about his real subject are presented only indirectly in sentences that are *direct* statements about other matters. The formula offered above reduces the likelihood that you will obscure your point by this particular kind of indirectness.

Indirectness may result not only from a poorly chosen subject, but also from a poorly chosen verb. By using a weak, general verb a writer may then be forced to work in the verb idea as a noun or adjective. For example, he might write:

make an adjustment instead of *adjust*

engage in a discussion instead of *discuss*

give consideration to instead of *consider*

put on a demonstration of instead of *demonstrate*

achieve an improvement in instead of *improve*

This is not to suggest that you must express *every* idea as a direct statement. If you do, you will make it hard to distinguish between the important and the less important. Consider for example: "We are now using the process described in the enclosed leaflet. It is a continuous-flow process. Last year we used the batch process." Every fact is expressed directly, but it would be better to write, "We are now using the continuous-flow process described in the enclosed leaflet rather than the batch process that we used last year." The revised version is more effective because it is a direct statement of the major idea, which stands out distinctly because lesser matters are referred to in an incidental manner only.

Precision

All too often the subject of precision is approached as if it concerned no more than the use of words with correct understanding of their meanings. Writers are warned, for example, not to confuse *imply* with *infer,* *liable* with *likely, fix* with *repair,* or *unique* with *unusual.* Most of the discussions along this line contain valid and useful information—unfortunately combined with many refinements that are based on textbook traditions rather than on first-hand observation of actual usage.

So far as such questions of general vocabulary are concerned, the Glossary of Usage at the end of the book covers this aspect of precision in enough detail to guard against the most likely errors. It includes the textbook favorites because there are still many people who value these traditional distinctions.

Precision in the use of technical terms is not covered in the Glossary because each line of work has its own extensive technical vocabulary. The most that a general discussion can do is to alert you to the need for mastering the meaning of each term in your field as you encounter it, and to urge that if you do much writing in a field where terminology is rapidly changing and developing, you invest in any special publication that lists and defines the terms you must use. Also, don't underestimate the help that you can get from the latest dictionaries—unabridged or even collegiate. And don't underestimate the extent to which you make yourself look immature if you use technical language incorrectly.

But precision is more than just a matter of words; it is also a matter of sentence structure. Many a writer who knows the meaning of each word that he uses will construct sentences that do not actually say what he intends. Consider for example the statement, "Test plots using various species give an average range of life of 19 to 25 years, with a probable average of 22 years." According to this sentence, it is the *plots* that use the species and give the results. But in point of fact, the plots neither use the species nor give the results. It is the tests, not the plots, that give the results and it is the scientists performing the tests who use the species. One way of expressing the idea precisely—certainly not the only way— would be, "Tests of various species, each performed on a separate plot, indicate that the range of life is 19 to 25 years and that 22 years is the probable average."

Another example of lack of precision is the sentence, "The material should be of a hardness and a toughness that will possess good wearing properties." According to this sentence, the hardness and toughness *possess* wearing properties. In point of fact, they *are* properties. A precise restatement would be, "The material should be hard enough and tough enough that it will wear well."

Objecting to lack of precision in sentence structure is not just quibbling about trivial details. A sentence that lacks precision in structure is like a photograph taken by a camera that is not properly focused. We may be able to see the picture, but the blurred lines are annoying and distracting. It is a writer's job to say exactly what he intends to say rather than just coming close enough to the intended meaning for his reader to figure it out. And the major reason for failure to do this job is writers' failure to check their own work carefully enough to notice what they have said—or in other words, to make sure that the statement made by each verb applies to that verb's grammatical subject.

Choice Between Active and Passive Voice

The style of many passages can be improved by changing passive voice of verbs to active voice. Following are typical examples:

1. It is maintained by the contractor that . . .
2. It is believed that . . .
3. Your letter has been received by us and . . .

The first of these sentences has a meaningless subject. The second not only has a meaningless subject but is also evasive about who does the believing—which may be a fact of considerable importance. The third is awkward and unnatural. The three sentences could be improved by change of voice, as follows:

1. The contractor maintains that . . .
2. I believe that . . . (if not *I*, some other word showing *who* believes)
3. We have received your letter and . . .

Yet in spite of the frequent overuse of the passive voice, it is a legitimate and useful form, and sometimes preferable to the active. For example, "The concrete was damaged by the cold weather" is better than "The cold weather damaged the concrete"—assuming that it is the concrete, not the weather, that we are discussing. Likewise, the passive voice in "The foam should be skimmed from the vats once an hour" is entirely satisfactory, since the skimming is the important fact and the question of who performs the action is not significant.

The passive voice is called for in a sentence such as, "The samples are collected by the foremen, examined by the inspector, and sent by air to the main office." To use the active voice we would have to write, "The foremen collect the samples, the inspector examines them, and an airplane carries them to the main office." This sentence, with its three different subjects, obscures the fact that the writer is really trying to tell us about the samples.

It is unfortunate that the terms *active* and *passive* are used to identify the two voices of verbs. Careless thinking makes some writers identify *active voice* with *active verb*. But the facts do not justify such an identification, as we can see when we look at two more sentences:

In the darkened room the mother softly hummed a lullaby to her quietly sleeping baby.

The building was shattered by an explosion.

The verb *hummed* in the first sentence is in the active voice but certainly does not convey a picture of vigorous activity. The verb *shattered* in the second sentence is in the passive voice but conveys just as much a sense of activity as if the sentence ran, "An explosion shattered the building." In brief, the extent to which a verb gives an impression of action depends more upon its actual meaning than upon the writer's choice of voice.

A sound guideline in deciding when to use the active voice and when to use the passive is found in the preceding discussion of directness—*that is, use a subject that shows what your sentence actually concerns, and use a verb that says what you really want to say about that subject.* If you will do this there is little danger that your use of voice will damage your style. Yet the warnings against excessive use of the passive may be justified, for the passive voice actually *is* overworked by many writers, it often *does* weaken their style, and it is often a symptom that calls attention to lack of directness.

CONCISENESS

Lack of conciseness, a defect in the writing of many people whose work is good in other respects, is a major cause of complaints by busy readers. Therefore, you should learn how to trim out every word that can be spared when the occasion justifies your taking the time to do so, and should try to avoid wordiness even when writing a paper that you will have little opportunity to revise.

To be sure, you can carry conciseness too far. You will not help your reader by cutting out so many words that you sacrifice clearness, readability, naturalness, precision, and proper application of emphasis. Nothing said in this discussion should be taken as encouraging such a sacrifice.

If you merely look over your work in a general way, you will probably find opportunities to reduce its length without losing anything of value. You will do a better job, however, if you know what to look for; that is, if you know the causes of wordiness. Some of these are taken up in the following discussion.

Repetition

Repetition for the sake of clearness or emphasis is sometimes desirable, but unintentional repetition is a major cause of wordiness. Many a writer uses *spring of the year,* for example, when the single word *spring* would be sufficient, or says that costs *rise to a higher level* when he need only say that *costs rise*. Other examples of such repetition are *a period of three months* (repetitious because three months *is* a period) and *the specimen was placed on the balance and weighed* (repetitious because the fact that it was weighed clearly implies that it must have been placed on the balance).

A slightly different kind of repetition is seen in the sentences, "In one respect, the house was not in good condition. Its roof leaked badly." If the writer had been telling us of several defects, a general statement might have been desirable as a topic sentence; but since there was only one defect to mention, it would have been enough just to say that the roof leaked. Words are wasted when we are told the same fact twice, once in a general way and once in a specific way.

Wordy Phrases

The English language abounds in phrases that convey little meaning but are sometimes necessary in order to make grammatical construction clear or to make the flow of words smooth and natural. If your writing is to be concise you should be alert for opportunities to eliminate these phrases. For example, you should avoid *in the event that* when you could substitute *if, due to the fact that* when you could use only *due to* or *because*, and *has proved itself to be* when *has proved* or just *is* would be sufficient. Similarly, *prior to the time that* is a wordy version of *before, at the present time* means only *now*, and *during the years between* could be cut to the single word *between*.

Use of General Rather Than Specific Words

We have already discussed some of the reasons why general words are undesirable; in addition, the damage they cause to conciseness is sometimes ample reason for avoiding them. For example, when a writer begins a sentence by saying, "They were fastened together," he then must add "by means of staples," "with rivets," or something of the sort to tell *how*. If he says, instead, "They were stapled (or welded, or glued, or riveted) together," his verb would give the full information without the assistance of a modifying phrase or clause.

Other examples of wordiness caused by use of needlessly general words would be: *transported by means of trucks, kept out by the construction of fences,* and *made contact with him by telephone.* These could be replaced, respectively, by *trucked, fenced out,* and *telephoned him.*

Needlessly Complicated Structure

Simplicity has been discussed separately because it is desirable for its own sake as well as for conciseness. You probably noticed in the examples that when a sentence was simplified it usually was shortened. The following illustrations will emphasize this effect further.

Complicated and Wordy

1. It is essential that we take these precautions if our crews are to be safe.
2. There are four dealers in Kansas City, and any of them can supply us with spare parts.
3. The condition of the machinery that is now located in the basement is not good enough that renovation would be justified.

Simple and Concise

1. These precautions are essential to the safety of our crews.
2. Four dealers in Kansas City can supply the spare parts.

3. The machinery in the basement is not in good enough condition to justify renovation.

One more fact—often overlooked—should be brought out here. If you simplify your sentences to such an extent that you use primer style, your writing will be wordy even though each sentence may be as short as you can make it. When too many sentences are short and simple, the repetition of certain words and phrases is unavoidable. Thus as you revise for the sake of conciseness, you should watch for opportunities to cut out words and phrases by combining sentences as well as by shortening them —though you will also need to guard against making your sentences too long by such a process. The following specimen shows how combining sentences can lead to conciseness.

Primer Style

You requested that a site investigation be carried out on area 896. The purpose of the investigation was to determine the depth of the water table. This investigation has been conducted by Samuel Scott and myself. We sank several test holes, drilling them to a depth of 20 feet. (49 words)

Mature and Concise Style

As you requested, Samuel Scott and I have investigated area 896 to determine the depth of the water table. We drilled several test holes to a depth of 20 feet. (30 words)

General Looseness of Style

There are times when wordiness results from mere looseness of style. Following are some examples.

Loose Style

We first tested three samples at room temperature, and when these tests had been completed we heated the others to a temperature of 150 deg. F and subjected them to the same tests.

When the choice of a new truck is made, the length of the body on the model chosen should be at least 18 inches greater than the length of the body of the truck that we are using at the present time.

Compact Style

After testing three samples at room temperature, we tested the others at a temperature of 150 F.

When a new truck is chosen its body should be at least 18 inches longer than the body of the truck we are now using.

Superconcentrated Style

One final word of caution: when conciseness is carried too far, the result is a superconcentrated style, as in the sentences that follow.

Preventing catalyst selectivity deterioration is difficult.

The machinery repair cost question demands attention.

When a reader encounters sentences like these, he does not grasp their meaning until he stops and figures out the relationship of the words they contain. There simply are not enough functional words (prepositions, conjunctions, and articles) to make the structure clear. A looser style would be better, as for example:

It is difficult to prevent the selectivity of the catalyst from deteriorating.

The cost of repairing the machinery demands attention.

In brief, conciseness is not just a means of saving space. It is also—often primarily—a matter of saving the reader's time. And you will defeat your own purpose if you eliminate so many words that you make your material harder to read and force your reader to spend more time on it than he would have spent on a longer version.

SUMMARY ON STYLE

Two qualities are absent from the preceding discussion: *clearness* and *readability*. Their omission does not mean that they are unimportant. On the contrary, it would be impossible to overstate their importance. Whatever else we may do to improve our style, clearness and readability are the end results we hope to achieve. But neither of these qualities can be attained by applying a separate technique. Our style becomes readable when we choose our words intelligently, write sentences of suitable length, develop such qualities as simplicity and directness and conciseness—in fact do all the things that have been recommended. And clearness, too, is produced by doing all these things and also, of course, by attention to such commonplace matters as reference of pronouns, parallel construction, accurate choice of connectives, punctuation—all the fundamentals of English. Thus clearness and readability have not been overlooked here. Each of them is simply the result of so many different causes that an attempt to discuss it would lead us to the very headings under which the subject of style has been covered.

To exhaust the subject of style would be impossible even in a book-length treatment, but it would be wrong to close without pointing out that in regard to each of the desirable qualities discussed, one warning has always been included: don't try so hard to develop this quality that you sacrifice other qualities equally desirable.

The warning concerns not only the sacrifice of qualities we have discussed but also the sacrifice of other values. Sometimes, for example, if you try to make a sentence or clause as simple and direct as possible, you may prevent it from being parallel to some other sentence or clause that it should resemble. On another occasion, phraseology that looks desirable at first may need to be avoided because it results in unpleasant, accidental rhyme or in excessive repetition of some one sound, word, or phrase. Again, an effort to make a sentence more concise may destroy the intangible grace and rhythm that make writing smooth and pleasant to read.

Our discussion of style should therefore end with one general piece of advice: pay conscientious attention to the principles that have been presented; but when the result of following them bothers you—when you feel that a revision you are considering simply does not seem right even though you do not quite know why—you will probably do well to trust your instinct and express yourself in a way that does not clash with your convictions about what sounds best.

EXERCISES

Exercise 1

Improve the diction of the following sentences as indicated.

A. Make the following sentences less pompous.

1. The developments occurred subsequent to the end of the fiscal year but prior to the date of this report.
2. We are doubling our efforts to instigate procedures that will secure more participation by staff members in this activity.
3. I am not in possession of any information relative to the subject.
4. Conditions were very bad because of the shortage of janitorial personnel.

B. Replace language that is needlessly technical by substituting ordinary language.

1. We should not reject the plan because of considerations that are highly stochastic.
2. It should shed water well because it has imbricate scales.
3. The danger of fire was great because the underbrush was in an extremely dehydrated condition.
4. This plant, which we found in the ecotone, had hispid stalks and linguiform leaves. Each leaf had a reddish limbus.

C. Reduce the vagueness of the following sentences. If you must invent facts in order to be more specific, you are free to do so.

1. These caterpillars are sometimes carried for a considerable distance by the wind.
2. The work is now quite a bit behind schedule, but we expect to remedy this condition within a reasonable length of time.
3. When the weather is cold enough that the furnace is running most of the time, the motor should be oiled occasionally and the filter should be cleaned frequently.
4. During the first month, the number of faulty parts produced was

relatively small, but by the time the second month was over it had increased by a substantial amount.

D. Decide for yourself what is wrong with diction in the following sentences and make changes necessary for improvement.

1. Greater lateral dispersion will result when the nozzles from which the droplets are ejected are moved toward the wing tip, when the mean diameter of the droplet spectrum is reduced, and when the airplanes fly at a greater altitude.
2. It is possible that different substances in the form of particulate matter are responsible for the lachrymal activity.
3. What this incident portends is impossible to prognosticate.
4. The loads borne by the three extensions are equiponderant.
5. They have been instructed to slow down the speed of the belt conveyor in five-foot increments.
6. We recommend that action be taken to make some parts of the room less crowded.
7. The ceremonies that will transpire subsequent to April 1 will signalize consummation of a Brobdingnagian engineering accomplishment.
8. There were several rank raises; and since these were sometimes misunderstood, an explanation of the decision reasons was necessary.

Exercise 2

Break each of the following long sentences into shorter sentences. If it is necessary to change the order of the ideas, feel free to do so.

1. Due to the fact that a $25,000 contract has been let for additional warehousing space and also because it is necessary to invest approximately $11,000 more in bulking boxes, the anticipated capital outlay next year will be $36,000, and it has been decided by your board of directors that it would be advisable to increase the working capital by issuing more certificates this year than normally. (Change to 3 sentences.)
2. The back machine girder and columns had to absorb the seismic force because, as we have pointed out, the back bearings were fixed whereas the front bearings were free to move; and therefore the whole horizontal seismic force of the dryer rolls would be transmitted to the back of the dryer frames. (Change to 2 sentences.)
3. The procedure for running a profile before the size press is too dangerous, for it forces a man to remain inside the machine on a catwalk beside the last dryer for ten minutes, and if this man were to pass out because of the heat he would fall to the basement. (Change to 2 or 3 sentences.)
4. It has sometimes been observed that eye irritation may be considerably less (or even nonexistent) inside a building than directly outside even when ventilation is sufficient to change the air in a building in four minutes, and in some chamber experiments it has been observed that air taken directly from a hole in a chamber may be substantially more irritating than air removed through a duct system. (Change to 2 or 3 sentences.)
5. The axle-scoring test, instrumentation for which includes thermocouples in the rear axle housing and on the transmission dipstick, a

fifth wheel for accurate speed indication, an accelerometer, and a stop watch to time acceleration, is probably the most useful method of evaluating the effectiveness of a lubricant in preventing gear scoring. (Change to 2 sentences.)

Exercise 3

The following passages are written in primer style. Rewrite each, reducing the number of sentences as indicated. Changes in order are permissible but each revised version should be smooth, natural, and free from stringiness. The sentences that you produce should bring closely related ideas together and leave less closely related ideas in different sentences.

1. The machine columns could not be evenly spaced. Instead, they had to be spaced to suit the machine design. This has been pointed out earlier. Two uniform loads were therefore developed. One was for the wet end. The other was for the dry end. (Reduce to 2 sentences.)

2. Various yardsticks are used in business generally. Many of these can be applied to the chemical industry. Many of the conclusions these yardsticks lead to, however, must be qualified. This is true because the chemical industry is unpredictable. Scientific breakthroughs can occur at any time. These breakthroughs are impossible to foresee. In the immediate past, breakthroughs caused great changes in the textile and rubber manufacture. Similar breakthroughs could occur in the future. One possible area is that of inorganic polymers. A breakthrough in this area could cause radical changes in several major industries. (Reduce to 5 or 6 sentences.)

3. Buildings on a college campus are often widely separated. A central fire alarm system is therefore essential. In such a system, most of the fire alarm equipment is located in one building. This should be a building where someone is on duty 24 hours a day. Each building on the campus comprises one fire zone or more. The number of zones in a building depends on its size. If there is a fire, a transmitter in the zone concerned sends a coded signal to the alarm panel. From this panel the alarm is relayed to coded bells in important locations. One such location is usually the president's home. Others include the guard desk and the power plant. (Reduce to 4 sentences.)

4. Seepage through the bridge decks became a serious problem. It led to deterioration of the deck and the steel below. The first effort to solve the problem was the use of a bituminous cap on the deck. The cap, however, proved to be detrimental. The deterioration was not retarded. Instead, it was hastened. This occurred because moisture seeped through the cap and was trapped against the underlying concrete. Along with the moisture, chlorides used in snow removal also were trapped. (Reduce to 4 sentences.)

5. It would be hard to estimate the cost of building a road network such as this. The plans would take long study and calculation. Likewise, no exact figure for the income could be given in advance. Such income would depend on the publicity given the project. It would also be dependent on the mineral wealth found. However, there would be a substantial net income as well as savings in resources. It seems likely that in the long run, these would nearly offset the cost of the roads. (Reduce to 3 sentences.)

Exercise 4

Improve the following sentences by making their structure simpler, more direct, or both. (As you do so, you will sometimes make them more concise.) If necessary, study a sentence until you clearly understand what the writer was trying to say, and then rewrite it entirely.

1. As indicated by your representative in remarks made by him during his recent visit, we are in agreement upon the desirability of frequent inspections.
2. In line with your request, we have viewed and reviewed the current territorial vacancies with an eye toward minimizing to an optimum extent the cost of moves necessary to filling open territorial vacancies.
3. Core analysis is of value to the engineer when he is faced with a decision as to the advisability of testing a formation.
4. In general there is an increase in precipitation with an increase in elevation; and broadly speaking, the regions of highest annual precipitation coincide roughly with the regions of lowest mean temperature while the dryest sections lie within the areas of highest annual mean temperature.
5. He entertains a feeling of distrust toward government regulation.
6. When the company experienced a decline in its business it effected a reduction in the number of its employees.
7. The forcing of the sulphur to the surface is accomplished by pumping hot water into the hole.
8. There are three streets used by this traffic. These streets are Main, Washington, and Jefferson.
9. The structural design of the building is such as to provide sufficient strength for the support of the machinery.
10. Repainting of the walls should be done as soon as the weather permits.
11. The noise that was caused by the operation of the compressor caused many of those who reside in the area to feel resentful.
12. There will not be many occasions when it will be necessary for us to rent equipment.
13. Such a device would involve a cost factor in the approximate range of $150.

Exercise 5

By exercising your imagination you can discover what the writer intended to say in each of the following sentences. Revise each sentence as necessary for the sake of precision.

1. The proposal will be located too far from the existing plant.
2. The source of current will be obtained from a generator.
3. The discussion includes the tools used in the process.
4. The date of the erection of the building is unobtainable, but appears to have been built for a long time.
5. The construction of the building is of brick, painted buff with brown trimming around the windows.
6. When the wall is ready to be poured, the top of the footing is washed.
7. My experience includes work on a survey crew, operation of a power shovel, and an attendant in a service station.
8. The materials we will need are glue, plywood, screws, a hammer, and a saw.

9. The need for thorough cleaning is of great importance, for otherwise the joint will be weak.

Exercise 6

Revise each of the following specimens so as to make it concise.

1. In this report there is a statement to the effect that aggregate deposits are present in great abundance in the vicinity of this route.
2. We have in our own files statements made by men who have worked for the company in the past, and these statements contradict the company's claims.
3. This device is constructed with a shape that is similar to that of a pear.
4. The fuse is of such a length that some of it remains protruding from the mouth of the hole.
5. I have held personal conversations with several architects and have learned in these conversations that the amount of work they are offered is greater than they are able to handle.
6. It is the recommendation of the committee that steps be taken to ascertain the economic value of the services of these engineers and give publicity to such services.
7. Even though it is impossible in actual practice to attain thermal efficiencies that are ideal, the mercury-steam cycle looks favorable from the standpoint of efficiency.
8. Four materials were considered by us for use in waterproofing the interior. These materials were mortar cement, powdered metal, soap, and bituminous products. Only two of these materials, however, were found worthy of detailed study under the existing conditions. These two were mortar cement and powdered metal.
9. The tank that has a capacity of 6000 gallons can be filled in a period of 15 minutes.
10. The cut will be 80 feet in depth, will have a top width of 200 feet and will extend for a length of 1900 feet.

3

ORGANIZATION

If you are to be effective in technical writing, you must be able to do more than just express each separate fact and idea clearly. You must also be able to organize those facts and ideas in a manner that will show how they are related to each other and to the paper as a whole.

Good organization is the result of planning your job of writing in advance. To be sure, when a piece of writing is to be short and simple, planning it may be only a matter of deciding what material to include and how to arrange it. But when the mass of material to be presented is substantial and the relationship of facts and ideas is complicated, the planning must be done with care if the result is to be satisfactory.

The plan for a longer piece of writing is usually in the form of an outline. This is an excellent practice because the very process of creating a good outline often forces a writer to clarify his thinking and to settle questions of thought relationships that might otherwise go unnoticed. In this chapter, however, the emphasis will be on the outline as a plan that will help you to produce an effective piece of writing rather than as an end in itself. This is no trivial distinction. Many an outline that seems at first glance to be a fine specimen turns out to have flaws when put to use as a writing guide.

RESISTANCE OF SELECTED PAINTS TO CHEMICALS

I.   Alkyd paints
   A.   Moderately good resistance
      1.   Moderately good resistance to dilute mineral acids
      2.   Moderately good resistance to neutral salt solutions
   B.   Fair resistance
      1.   Fair resistance to oils and greases
      2.   Fair resistance to gasoline
      3.   Fair resistance to detergents
II. Phenolic paints
   A.   Good resistance
      1.   Good resistance to mild mineral and organic acids
      2.   Good resistance to salt solutions and water
      3.   Good resistance to oils and greases
   B.   Fair resistance
      1.   Fair resistance to dilute alkalis
      2.   Fair resistance to strong detergents
   C.   Poor resistance
      1.   Poor resistance to concentrated alkalis
      2.   Poor resistance to concentrated mineral acids
III. Rubber Paints
   A.   Butadiene styrene capolymer paints
      1.   Good resistance
         a.   Good resistance to mineral acids during intermittent contact
         b.   Good resistance to alkalis and strong detergents
      2.   Poor resistance
         a.   Poor resistance to mineral acids
         b.   Poor resistance to organic acids
   B.   Chlorinated rubber paints
      1.   Good resistance
         a.   Good resistance to moderately concentrated mineral acids
         b.   Good resistance to moderately concentrated organic acids
      2.   Moderately good resistance
         a.   Moderately good resistance to dilute alkalis
         b.   Moderately good resistance to strong detergents
      3.   Poor resistance
         a.   Poor resistance to strong alkalis
         b.   Poor resistance to concentrated mineral acids
         c.   Poor resistance to ketone and ester solvents

Figure 1.   Specimen Outline Showing Correct Physical Form.   This specimen illustrates a simple system of indentation and shows the ordinary symbols to precede four ranks of points. (For decimal-system symbols, see Chapter 4.) Though single spaces have been used between lines, double spacing or a combination of single and double spacing is acceptable.

Of course an outline may also be used for other purposes. It may be submitted to the person who will eventually receive your completed paper so that he can see whether you are on the right track, or may serve as a source of headings for inclusion in the completed paper. However, any outline that turned out to be unsatisfactory as a plan to use while writing would also be unsatisfactory for the other uses. Thus, the emphasis placed here on outlining as a method of planning is justified from every point of view.

If an outline is to function effectively, it should meet the following requirements:

1. It should cover the subject as you have narrowed it down after carefully considering the purpose of your paper.

2. It should be based not only on your consideration of the subject but also on any knowledge you may have about the readers—their reasons for reading, their attitudes, their familiarity with the subject, and anything else that will affect their reception of your ideas.

3. It should be specially designed to accommodate the specific facts and ideas that you want to present.

4. It should give a sense of continuity—of organic unity—rather than being merely a collection of headings that fall within the scope of the subject. (This fourth requirement is less vital in some kinds of writing —for example an instruction manual intended to be used for reference purposes rather than read as a whole—but even when continuity is not essential, the pattern that you create should be systematic, not haphazard.)

THE PROCESS OF PREPARING AN OUTLINE

It would be foolish to pretend that there is an easy way of organizing a complex mass of facts and ideas, and equally foolish to maintain that such a result may be accomplished by only one method. The present approach to the problem is not offered as either an easy method nor as the only method. It is simply a systematic procedure that will usually reduce to a minimum the difficulty of getting good results.

One principle should be made clear at the outset: before you can make an outline that will serve its purpose, you need to decide, in the main, what material you will use in the paper you expect to write. If you disregard this principle you will often find that when you gather your facts and ideas, they will not fit into the organization you have decided upon. It is impossible to be sure of the best organization for your material until you know what that material is.

Acting on this principle, you can proceed as follows:

1. Think about your subject and the function your paper is to perform,

and gather information about the subject if necessary. As you do so, jot down your facts and ideas in the form of rough notes. You will probably add or eliminate material later, but so far as possible you should make notes that cover the substance of your paper.

2. Study these notes, and group together material that seems to be related. As you do so you can usually settle upon a tentative heading for each group—one that will later form the basis for a point in the outline. If necessary, postpone a decision about where to place doubtful points.

3. Taking into consideration both your purpose in writing and your raw material (the latter now being grouped under headings that indicate its nature) decide upon the main points of your outline and hence upon the main divisions of your discussion. There should seldom be more than five or six main points, because a reader will have a hard time grasping your over-all plan if there are too many main divisions. (If you are writing something to be used only for reference rather than to be read as a whole, the desirability of holding down the number of main divisions is not so great.) After you choose your main points, you will probably have to place some of the groups of material as subdivisions of larger groups; in fact, some of the groups were probably made subdivisions when you formed your original groupings. In any event, your main points will not result from just *cutting up* the subject; they will also result, at least in part, from a process of *building up* main points from the raw material.

4. Bearing in mind not only the logic of the subject but also the attitudes and abilities of your probable readers, arrange your main points in a suitable order.

5. Now apply to the first main point the same treatment that you applied to the entire subject. Thus work out and arrange the highest rank of subpoints under your first main point.

6. Either apply the same treatment to the other main points or else continue working on the first main point until you have organized its contents to the extent that you consider necessary. (At this stage, the order in which you work on one or another part of your outline will probably depend on the order in which your ideas mature and your facts become available.)

The preceding method of outlining is offered as a general guide and should not be regarded as a straitjacket. There is no reason that you should not depart from it when the way in which your ideas develop makes it desirable to do so. For example, you may have in mind a possible list of main points before you begin to jot down notes. You may develop ideas for handling some of your material at lower levels before you are certain what your main points will be. It is advisable, however, to regard such ideas as merely tentative until you see how they fit into the pattern that emerges from the general procedure recommended.

This procedure has the advantage of avoiding two other approaches to the job, both undesirable. One of these is to decide first upon the first main point, develop it in full, then choose and develop a second main point, and so on until the outline is complete. (Some people do this because it seems natural to write out the points of an outline in the order in which they appear on the page, just as they write ordinary text.) The other is to decide upon the main points only after considering the subject as a whole, and then to work out subpoints and sub-subpoints—trusting to luck that the specific facts and ideas to be expressed will fit into the framework thus developed. Although the procedure recommended also consists of forming a general, over-all plan and then working out the details, it is based on consideration of the material that must be handled when the plan is put to use.

GIVING SUITABLE RANK TO YOUR POINTS

The question of how to decide on the rank to be given to the various points of an outline calls for further comment. Sometimes the decision about the rank of each point is dictated by facts beyond our control. For example, it might be essential to base a discussion of a college or university on its formal organization. Thus it would be unsuitable to make a point covering a department equal in rank to points covering entire colleges, even if the department taught more courses, handled more students, and spent more money than some of the colleges.

Much of the time, however, a writer is free to use his own judgment. Suppose, for example, that in a certain area the acreage and value of each of two kinds of grain equaled or exceeded the combined value of all the fruits. In this case it might be not only permissible but actually desirable to make the point covering each kind of grain equal in rank to the heading *Fruits.*

With a reasonable amount of ingenuity, you can usually give each point the rank that its actual importance calls for without producing an illogical result. To be sure, if points such as "Grain" and "Wheat" were given equal rank, the equality would not be defensible because one includes the other. But if wheat happened to be especially important on one specific occasion, it would be possible to change "Grain" to "Grains of Lesser Importance," and thus justify equal rank for the point "Wheat." There would then be nothing wrong with taking up "Barley and Oats" as subpoints under "Grains of Lesser Importance." Thus the rank of the points mentioned could be made to reflect accurately the importance of the material covered by each of them.

In brief: when we are not forced to follow a pre-existing pattern over which we have little or no control, we should create a pattern that gives each point the rank its actual importance justifies, but one that is free from such flaws as faulty subordination and faulty coordination, which will be discussed later in the chapter.

ARRANGEMENT OF POINTS

Sometimes arrangement of material may be based on a recognized principle—the chronological order, the order of location, or the order of increasing difficulty, for example, and sometimes it may be based on reasons peculiar to the particular occasion. But in any event, the arrangement should not be left to chance, but should result from a conscious decision about what is best.

Moreover, unless a piece of writing is to be short, no single system is likely to govern the arrangement of *all* the material in the outline. We may often arrange our main points according to one principle and our subdivisions according to another. Indeed the very nature of our sub-points may make it impossible to arrange them on the basis that governs the main points. When the main points, for example, are based on what is to be done at different times during the year and the subpoints are based on what is to be done at certain places or by certain persons, the chronological arrangement used for the main points could not possibly apply to the subpoints.

In addition to the nature of the material itself, there is another important point to consider. When you make an outline you are not just planning how to write about a subject; you are also planning how to communicate with your readers in a manner that accomplishes the result desired. The best arrangement, therefore, is one that is based not only on the logic of the subject but also on the reader's readiness to understand and accept your facts and ideas. Effective arrangement must often grow out of such considerations as: Who will the reader be? Why is he reading? What attitudes, what prejudices—so far as we know—does he already have on the subject? What questions will come into his mind first?

A good example of such considerations is seen in the widely used pattern that places conclusions and recommendations of a report before the body. According to logic, the evidence should precede the conclusions, but many organizations reverse the order because the reader wants to know at once what is recommended.

CHECKING AN OUTLINE FOR ERRORS

However carefully the first draft of an outline is made, errors in organization are likely to creep in. The first draft should therefore be checked over with the following points in mind:

1. There should never be a single main point. (Do not count *Introduction* or *Conclusion* as main points.) If there is, further examination will show (1) that this single main point covers the entire subject and hence is not a main *division* of the material, (2) that some of the material placed under this main point does not belong there, or (3) that the full subject has not been covered.

2. There should usually be no more than five or six main points. If an outline must be long, the increased length should result from the use of more subpoints and sub-subpoints rather than from the number of main points.

3. There should rarely be a single subpoint. That is, there should rarely be an A without a B or a 1 without a 2. The only justification of a single subpoint is the need of treating two or more closely related points in the same manner.

4. There should be no faulty subordination. That is, no subpoint should be placed under a main point where it does not belong. (It might be equal in rank or might belong under some other main point.)

5. There should be no faulty coordination. That is, no point should be shown as equal to another when it is logically subordinate.

6. There should be no overlapping among the main points or among subpoints of equal rank under the same main point. This flaw may result from faulty coordination or from other causes.

GENERAL SUGGESTIONS

Classification

The term *classification* here refers to the establishing of divisions. For example, an outline on erosion control in the United States might have four main points:

I. Erosion control in the East
II. Erosion control in the South
III. Erosion control in the Midwest
IV. Erosion control in the West

Each of these points might be subdivided thus:

A. Erosion control in the past
B. Erosion control in the present
C. Erosion control in the future

Some classification of this sort is often necessary and valuable, especially at the upper levels of the outline. Moreover the outline produced by classification is usually clear, orderly, and apparently logical. There is a real danger, however, that because classification is so easy, it will be carried too far. The resulting outline might contain some headings that are unnecessary because there is nothing much to say about them, and other headings that call for the same material in two or three places. Also, such an outline often fails to provide the headings that would be most useful in organizing the specific facts and ideas to be presented.

Another defect resulting from excessive classification is that it leads to subpoints that always bear the same relationship to their main points. In a sense this relationship does always exist; that is, the discussion under a subpoint is always part of the discussion of the main point. But the thought relationship can vary. For example, suppose a main point concerns the decline in the production of metals. Mere classification would probably result in such subpoints as ferrous and nonferrous metals, and sub-subpoints such as lead, silver, and zinc. But perhaps there would be no reason for such division into parts. Perhaps, in a discussion that applied to all the metals, we mght wish to present first the evidence that a decline is imminent, second, its causes, and finally its probable consequences. Classification is unlikely to provide headings that cover these latter kinds of material.

One virtue of the procedure recommended at the beginning of this chapter is that by reducing the likelihood of excessive classification it also reduces the likelihood of our producing an outline that appears logical and orderly but later turns out to be unsuitable for our purposes.

Parallel Treatment of Similar Points

Though the desire for parallelism should not lead you to jam any portion of your paper into an unsuitable organization, it is sound practice to organize similar points in a similar manner so far as the subject matter permits. Such a practice enables your reader to become familiar with the pattern and read more efficiently.

When your outline is to be scrutinized by someone else, parallel phraseology as well as parallel organization becomes desirable. Main points should be phrased alike so far as possible, and subpoints of equal rank falling under the same superior point should also be phrased alike. This treatment is recommended not because arbitrary rules demand it, but because it makes an outline easier to grasp.

Avoidance of Undesirable Extremes

It is often necessary, in preparing an outline, to balance between two extremes, either of which would be undesirable. It is undesirable, for example, to have too many ranks of points; but it is also undesirable to have a long string of subpoints of equal rank—perhaps eight or ten— under the same main point. Such a string might better be divided into two or three parts. Instead of naming in a single list ten advantages of a certain process, for example, you might do well to subdivide them into different *kinds* of advantage and name the specific advantages as points of a lower rank. Whether this would be an improvement, however, would depend on whether this change would create an outline with too many ranks.

Further, it will constantly be necessary to decide whether to make your points long enough so that each is self-sufficient, or whether to keep each point short so it may be grasped at a glance.

Logical Allotment of Space

The space devoted to various points in an outline should be roughly proportionate, if possible, to the amount of space they will occupy in the paper to be written. Thus a reader will not be misled about which points will comprise the bulk of the paper.

Clearness in the Outline

You should take special pains to make your outline a clear enough record of your plan so that a reader can understand it. This should be done even if you yourself are the only probable reader. Many a writer, when he is not able to write from his outline immediately, finds it hard to remember his own intentions later on, and runs into trouble unless his outline is clear enough to refresh his memory.

Each point should be worded so that its meaning is impossible to misconstrue. It should be broad enough to cover all the material you intend to place under it, but not so broad as to cover more material than you intend to present.

Not only the individual points but also the relationship among different points should be clear—especially the thought relationship between a main point and its subpoints. Some outlines fall so far short of meeting this requirement that a main point and its subpoints do not even seem to cover the same material. If such a discrepancy exists in your outline, you need first to decide whether you actually *do* have in mind two different bodies of material, or whether your plan is sound but is not clearly recorded. In the former case, either the main point or the subpoints must be moved—or else discarded. In the latter, the phraseology must be changed so that the soundness of your plan becomes apparent. It is advisable to check this kind of defect by asking yourself two questions about each doubtful portion: (1) If someone first read the main point and then the subpoints, would it be clear that the main point could be discussed under the subpoints used? (2) If someone read the subpoints first and then the main point, would he see that the main point covered the subpoints without going beyond them?

Sentence or Topic Outlines

In many discussions of outlining, the distinction between the sentence and the topic outline is given considerable attention. When no one except the writer will see the outline, this distinction is obviously unimportant. Indeed, it is unlikely to be considered important in any circumstance. In many excellent outlines, sentences are used for some points and topics or other types of phraseology for others. Unless the points of an outline are to be used as topic headings—in which case they should all be topics—there is no reason to avoid variation in form if the principle of parallelism, already discussed, is complied with. This principle applies not as a special requirement of outlining but as a general principle to be observed in any writing, whether it be an outline or text.

FINAL CHECK OF AN OUTLINE

When you approach the completion of an outline, you can check your work by considering the following questions:

1. Does your outline have a desirable number of main points?
2. Do your main points cover the subject, and will they lead to the best main divisions of material in view of your purpose and your readers?
3. Have you provided for the inclusion of the specific facts and ideas that you want to present?
4. Is the outline free from points that are not really called for?
5. Is your outline free from classification that serves no useful purpose?
6. So far as the subject matter permitted, have you used parallel organization where it should be expected?
7. Have you balanced properly between the desire to avoid long series of equal points and the desire to avoid points of too many ranks?
8. If you have any single subpoints, can you justify them?
9. Have you avoided faulty subordination?
10. Have you avoided faulty coordination?
11. Have you avoided overlapping points?
12. If your outline is to be examined by someone else, will it create an impression of clearness and continuity?
13. If your outline is to be examined by someone else, will it give a reasonably accurate impression about the relative amount of space the various points will occupy?

EXERCISES

Exercise 1

Following are fragments of outlines, each of which contains one or more weaknesses in organization. Point out in one or two sentences the weakness or weaknesses you find in each.

(1)

A. Possible damage to wild life
   1. Possible damage to deer
   2. Possible damage to elk
   3. Possible damage to bear
B. Possible damage to birds

(2)

I. Weather problems encountered
  A. Severe winters
  B. Heavy snowfall
  C. Subzero temperatures
  D. Pleasant summers
II. Shortages of materials
    Etc.

(3)

II. Discovery of the new method
  A. Successful use in the laboratory
  B. Successful use in the pilot plant
  C. First successful full-scale use
  D. Rise to dominant position in the industry

(4)

I. The Ozalid process
  A. Equipment
    1. Machines needed
    2. Cost of machines
    3. Availability
  B. Skill needed by the operator
  C. Potential uses
    1. The jobs it can do well
    2. Its limitations
II. The offset process
  A. Principle of operation
  B. The jobs it can do well
  C. Its limitations
  D. Equipment needed
    1. Cost
    2. Availability

(5)

A. Types of heating considered
   1. Oil furnace
   2. Gas furnace
   3. Electricity
   4. Radiant heat

(6)

I. Glass containers
  A. Advantages
    1. Convenience
    2. Economy
  B. Disadvantages
    1. Breakability
    2. Inconvenience of shapes available
II. Metal containers
  A. Durability
  B. Convenience of shape
  C. Inconvenience in use
  D. Costliness

(7)

I. The excellence of the new motor
  A. Its increased power
  B. Its economy of operation
  C. Its durability
II. The improvement of the body
  A. Its new roominess
III. The new provisions for safety
  A. The improvement in the brakes
  B. The improvement of visibility

(8)

A. Reasons for raising the new species
   1. Its resistance to blight
   2. Its resistance to insects
   3. Its resistance to drought
B. Added profit from planting the new species
   1. The savings in cost of harvesting
   2. The higher price it commands

(9)

I. The electric power available
  A. Power from steam plants
  B. Power from hydro-electric plants
  C. Power from privately owned plants
  D. Power from government-owned plants

(10)

I. The proposed Grandeau dam
  A. Information about water it would provide

       1. Minimum run-off in the past
       2. Losses from leakage and evaporation
   B. Information about the damsite
       1. Suitability of site for the height of dam proposed
   C. Costs
       1. Cost of construction of the dam
       2. Other costs

Exercise 2

Following is a list of some of the considerations that influence companies' decisions about where to build new plants. Make an outline based on this information. You may add other considerations if you think of any, or may subdivide items listed. The arrangement of items in the list is intentionally unsystematic.

Markets	Living conditions
Raw materials	Communication facilities
Recreational facilities	Climate
Community planning	Police and fire protection
Transportation services	Utilities
Competitors	Taxes
Construction costs	Regulatory laws and practices
Labor	

Exercise 3

Make an outline for a paper about Butler Steel and Aluminum buildings, using as material the unorganized list of facts provided below.

There should not necessarily be a point in your outline for each item in the list. On the other hand, a single point in your outline may cover two or three items in the list; or there may be items in the list that overlap, just as your own notes will occasionally overlap as you jot them down before making an outline for one of your own papers. In short, the items are not points of an outline. They are merely facts that the paper would include. *You* are to make up for yourself the points that an outline would need to contain in order to accommodate the facts.

It is not necessary for your outline to cover every item on the list, but it should include most of them. It may also include any facts that you need to make up for yourself so that your particular treatment will not contain gaps. Remember that there is no single, correct treatment for the material. The purpose of this exercise is merely to give you a chance to make up an outline without having to spend time looking up information, and to provide a basis for class discussion by permitting comparison of the treatments worked out by a number of people.

   1. Butler buildings may be 20, 32, or 40 feet wide.
   2. The 20-foot width has a basic length of 48 feet and may be lengthened in multiples of 12 feet.
   3. The 32-foot width has a basic length of 60 feet and may be lengthened in multiples of 12 feet.
   4. The 40-foot width has a basic length of 100 feet and may be lengthened in multiples of 20 feet.

5. The 40-foot width has straight side walls 14 feet high. Side walls of the other sizes are also straight.
6. These buildings have no posts inside and are therefore free from obstructions. They have no trusses. Because of this and because side walls are straight, all the space can be utilized.
7. These buildings are meant to be erected on 8-inch concrete foundations.
8. The sides, ends, and roof are made of corrugated aluminum.
9. These buildings can be widened by setting two units side by side and omitting the interior walls.
10. An adjustable louver for ventilation is present in all end sections of the 40-foot width.
11. Windows are a type that can be opened for ventilation.
12. Erection of these buildings takes only a few days.
13. The end section for the 40-foot width can have two windows and a large sliding door big enough to drive a truck through.
14. Each side section for the 40-foot width may have from zero to three windows.
15. The 32-foot width may have either a small door for persons or a large door for cars and trucks in any section, either end or side.
16. The side section as well as the end section of the 40-foot width can have large sliding doors.
17. It is easy to insulate the sides and ends of these buildings.
18. The buildings are weather-tight. The aluminum walls, ends, and roofs are noncorrosive.
19. An erection manual is furnished when a building is purchased.
20. A mobile crane makes erection easier but is not essential.
21. For all three sizes, a front of brick, stucco, or wood can be substituted for an end section. (That is, it would be built specially by the purchaser, who might thus provide improved appearance, display windows, etc.)
22. The buildings can be used for many farm, industrial, and commercial purposes.
23. All the parts are ready to erect, so it is only necessary to bolt them to the foundation and to each other. The entire fastening is by means of bolts.

Exercise 4

The following table indicates the kinds of information that might be included in a paper telling how certain work was progressing. It does not, of course, attempt to provide the details that would comprise the substance of the paper. Make three outlines, each with a different basic organization, that cover the information indicated.

You may not consider all three bases equally good, but that does not matter. The purpose of the assignment is merely to illustrate that the same material may often be handled in different ways. Realization of that fact makes it more likely that when you organize the contents of something you must write, you will devote some time to figuring out the best approach on that particular occasion rather than adopting some pattern because it looks easy or because it happens to be the one that you think of first.

STATUS OF SUMMER WORK ON CAMPUS BUILDINGS

	Buildings			
Kind of Work	Administration	Science	Music	Classroom
Repairs	completed	not started	not started	completed
Remodeling	completed	under way	not started	completed
Redecoration	completed	completed	completed	not started
New lights	none planned	under way	under way	not started

Exercise 5

Following is a list of general subjects to be used as a basis for outlines, either as they stand or as you adapt them. Choose one or more of them and make an outline containing 15 to 30 points. These outlines may be topic, sentence, or a combination as directed by the instructor. They need not be "thought content" outlines unless the instructor requests that you make them so.

An attempt has been made to name subjects on which you have or can easily obtain enough facts to use the outlining procedure recommended. Supply a title for the paper that you would presumably write, so that your subject will be more specific than those listed.

1. The criteria you will consider when you apply for or accept employment after graduation.
2. The difference between old and new buildings on your campus or in some other area you are familiar with.
3. Accessories for modern automobiles.
4. Reasons for the popularity or unpopularity of some type or make of automobile.
5. The curriculum in which you are seeking a degree (specific subjects and kinds of subjects it includes, types of work to be called for, difference between courses taken in earlier and later years, etc.).

4

MECHANICS

Our discussion of mechanics here will be limited to brief instructions on manuscript form, technical style, hyphenation, decimal numbers for headings, equations, and documentation. Punctuation, capitalization, spelling, and other points that concern all writing are covered in the handbook.

MANUSCRIPT FORM

Much of the time, technical writing does not demand any special manuscript form. In such cases the following general instructions should prove sufficient.

1. Ordinary manuscript should be typed on one side of $8\frac{1}{2}$-by-11–inch white paper of good quality. Double spacing is usually preferable to single, though single spacing with double spacing between paragraphs is standard in letters and often desirable in reports.

2. The margin at the top should be 2 to $2\frac{1}{2}$ inches on

the first page and 1 inch on other pages. Other margins should be: left, 1 inch; right, ¾ of an inch to 1 inch; bottom, 1 inch. If a manuscript is to be bound at the side, the left margin should be increased by ½ or ¾ of an inch. If it is to be bound at the top, the top margin should be increased to 2 inches.

3. The beginning of each paragraph should be indented five spaces.

4. Unless a separate title page is used, the title of a paper should be placed on the first page, centered on the first line. It may be entirely in capital letters, or, if the author's name does not follow, may be underlined and written in upper and lower case (capital letters to begin each important word, small letters elsewhere).

5. If the name of an author accompanies the title, it should be centered a double space below the title and should be upper and lower case. There should be three or four blank spaces between it and the text.

6. The page number is ordinarily placed in the upper right corner of each page except the first, from which it is omitted. If a paper is bound (not clipped) at the top, however, the page numbers should be centered in the bottom margin.

7. Long quotations (75 words or more) should be single-spaced except for double spacing between paragraphs. Margins adjoining such quotations should be increased by ½ to ¾ of an inch on each side.

8. Ordinarily, manuscript should be fastened together by means of paper clips or not at all, and should not be folded. Occasionally, however, especially when it is placed in final, permanent form, it should be semi-permanently fastened in a cover that opens at the side, or provided with backing paper and stapled together at the top.

9. Manuscript to be submitted for printing should never be fastened permanently. In such manuscript, figures should not be attached to the copy. Rather, an identifying number should be written on the figure's back and a note should be inserted in the manuscript to indicate where the figure belongs.

TECHNICAL STYLE

Technical style, in the present context, concerns the form in which numbers are written and the use of abbreviations. In this discussion, suggestions will be offered to help you determine when to use technical style and how to use it correctly.

Use of Figures or Words for Numbers

Numbers in Ordinary Style. Before the use of numbers in technical style can be explained, it is first necessary to recall the conventions that govern their use in ordinary writing. *The basic rule in ordinary writing is: If a number can be expressed in no more than two words, it should be written out. Otherwise, it should be expressed in figures.* (Examples: *four, seventeen, twenty-seven, one hundred, one thousand;* but *114, 1198, 14,456.*) There are many modifications to this rule, the most important of which follow:

1. Figures are never used at the beginning of a sentence. Such numbers must be written out, or else the sentence must be changed so it does not open with a number.

2. All numbers in a series are written in the same form—preferably in figures if any number in the series is long enough to call for use of figures.

3. There are many special uses in which figures may or should be used regardless of the size of the number. These include degrees of latitude and longitude or of temperature, prices, scores, time of day, dates, and tabular statistics.

4. For extremely large numbers a mixed form is widely used which is extremely easy to write correctly and to read accurately. (Examples: *50 billion, 125 million, 6.4 billion.*)

Numbers in Technical Style. In technical style, numbers are more likely to be written as figures. The main differences between ordinary and technical style are as follows:

1. In technical style, 10 and all numbers above are expressed as figures. Any number below 10 is written out, except as mentioned below.

2. In technical style, a number that precedes a unit of measurement is written as a figure even if it is below 10. (Examples: *6 inches, 4 hours, 8 cubic yards;* but *six hoes, three stories, eight gusset plates, four arches.*) Writing out a number as a word is especially undesirable when it precedes a unit of measurement that is abbreviated.

3. In a passage where numbers are especially frequent, all numbers may be expressed as figures. (Example: *He used a crew of 3 carpenters, 1 plumber, 6 laborers, 1 foreman, and 1 timekeeper.*) This is particularly desirable when statistical information is being presented.

4. When one number appears immediately after another as part of the same phrase, one of the numbers is spelled out. (Examples: *7 six-inch timbers, two 7-man crews.*) It is preferable that the shortest number be the one spelled out; but when two such terms are close together, the same form should be used for both.

5. Numbers that are merely approximations are often written out, regardless of their size, unless the result would be cumbersome. (Examples: *The company has enough timber to operate for twenty years. The building should stand for fifty years.*)

6. Sums of money are expressed in figures. (Examples: *$7.95, $5* or *5 dollars, $0.80* or perhaps *80 cents.*)

7. Technical style tends to use decimals rather than ordinary fractions, partly because decimals are easier to write on a typewriter. In a decimal fraction with a value less than one, a zero is placed before the decimal point (*0.719*). It may at times be desirable also to add a zero *after* the decimal point to show exactness (*6.840*).

8. Decimal fractions should not be used to express information for which ordinary fractions are customary, nor should they be used when accuracy would be misrepresented. For example, *2.375* inches should not replace *2⅜ inches,* since this measurement is not accurate to the thousandth of an inch.

The preceding rules do not answer every possible question; if they did, they would be too long and complicated to be useful. Moreover, there are times when two rules may conflict with each other. Hence there are problems you will have to solve by using your own judgment. Most of the time, however, these rules will make it possible for you to choose between figures and words with confidence that the form you decide upon will be acceptable.

Use of Abbreviations in Technical Style

As any reader may observe, abbreviations are used more frequently in technical writing than in writing in general—so frequently, in fact, that their use is clearly the result of a special set of conventions. If you are to decide intelligently when to follow these special conventions, you will need to know the underlying reason for their existence.

Abbreviations are justified not because they make the writer's work easier—though they may have that effect—but because they assist the reader. In technical writing, certain terms related to the field of discussion may be used over and over again. To write them out in full would take more time and space; but more important, it would make what is written harder to read. This is especially true when the terms are phrases rather than single words. It might be necessary, for example, to write *parts per million, feet per second, revolutions per minute,* or *board feet* eight or ten times in a single brief paragraph. Written out in full, these terms might occupy so much space that the remainder of the material would be overwhelmed; yet each of them expresses only a single concept and would actually be clearer and more compact if expressed by a single symbol. Hence abbreviations that shorten such phrases to a few letters have come to be recognized and may be used when they serve a useful purpose.

If terms for which there are abbreviations do not appear often enough to be a problem, however, nothing is gained by abbreviating them. In fact, unless they are numerous, abbreviations are distracting and annoying; they look peculiar, and they hinder rather than assist communication. Therefore it is advisable to refrain from using the technical abbreviations unless the terms appear frequently. When you decide, after considering the points mentioned, to abbreviate in accordance with technical style, you will have sound authority for what you do if you comply with the following rules:

1. Unless it is extremely short, a term denoting a unit of measurement is abbreviated when it follows a figure. Examples are *inch, yard, pound, ounce, gallon, cubic yard, revolution per second, watt, board foot,* and *horsepower.* Unless it follows a figure, however, none of these terms is abbreviated. One would write *63 ft, 2300 rpm, 435 ppm, 125 hp, 50 cc;* but, "It is expressed in *horsepower*" or "The measurement is converted into *cubic centimeters.*"

2. An abbreviation *for a unit of measurement* is always shown as singular. You should use *lb,* not *lbs; bbl,* not *bbls, gal,* not *gals.*

3. A few extremely short terms denoting units of measurement are not abbreviated. Among these are day, mile, and acre. Since usage is not consistent, no exhaustive list can be given. Systematic personal observation is the only way to be sure about the customs in your own intended profession.

4. In many professions there are terms in addition to units of measurement that are used with extreme frequency and consequently are abbreviated when it is reasonable to believe that the readers addressed will grasp the meaning instantly. Some examples are: *a-c* for *alternating-current* used as an adjective, *F* and *C* for *Fahrenheit* and *Centigrade, cp* for *chemically pure, el* for *elevation, emf* for *electro-motive force.*

5. Even when you are using the technical style of abbreviation, there are many terms that you may abbreviate or not according to the dictates of your own judgment, provided you handle each term consistently.

6. The fact that technical style permits the use of abbreviations does not mean that it permits the use of arbitrary signs for words. You should write *8 in.,* not *8";* *12 by 15 ft,* not *12' × 15'; percent,* not *%.*

There are a few exceptions to this rule. It is correct to use the dollar sign, and in appropriate context the use of ¢ would be permissible. Degrees are another exception. Three forms are widely used to indicate degrees of temperature: *84° C, 84 C,* and *84 deg C.* (The same forms could be used for degrees Fahrenheit.) Degrees, minutes, and seconds of angles or degrees of latitude and longtitude may be expressed by signs. It would be correct, for example, to write *21° 55' 15".* However, for the sake of easier typing it seems desirable to avoid the sign for degrees.

7. Capitalization need not be affected by abbreviation. Abbreviations are not ordinarily capitalized unless the terms they stand for are capitalized.

8. In some professions, notably engineering, it is customary to omit the period after many abbreviations. In deciding whether or not to use periods, you should follow the practice of books and magazines in your own field. Even in engineering, however, the period should be used if omitting it could cause confusion, for example in the abbreviation for *inch*. Also, the period should always be used after abbreviations that do not result from technical style but would be used in writing in general— for examples: *a.m., p.m., c.o.d., B.C., Fig.,* and abbreviations used in footnotes and bibliographies, such as *ibid., op. cit., Vol., p.,* and *ff.*

9. One final rule about abbreviation will settle many questions: When in doubt write the word out.

Any collegiate dictionary contains many pages of the abbreviations that are in current use. Unfortunately, however, the editors of *Webster's Seventh New Collegiate Dictionary* have omitted periods after all abbreviations in their list and thus somewhat reduced its usefulness.

HYPHENATION

Terms that create questions about hyphenation occur with unusual frequency in technical writing, and usage is so far from uniform that even such an extensive treatment as the one in *Webster's Seventh New Collegiate Dictionary* is carefully phrased so that it merely comments on tendencies rather than offering rules. As a matter of fact, a definitive set of rules would be almost impossible to draw up; and even if such a listing were possible, the exceptions would be so numerous that even full mastery of the rules would not prevent the necessity of frequently looking up an individual term. Nevertheless, you will be able to settle a great many questions by applying the following brief principles:

1. In writing a term formed by placing a prefix in front of a word, you will almost always be safe if you use the solid form. Such a term may be hyphenated, however, to permit internal capitalization (*pre-Cambrian*) or to clarify pronunciation or meaning (*reform, re-form; re-employ; re-anneal; intra-atomic*). *Self* is an exception to the general rule; when used as a prefix it is always set off by a hyphen (*self-sufficient*).

2. A compound adjective is usually hyphenated, especially when it precedes and directly modifies a noun (*time-consuming method; all-inclusive statement; 60-horsepower motor*). It is somewhat less likely to be hyphenated if used as a predicate adjective (*the man was hard-hearted; the rules were all-inclusive; but the job was half completed; the method was up to date*). However, a chemical term, for example *carbon monoxide* or *calcium chloride,* is not ordinarily hyphenated even when used as a compound adjective. Also, one should not hyphenate such terms as *easily answered* even when they appear in phrases such as *easily answered question.*

3. Compound nouns are more likely to be written as separate words or as solids than to be hyphenated. A few special types that are hyphenated are exemplified by the following terms: *cave-in, motor-generator, weigher-in, I-beam, foot-pound.*

4. Compound verbs vary, but the type shown in the following sentences is hyphenated: *They double-tracked the railroad. They dry-cleaned the canvas.*

5. Usage in hyphenating compound adverbs varies widely, but a hyphen is always used in a compound adverb formed by adding *ly* to a hyphenated compound adjective (*half-heartedly, quick-wittedly*).

6. Try to avoid writing sentences in which you would be forced, if you followed the customs of hyphenation, to create a form that is unclear or illogical. Many problems are best settled not by consulting rules for hyphenation but by revising the sentence so as to get rid of the troublesome term. (Undesirable: *a mercuric chloride-activated compound; a 7 by 16-foot area; the North Dakota-South Dakota boundary.* Improved: *a compound activated by mercuric chloride; an area of 7 by 16 feet; the boundary between North Dakota and South Dakota.*)

7. To carry rule 6 further: Long, unwieldy compounds are poor style, and instead of trying to decide how to hyphenate them it is better to refrain from using them. (Undesirable: *internal-combustion-gasoline-engine cylinders; a piece of 1½-inch-inside-diameter pipe.* Better: *cylinders for internal-combustion gasoline engines; a piece of pipe with an inside diameter of 1½ inches.*)

8. It is important to remember that the same term may be hyphenated in one usage and not in another. (*The blast-furnace crew worked overtime,* but *A new blast furnace is under construction. The shut-down was unavoidable,* but *The plant is to be shut down. We plan to hard-surface the highway,* but *The highway has a hard surface.*)

THE DECIMAL SYSTEM OF NUMBERING HEADINGS

You have probably seen the decimal system of numbering headings in instruction manuals, specifications, and perhaps in some of your textbooks. It is useful when frequent reference to some specific section of the material will be necessary. In this system, a number is placed before each heading in the text, and also before each heading in the table of contents if one is used.

The following examples show how this system, by use of Arabic numerals and decimal points, indicates the rank of each point and identifies the superior point under which the lesser points appear.

1 main point
1.1 subpoint under first main point

1.2 second subpoint under first main point
1.2.1 subpoint under 1.2
1.2.2 second subpoint under 1.2
2 second main point

Unlike the numbers used in an ordinary outline, each number in this system is complete and self-sufficient. That is, the number preceding a point includes the numbers of points of higher rank under which it is taken up. Because of this fact, and because its numbers are compact and easy to include in text, the decimal system does its job extremely well. When there is no necessity of frequently referring to some specific section of the text, however, it is undesirable because it gives the text a cluttered appearance and serves no added purpose.

EQUATIONS

When equations appear frequently in a piece of technical writing, each equation is set apart from ordinary text. Following is a typical example.

. . . The formula for heat flow under these conditions is

$$Q = \frac{k(T_1 - T_2)At}{d}$$

where

$$Q = \text{heat flow,}$$
$$k = \text{coefficient of thermal conductivity for the refractory material,}$$
$$T_1 - T_2 = \text{temperature drop from hot face to cold face,}$$
$$A = \text{area of the wall,}$$
$$t = \text{time,}$$
$$d = \text{thickness of the wall.}$$

Note that the alignment is based on the "equal" sign. Note also that punctuation is just as it would be if the material were placed in regular lines of text rather than set apart.

DOCUMENTATION

As a technical writer you will often use information obtained from printed sources. Consequently, you will need to acknowledge your indebtedness, partly as a matter of courtesy and honesty, and partly because you serve your readers' best interests by doing so. This acknowledgment of sources is referred to as documentation.

By acknowledging sources you may perform various functions: You may show the source of quotations or the authority for statements that might arouse skepticism; you may indicate the extent of your study, and thus build confidence in your remarks; or you may show the reader where he can obtain additional information.

Four methods of documentation are common in technical writing: (1) footnotes only; (2) an alphabetical list of references (no footnotes and no citation of this list in the text); (3) a numbered list of references, and citations in the text referring to these numbers; and (4) footnotes plus a bibliography.

In choosing among these methods you should take into consideration both the functions you need to perform and the customs that prevail in your own particular field. The following discussion is to assist you in selecting the appropriate system of documentation and to provide forms that you may follow in using any of the systems.

Footnotes

If you do not expect to cite sources very frequently and if your total indebtedness to references is not very great, footnotes alone will often be the most satisfactory system of documentation.

A footnote may be used for various purposes. It may merely explain something in the text that will be clear to most readers but not to all; it may provide additional comments or facts that would destroy continuity if placed in the text. These uses, however, are unrelated to documentation and may occur even in undocumented work. Footnotes used for documentation usually perform one or more of the following functions: (1) identify the source of a quotation; (2) acknowledge indebtedness for facts or ideas; (3) cite authority for some statement that might arouse skepticism; and (4) indicate sources for additional information.

Footnotes should not be used unless they are needed. There is no reason to use a footnote in support of a statement that your readers are unlikely to question or can easily verify without assistance, nor to identify a brief quotation used only because of its striking phraseology.

Footnotes used for documentation should be numbered. Sometimes all the notes applying to each page are placed at the bottom of the page itself. In this event, each page may begin with footnote 1, or there may be a single sequence of numbers for all the footnotes in a paper. Sometimes all the footnotes are placed at the end of the paper, sometimes at the end of each section. In this event a single sequence is used for numbering all the footnotes at any one location. Placing the footnotes on the pages to which they apply makes it easier for the reader to consult them. Placing them all in one location eases the work of the writer, and of the printer if manuscript is to be printed. Also, it permits the reader to see in one place all the references that have been cited.

The presence of each footnote is indicated by inserting its number in the text at the appropriate place. If the footnote identifies the source of a quotation, the number is placed at the end of the quotation. If the note applies to material that is not directly quoted, the number is placed at the end of the material that the note concerns. (The text must of course be phrased so that it shows where the application of the footnote begins.) Some forms permit a writer to place this number in parentheses on line with the regular text, but more frequently the number is raised half a space above the line, thus: ". . . Using this system, it was possible to produce about 3,000,000 lumens of light." [2] As can be seen, the number identifying the footnote follows all other punctuation and is not preceded by a blank space.

Regardless of their location, footnotes are ordinarily separated from the text by a solid line beginning at the left margin and extending 1½ inches (15 or 18 spaces) toward the center of the page. This line is a double space below the last line of text and a double space above the first footnote. A double space is left between two footnotes, but single spacing is used within the footnote itself.

The form of footnotes varies in minor respects, but most forms are similar in general arrangement and content. A footnote usually answers the following four questions, so far as possible, in the order indicated: (1) Who said it? (2) What was the title of the piece of writing in which he said it? (3) Where or by whom was this writing made available? (4) On what page or pages may the material cited be found? The following examples show widely used forms for footnotes citing various types of material. They are numbered as if they appeared together, but it is unlikely that so many footnotes would be found on any single page.

Forms for Footnotes

For a book with one author:

1. James Brown, Casebook for Technical Writers (San Francisco: Wadsworth Publishing Company, Inc., 1961), pp. 74-77.

For a book with two or more authors:

2. R. L. Turner and R. O. Byers, Engineering Problem Solving Techniques (West Lafayette, Indiana: Balt Publishers, 1959), pp. 51-53.

For a book with no author given:

3. The Chemical Industry Facts Book, 4th ed. (Washington, D.C., Manufacturing Chemists Association, Inc., 1959), p. 123.

For an edited book:

4. Lawrence V. Ryan, ed., A Science Reader (New York: Holt, Rinehart & Winston, Inc., 1960), p. 224.

For an article in a book:

5. John E. Hove, "Nuclear Materials and Problems," in Materials for Missiles and Spacecraft, ed. Earl R. Parker (New York: McGraw-Hill Book Company, 1963), p. 326.

For a magazine article (signed):

6. William Pease, "An Automatic Machine Tool," Scientific American, September, 1962, p. 64.

For a magazine article (unsigned):

7. "NBC Prepares for the Conventions," Radio Age, April, 1948, p. 23.

For an article in an encyclopedia:

8. "Pollination," The Encyclopedia Americana (1955), XXII, 320.

For an article in a newspaper:

9. The New York Times, March 1, 1964, Sec. 1, p. 5.

For a numbered report (or technical paper or any similar citation):

10. United States Bureau of Reclamation, Tests on Unreinforced Concrete Pipe. Report No. SP-27, August 8, 1950, U.S. Government Printing Office, Washington, D.C., p. 11.

For an address:

11. B. D. Fried, Shock Waves in a Moderately Hot Plasma (paper presented to the Division of Plasma Physics, American Physical Society, Monterey, California, December 3, 1959).

For a reference to a secondary source:

12. John Von Neumann and Oskar Morganstern, Theory of Games and Economic Behaviour, as quoted in Howard P. Emerson, "A Mathematics Foundation for Engineers," Journal of the Franklin Institute, April, 1953, p. 61.

For a thesis or dissertation:

13. Stanley G. Abramson, Oxygenation of Solutions of Cobalt (II) Ion and Triethylenetetramine (Doctor's dissertation, University of Idaho, 1964).

As mentioned earlier, the form of footnotes varies in detail. Different systems of punctuation are used. Some forms indicate the volume and issue of magazines, and some omit this information. Indentation is sometimes hanging (first line extending to the margin and the other lines indented) rather than in paragraph form. Footnote numbers are sometimes raised half a space and set flush against the footnote. And some highly specialized scientific books and periodicals use abbreviation far more extensively than is customary elsewhere.

In many respects, however, usage is well established and should be complied with. The title of a book, magazine, or other independently printed reference should be underlined (the equivalent of italics in print), but quotation marks should be used for articles in a magazine, separate units of a collective work, and other writings that are not separately printed. Since footnotes are not alphabetized, the name of an author is arranged in normal order and should be shown exactly as it appears in the original. A publisher's name should be used exactly as it appears on the title page of a book. If it is known that a publisher's imprint has changed since publication of the book, it is proper to give the new imprint provided the form used is precisely as sanctioned by the publisher. A title, the first time it is mentioned, should appear exactly as in the original, although it may be shortened in later citations. That is, a footnote referring to a book may be reduced to the name of the author, the title, shortened if necessary, and the page number; and the name of a periodical or organization, if long, may be sharply abbreviated.

Since a footnote need not repeat information already given in the text, if an author's full name appears in the text, it may be omitted from the footnote. If only an author's last name appears in the text, however, the footnote should provide the full name. The question as to whether the name of an author or any other information belongs in the footnote or in the text can be settled by applying the following principle: whatever is actually part of the message belongs in the text; what is provided merely as documentation should be in the footnote.

Certain abbreviations are widely used in footnotes, the most common being *ibid.* and *op. cit. Ibid.* is the abbreviation for *ibidem,* Latin for "the same." *Op. cit.* is the abbreviation for *opere citato,* Latin for "work cited." (Italics are used because the terms are foreign; in a typed paper they would be underlined.) *Ibid.* without a page number indicates that a reference is exactly the same as the one immediately preceding it. *Ibid.* followed by a page number indicates that the two references are the same except for the page. *Op. cit.,* which is preceded by the name of the author unless he was named in the text, is used when a reference has already been named but other references have intervened. Obviously, *op. cit.* cannot be used if more than one work by the same author has been named. In order to spare the reader the necessity of turning back to preceding pages, it is best to use *ibid.* and *op. cit.* only to refer to a footnote on the same page. *Loc. cit.* (Latin for *loco citato,* place cited) is sometimes used in much the same manner as *ibid.* but is less definite. *Passim* (Latin for here and there) is used to indicate that ideas have been gathered from various places in a reference, perhaps within a stated succession of pages. *Cf.* (Latin for *confer,* compare) is used just as *compare with* might be used.

It seems desirable, however, in the interests of effective communication, to hold the use of a foreign language to a minimum; more and more technical writers are coming to the conviction that *ibid., op. cit.,* and *cf.* are the only Latin abbreviations that are really necessary, and some are even omitting the underline or italics that identify *ibid.* and *op. cit.* as foreign.

Alphabetical List of References

Often, in technical writing, documentation is limited to an alphabetical list of references, headed either *References* or *Bibliography.* Such a list may include only the sources from which you drew specific information, may be broadened to cover material that contributed to your general background, or may even include references that merely would be helpful to a reader who wants additional information.

Obviously, a list of references not cited in the text conveys only a limited amount of information. It does not tell a reader where you obtained specific facts, but merely shows him whether you have examined a satisfactory number of authoritative, up-to-date references before writing. Still, the evidence that you consulted good authorities makes your statements more convincing; and the use of this system does not prevent your mentioning, in the text, the sources of specific facts when you think that such information is important. Whatever its limitations, the use of nothing more than a list of references is an extremely common method of documentation and therefore must be judged adequate to the needs of many occasions.

The form used for the individual entries in a bibliography or list of references closely resembles the form used in footnotes. The main difference is that the last name of an author is placed first in order to facilitate alphabetical arrangement. When more than one title by the same author is listed, a solid line one half inch long is often substituted for the author's name in the second and later entries. Titles are indicated as in footnotes: quotation marks for a title such as that of an article in a magazine or in a book, and an underline, the equivalent of italics, for the title of an independent publication. Two or more references by the same author are alphabetized by title.

Details may vary, but the following alphabetical list illustrates a form that is widely used and covers most types of entry.

References

Brown, Leland, Communicating Facts and Ideas in Business. Englewood Cliffs, N.J.: Prentice-Hall, Inc., 1961.

Forbich, L. R., "Effect of Reagents on Heat Liberation Characteristics of Portland Cement." Proceedings of the American Concrete Institute, XXXVII, 1940.

"Ground Water," Encyclopaedia Britannica (1963), X, 910-12.

Hartman, Martin A., "A New System Lubricant for Rocket Engine Gear Boxes," Lubrication Engineering, March, 1962.

Kinney, S. P., and E. W. Guernsey, Occurrence, Distribution, and Significant Characteristics of Alkali Cyanides in Iron Blast Furnaces, U.S. Bureau of Mines Technical Paper No. 390. Washington, D.C.: Government Printing Office, 1926.

Ludwig, Norman C., "Effects of Sodium Chloride on Setting Properties of Oil Well Cements," Oil and Gas Journal, May 24, 1951.

————, Retarded Cement and Method of Making. U.S. Patent No. 2,429,211, 1949.

"Modern Calender and Supercalender," Paper Trade Journal, November 18, 1963.

Prochnow, Herbert V., ed., <u>American Financial Institutions</u>. Englewood Cliffs, N.J.: Prentice-Hall, Inc., 1951.

<u>Second Report on Refractory Metals</u>. Iron and Steel Institute, Special Report No. 28, 1942.

Numbered List of References

To make documentation more explicit without the use of footnotes, a numbered list of references is frequently used in place of an alphabetical list. Thus a reference can be cited by inserting its number into the text. If this method of documentation is used, the list of references is limited to materials that are definitely cited, and the entries are arranged in the order in which they are first cited. The form of the individual entries is identical with the form used in an alphabetical list except that authors' names are usually arranged in the normal order. The following brief list should be a sufficient illustration of form.

References

1. Norman C. Ludwig, "Effects of Sodium Chloride on Setting Properties of Oil Well Cements," <u>Oil and Gas Journal</u>, May 24, 1951.
2. Leland Brown, <u>Communicating Facts and Ideas in Business.</u> Englewood Cliffs, N.J.: Prentice-Hall, Inc., 1961.
3. S. P. Kinney and E. W. Guernsey, <u>Occurrence, Distribution and Significant Characteristics of Alkali Cyanides in Iron Blast Furnaces</u>, U.S. Bureau of Mines Technical Paper No. 390. Washington, D.C.: Government Printing Office, 1926.
4. Herbert V. Prochnow, ed., <u>American Financial Institutions</u>. Englewood Cliffs, N.J.: Prentice-Hall, Inc., 1951.

To insert the number of a reference into the text of a paper, either of the following forms may be used:

The temperature loss rarely exceeded 2.9 deg F for 100 lb of ore (7). This information . . .

Tests performed by L. V. Smith /2/ showed the form of the curves to be similar to the form previously reported for austenite steels.

A numbered list of references should not be confused with the use of footnotes at the end of a paper. When footnotes are used, each has a separate number even though it may refer to a reference that has been cited previously. When a numbered list of references is cited, however, each reference is listed only once, and the same number is used each time the reference is cited. Also, as can be seen in the examples, the page of the reference from which material has been drawn is not always indicated when a numbered list of references is cited.

Like the alphabetical list of references, the list that is numbered and cited by number is used very widely, especially in writing that deals with agriculture. Thus it is apparently found satisfactory by a great many technical writers.

Footnotes Plus Bibliography

The most detailed system of documentation is that in which footnotes are supplemented by a bibliography. This system is used more frequently in scholarly work than in run-of-the-mill technical writing. It is suitable when references to sources are numerous and when a writer wishes not only to give the exact page number of every citation but also to show in one place all the references that he has consulted, regardless of whether he has cited them all specifically.

When footnotes are supplemented by a bibliography, their form is the same as that already illustrated, except that the publisher and place of publication of a book are not included. The form used for the bibliography is the same form that is used when there are no footnotes.

Final Comment on Documentation

It is impossible to discuss the subject of documentation without presenting a great many rules. Omission of any of these rules would have meant failure to answer questions that constantly arise; and the writer who does not know or does not look up the answers to such questions is likely to use forms that impress the reader as strange and awkward. Also, rightly or wrongly, a reader may form the impression that a writer who has not learned how sources are usually cited may be so inexperienced that he does not know how they should be used. And of course the conventional forms are preferable also because a reader will grasp the content faster if the form is familiar.

None of this should make us lose sight, however, of the fact that the purpose of documentation is to give the reader information that he wants or needs. Anyone who does much documentation will occasionally need to present information that does not fit into the conventional forms. When this is your predicament, there is no reason to be disconcerted. Following the conventional forms only so far as they fit the occasion, merely tell the reader the facts in the simplest, most concise manner that will be clear. One of the comforting facts about knowing the conventional forms is that you can feel free to improvise when it's necessary, undisturbed by the fear that you are betraying ignorance.

EXERCISES

Exercise 1

Following are sentences involving the use of numbers and abbreviations. Make the changes *technical style* would call for, but do not make unnecessary changes.

This is not an exercise in hyphenation and there are no errors in the use of hyphens. Make sure, however, that you do not create such errors in making corrections involving abbreviations and numbers. Remember that ordinarily hyphenation is not affected by use of technical rather than nontechnical style.

1. It seems likely that the known reserves of ore will permit operations for approximately 30 years.
2. Though the pressure rose to 125 psi, the valve failed to open.
3. Power is supplied by 12 135-hp motors.
4. The area available, as shown in Fig. 7, is only 14′ × 30′.
5. The clearance when the test was run was .031 inches.
6. The conveyor travels at a rate of 6–10 feet per sec.
7. The pipes that we tested had inside diameters of ⅝ in., 1.5 in., and 2¼ in.
8. During the past month there were fewer than ½ as many cancellations as we had anticipated.
9. The average thickness is about 0.125 inches.
10. 14 acres would be a suitable size.
11. The territory has an area of 160 million acres.
12. It was held at a temperature of 925 deg C for 45 minutes.
13. The tank had a volume of eight cu ft.
14. The tank had a volume of 8 cubic feet.
15. Since only a-c motors were available, a power supply consisting of a-c had to be provided.
16. Its capacity of 275 gals. is adequate.
17. How many cu ft of fill will be needed?
18. A depth of 18 in. will be sufficient.
19. We must place an order for six wheelbarrows, three power saws, 16 axes, 12 pulaskis, and 24 shovels.
20. The valves must be opened by 5:30 a m on Mondays.

Exercise 2

A. Each of the following sentences contains an expression that a writer might feel should be hyphenated or perhaps written as a single word. For the purposes of the exercise, they have been written as separate words. Rewrite in correct form each expression that needs to be changed. Although the treatment of compounds is far from uniform, you should attempt, in working this exercise, to follow the principles that were recommended in the chapter.

1. It is our policy to order nothing but service tested parts.
2. He advised us to use pre stressed concrete.
3. It would be safer to use flat bottomed boats.
4. The odor causing bacteria had to be destroyed. (The bacteria cause the odor.)
5. He inspected the fine ore bin carefully. (The bin is one in which fine ores are stored.)
6. They will hard surface the road next year.
7. The plans call for self regulating motors.
8. It was supported by 8 inch timbers.
9. The build up had been going on for a long time.
10. The small grain crop is unusually large. (The grains are small, the crop is large.)
11. This attitude was never expressed by pre Darwinian writers.
12. The high water mark was easy to see. (*High* refers to water, not mark.)
13. The high water consumption was a cause of alarm.

14. We must build up a reserve of raw material before we begin production.
15. We were handicapped by their un co operative attitude.
16. Three of the I beams were already in position.
17. The company will double track the entire stretch.
18. The motor generator is too small.
19. The storage capacity will be 750,000 acre feet.
20. We promised to re examine the entire record.

B. Improve each italicized expression in the following sentences either by inserting hyphens and/or by changing the sentence construction.

1. They must be provided with *outdoor surveying instrument adjusting* apparatus.
2. The *Washington State University University of Washington* sponsorship was agreed upon.
3. It would be advisable to use a *creosote coal tar* mixture.
4. A *nontaste imparting* filter is seriously needed.
5. A *steel quenching* tank was purchased. (That is, steel is to be quenched in the tank.)
6. Because of the decline in prices, the *low grade ore producing* mines were operating at a loss.

Exercise 3

Assume that the following statements are in papers where the source of specific material is cited. Indicate the statements that in your opinion call for citation.

1. Many an inventor is hazy about the fundamental principles that control the phenomena with which he deals.
2. "The main reasons Americans go to college, in the order of decreasing importance, have been demonstrated as being desire for money, snobbishness, the feeling for accomplishment *per se,* and intellectual curiosity."
3. Eighty per cent of the research work of college faculty in these fields is done on projects with a military purpose.
4. The work done on other instruments in the field of Nuclear Instrumentation is not of such vital importance as the work done in developing instruments to protect against radiation.
5. If this system of passing upon admissions were adopted, the technical schools could reduce the mortality of students for academic reasons by fifty per cent.
6. The legislation thus far passed by Congress is entirely inadequate to guarantee protection against damage by herbicides and insecticides.
7. "By the next decade vehicles may be making round trips to the planets, and we must reckon with the possibility that the returning vehicles may infect the earth with life from some other planet."
8. The International Atomic Energy commission can be counted upon to provide satisfactory guidelines for the peaceful use of outer space.
9. During 25 years of operation it is possible to save three million dollars in the cost of operating a single ship by automating the operation of its engine room.
10. "In industry the young engineer learns that if his decisions are correct half of the time, he may be doing all right."

Exercise 4

Assume that you have written a paper that you are documenting only by means of footnotes, and that you must include, on one page or at the end of the paper, the material provided below. Rewrite each item in the proper form.

1. A reference to page 45 of the 2nd edition of a book called Interplanetary Flight published by Temple Press, Limited in London in 1960. The author is Arthur C. Clark.
2. A reference to an article entitled Effect of Green Properties in Ramming of Sand, published in a magazine named Foundry in the issue for October of 1963. The page cited is 77.
3. A second reference identical to number 2.
4. A second reference identical to number 1 except that the page cited is 54.
5. An article by J. O. Jordan entitled Mine Gases, which appears in a book called Mine Ventilation edited by A. Roberts. The book was published by Cleaver-Hulme Press, Limited of London in 1960. The page is 76.
6. An article entitled An Age of Specialization written by William H. Colver, whose full name you have mentioned in your text. The article appeared on page 69 in a magazine, Metal Progress, in the May, 1964 number.
7. A reference to an unsigned article entitled Fuel-Solids Handling Surveyed, published on page 70 of a magazine named Power in November of 1961.
8. An unpublished address entitled The Role of the Engineering Technician in Industry. It was delivered in Moscow, Idaho, on May 1, 1964, to the Pacific Northwest Section of the American Society for Engineering Education by S. J. McDermott.

Exercise 5

A. Assume that you have written a paper that you are documenting by providing a numbered list of references and citing them in the text. The facts about each reference are provided below. Make a list of the items.

1. A book named Materials and Processes edited by James Frederick Young and published in 1944 by John Wiley and Sons, Inc., of New York.
2. A book by Walter Herman Bucher published by the Princeton University Press in 1933. Its title is Deformation of the Earth's Crust.
3. An article entitled An Improved Device for Locating Ground Faults in Power Distribution Systems, published in 1963 in the first quarterly number of the General Motors Engineering Journal. The author was I. J. Stricker.
4. A book published by Chemical Publishing Co., Inc. of New York. Its title is Time and Its Reckoning, and it was written by Barnard Way and Noel Green. The year of publication was 1940.
5. An unsigned article entitled Sixty Yard Dragline Goes to Work, published in a magazine named Excavating Engineer in the April 1964 number.
6. A piece of writing entitled Performance of Hot Water Panel Heating Systems and written by Walter S. Harris and Everett L. Sartain.

It was published as University of Illinois Engineering Experiment Station Bulletin number 453 in 1959.

7. A book by Walter Herman Bucher published by The Geological Society of America, New York, in 1952. Its title is Geologic Structure and Orogenic History of Venezuela.

B. Assume that you have written a paper which you wish to document only by means of an unnumbered list of references. Using the material in A of this exercise, make a list of references (call it a bibliography if you prefer) suitably headed but not having numbers before the items. Arrange the items in suitable order and place the material in each item in a suitable form.

5

SPECIAL
PROBLEMS

The special problems discussed in this chapter are those related to definitions, technical description, the explanation of processes, instructions, analyses, and technical or semitechnical papers and articles. Except for articles and perhaps instructions, you will find that the kinds of writing discussed do not usually appear as complete, independent papers, but as component parts of reports or other longer pieces. Nevertheless, each of them calls for special skills that may best be acquired by examining it separately.

DEFINITIONS

In writing about technical subjects you will continually find that in order to express your ideas clearly you must use a term that calls for definition. Sometimes a sentence definition will be sufficient, but there are times when an expanded definition is necessary.

The Sentence Definition

A sentence definition is a statement that contains the bare minimum necessary to cover the meaning of a term and thus to reveal the essential nature of the thing that the term stands for. Usually it consists of a single sentence; but if a single sentence would be long, involved, and hard to read, there is no reason that two or three sentences should be considered objectionable, in spite of the name "sentence definition." In addition to the term itself, this type of definition contains two other parts, the genus and the differentia. The genus indicates a classification or group that includes the term, and the differentia discriminates between the term and whatever else the genus includes. These parts are seen in the definition of a microscope as "an optical instrument (genus) consisting of a lens or combination of lenses for making enlarged or magnified images of objects (differentia)."

The genus must be chosen carefully. It must be accurate and should be as narrow as possible so that the differentia will not have to include an excessive amount of information. It would be better to identify asbestos, for example, as a nonmetallic mineral than merely as a substance. The differentia should contain enough information to draw the line between the term being defined and everything else that the genus might include.

A good sentence definition must be based on a clear understanding of the essential nature of the object for which the term stands. The definition of a pearl, for example, would need to emphasize the pearl's origin. Color, beauty, and value might also be mentioned; but unless the definition were based on the fact that a pearl is an abnormal growth within the shell of certain types of mollusk, it would not serve its main purpose.

The following sentence definitions may be studied as additional examples:

> A forest region is an area, frequently covering portions of several states, within which the forests are the product of climatic differences whose controlling factors are the total annual amount of heat and the total annual rainfall.

> Isothermal compression is the compression of a gas under such conditions that the heat generated by compression is removed as fast as it is generated, so that the temperature of the gas does not change. The meaning may be seen in that *iso* is a combining form meaning *equal* and that *thermal* refers to heat.

> The flash point of oil is the lowest temperature at which the mixture of oil vapor and air above the surface of the oil will flash up if ignited. The fire point is the lowest temperature at which the surface of the oil will catch fire and burn.

The Expanded Definition

Though a well-written sentence definition is logically complete, it often must be expanded if the reader is to realize all its implications, find answers to all the questions that may arise in his mind when he reads it, and see how it does or does not apply in specific cases. Sometimes it must be expanded by means of additional definitions which make clear the meanings of words it contains. Usually, however, it is expanded by one or more of the following methods: use of illustrative examples, comparison and contrast, listing of the component parts, and elimination.

Illustrative examples make a definition more concrete and sometimes, also, clarify its scope. A definition of *parasite* might be expanded by mention of tapeworms, sheep ticks, and other specific parasites each of which lives in or on some host from which it obtains food or shelter. Illustrative examples are helpful in that they make a definition concrete. There is danger, however, that the examples chosen will not be representative and will therefore create a one-sided picture. If all parasites listed were types that live inside the host, a reader might not notice that the term *parasite* includes types that live outside, even though the sentence definition had been broad enough to include them.

Comparison or contrast is a useful method of expanding a sentence definition because it facilitates discrimination between the term defined and other terms with which that term might be confused. The full meaning and exact limitations of *contagious disease,* for example, might not be realized until that term was compared with *infectious disease.*

A list of parts or divisions encompassed by a term will often help a reader to realize the full scope of the term. For example, a definition of *physics* might read, "Physics is the science that deals with those phenomena of matter involving no change of chemical composition." This statement may be complete in itself, but it would be possible to help a reader by pointing out that under this definition physics includes the science of matter and motion, mechanics, heat, light, sound, electricity, and the branches of science devoted to radiation and atomic structure.

Naming the parts that comprise something has a different purpose when done in a definition than when done for the sake of analysis. When we analyze something, it is assumed that the reader knows what the object is but needs to be told what its parts are; but when we name the parts for the sake of definition, the purpose of naming them is to let the reader know what the whole object is. Naming the parts of something for the sake of analysis is comparable to listing the ingredients contained in a cake—it being assumed that the reader knows what a cake is. Naming them for the sake of definition is comparable to listing the counties that comprise an electoral district so that people will know what is meant when the district is mentioned.

Expanding a sentence definition by elimination is a process in which a writer clarifies our understanding of a term by pointing out what it might seem to include but does not. In defining *insanity,* for example, it might be necessary to mention that the condition called insanity does not include feeblemindedness, imbecility, or any other condition of mental deficiency as contrasted with mental derangement. Elimination can never by itself serve as a complete definition, for essentially, definition is a process of telling what something is rather than what it is not. But by specifying some of the meanings that a term does not include, a definition makes it easier to see the *limits* of its meaning.

The foregoing methods of expanding a sentence definition may be used separately or in any combination. Any kind of material may be used, in fact, if it will help the reader to absorb and remember the sentence definition. The following example shows how a sentence definition has been made easier to grasp by being amplified.

> The term *cyclone,* when used with precision, means a storm that may range from 50 to 900 miles in diameter and that is characterized by winds of 90 to 130 miles per hour blowing in a circle—counterclockwise in the northern hemisphere—around a calm center of low atmospheric pressure while the storm itself moves from 20 to 30 miles an hour. This definition of *cyclone* includes the terms *hurricane* and *typhoon* but not the term *tornado*. The term *hurricane* is properly applied to a cyclone of large extent and suggests the presence of rain, thunder, and lightning. The term *typhoon* is used to refer to a tropical cyclone in the regions of the Philippine Islands or the China Sea. A tornado, however, is not a cyclone. Though it consists of whirling winds, it is much smaller in diameter. It is characterized by a funnel-shaped cloud, the narrow bottom of which extends to or almost to the earth. Its winds reach a velocity that far exceeds the velocity of the winds in a cyclone. Though a tornado is often popularly referred to as a cyclone, it is a distinctly different phenomenon from what a meteorologist calls a cyclone, and it results from different causes.

Point of View in a Definition

Many terms vary in meaning according to the context in which the term is used. When a lawyer uses the term *insanity* in a courtroom, he refers to legal insanity and intends to convey a meaning that is not usually in the mind of the average person who uses the term. If a psychologist were to define *normal human being,* his definition would differ from the one that would be offered by a physiologist or sociologist. Thus the point of view from which a definition is written may affect its contents.

There is nothing objectionable about a definition written from a special point of view. However, it is important that, unless the special point of view is obvious from the context, the definition itself mention it.

In technical writing, concerned as it is with specialized subject matter, the need of mentioning a special point of view occurs with unusual frequency. In particular, the difference between the scientific and the popular meaning of many terms should not be overlooked. A zoological definition of *insect,* for example, would include butterflies but not spiders;

but to a layman the term would probably include spiders but not butterflies.

The popular meanings of words are valid in ordinary circumstances. In technical work, however, precision is expected, and words that have exact scientific meanings should not be used or defined in a loose, casual manner. Consequently, when as a technical writer you address untrained readers, you should provide a scientific definition of any term that the reader might otherwise misunderstand.

The following specimen shows how a writer has recognized the obligation to define a term from a special point of view.

> To a farmer, soil is the substance on the earth's surface that supports plant life, while to the geologist *soil* is an ambiguous term meaning the substance that supports life in addition to the material from which it was derived. To the engineer, however, the term has a broader meaning.
>
> Earth or soil may be defined as *any unconsolidated material that can be excavated and handled with a pick and shovel.* Soils may include small boulders deposited by a glacier, the slick, greasy clays of the Mississippi Valley, beach sands, swamp slime, and even the tin cans, bed springs, cinders, and ashes of a typical city dump. Soils may be well-defined mixtures of a few specific minerals or heterogeneous mixtures of almost anything.[1]

Sometimes a point of view is special to the extent that a definition may become arbitrary. When government authorities, for example, establish grades of livestock and produce, each grade must be defined as exactly as possible. Though there may be a real difference between beef that is *prime* and beef that is merely *good,* the exact point where the distinction between the two grades is made is an arbitrary point. Similarly, to cite a long-established example, the exact amount of alcohol a beverage may contain before it is legally considered intoxicating must be set arbitrarily.

Definitions that draw arbitrary lines are especially common in specifications. Indeed, definitions are so important in specifications that a special section is often devoted to them. A typical example would be the definitions of *coarse aggregate* and *fine aggregate* that might be included in specifications in a contract that involved the pouring of concrete.

Even an individual is sometimes justified in writing a definition that is to some extent arbitrary. If there is disagreement about the meaning of some term, a writer may define it arbitrarily—not with the intention of settling the general controversy but merely to let the reader know which of the possible meanings he has in mind when he uses the term.

The following definition, drawn from a set of specifications, is a good example of an arbitrary definition.

---

[1] George B. Sowers and George F. Sowers, *Introductory Soil Mechanics and Foundations* (New York: The Macmillan Company, 1951), p. 2.

Rock excavation includes all solid rock in place which cannot be removed until loosened by blasting, barring, or wedging, and all boulders or detached pieces of solid rock more than one-half cubic yard in volume. Solid rock under this class, as distinguished from soft or disintegrated rock under common excavation, which also requires blasting before removal, is defined as sound rock of such hardness and texture that it cannot be loosened or broken down by hand-drifting picks. No material, except boulders or detached pieces of solid rock, will be classified as rock excavation which is not actually loosened by blasting before removal, unless blasting is prohibited and barring, wedging, or similar methods are prescribed by written order of the contracting officer.

The Effect of Purpose on Definitions

At first thought there would seem to be little need for comment on the purpose of a definition. The purpose, it would seem, is merely to make clear the meaning of the term to be defined. But further consideration shows that there is more to say.

Like any other writing, a definition is written because we are trying to communicate with a reader. Consequently, we face the question, "Who is the reader, and why does he need a definition of this term?" Whether a definition is good or bad depends in part upon whether these questions receive enough attention.

For example, you may need to define a term so that readers who are entirely unfamiliar with it, or who at best have a vague idea about it, may grasp its meaning well enough to meet their needs. Or, you may need to define a term so that readers who already understand its general meaning, or who at least have special knowledge in some field where the term is used, may use it as a basis for making fine discriminations.

The basic facts in a definition, and the language used, should both be affected by the question of which of these two conditions exists. Suppose we defined butanone as "a highly flammable liquid used as a solvent." On many occasions, nothing more would be necessary to accomplish our purposes; but if chemical matters were under discussion and chemists were among the readers, it would probably be desirable also to say that butanone is derived from acetone and to include its chemical formula. The point is that facts of more than one kind can be used to draw the line between what you are defining and all else with which the thing you are defining might be confused. And the question of what facts to include depends on whom you are addressing and on the specific purpose for which your definition will be used.

As for language—the advice in the chapter on style applies to definitions as it applies to other writing. If you want a particular definition to be useful to anyone who is not a specialist in the subject, it is best to avoid the use of words that are more technical than the term you are trying to define. A layman who did not know what is meant by *mumps* would learn very little from one dictionary's definition, "a specific, febrile disorder characterized by a non-suppurative inflammation of the parotid and sometimes other salivary glands." He would be better served by, "a contagious disease marked by inflammation and painful swelling of the salivary glands below and in front of the ear." Yet if one were giving instructions to medical students, the language as well as the additional facts would make the former definition the better of the two.

Most instructions on how to write definitions warn against the use of highly technical words. This warning should often be heeded, but it is based on the assumption that the purpose of a definition is to give the reader his first introduction to the term defined, and that the reader is unfamiliar with the technical vocabulary of the field involved. Sometimes this is true, but not always. When a definition is written to enable a scientist to pin down the meaning of a term with extreme precision, it may well be expressed in different language than would be used to give a layman a general understanding of the term. There are times when the very reason that the definition is brought into existence is the need for an exactness that ordinary language does not possess.

Still another condition may exist. A definition may be written to establish a special meaning of an ordinary word that science has adopted because no single word in its vocabulary will serve the purpose. An example would be the use of *doping* to mean, "adding minute, carefully controlled amounts of impurities to growing crystals of silicon or germanium." It is sheer nonsense to object to scientific language in a definition that exists in order to tell the special scientific meaning of an ordinary term.

In general, the point to remember about the effect of purpose on a definition is this: in writing a definition, as in writing anything else, always ask yourself, "Who will my readers be, and how can I write so as to meet their needs?" In any kind of writing, it is bad to concentrate on substance alone and disregard the reader and the function of the written material.

General Suggestions

1. Do not base your definition of a term on any word that comes from the same root as the term itself. To define *permeability* as the quality of being *permeable* does no more than tell the reader that permeability is a quality. (This rule will be modified in rules 2 and 3 that follow.)

2. Always phrase a sentence definition to match the grammatical form of the term defined. (This requirement rules out such sloppy phraseology as "Osmosis is when . . ." Even if one were defining a noun that means a time, it would be better to use such phraseology as ". . . is the time when . . . ," thus avoiding the use of an adverbial clause when a noun

is demanded by grammar.) Sometimes the need for grammatical consistency delays the moment when a writer comes to grips with his real problem. For example, the noun *fertility* is derived from the adjective *fertile*, so the first statement one might make in defining *fertility* is that fertility is the quality of being fertile. The real problem of definition would then consist of defining the adjective *fertile*.

3. In defining a term that consists of more than one part, concentrate your attention at the point where attention is needed. For example, in defining *soil physics* your main problem would probably be to show how soil physics differs from physics in general. Or in defining *biochemistry*, the main problem might be to differentiate between biochemistry and other chemistry. Of course, if you felt it necessary, you might first define the basic word (*physics* or *chemistry*) and then go on to the discrimination indicated above.

4. Be sure that a definition includes everything that should be included. If bird were defined as "a warm-blooded animal that flies through the air," the definition would exclude the ostrich, which is a bird even though it does not fly. There is no reason, however, that you should not resort to a device constantly used in dictionaries and insert the word *usually*, so that you can utilize a helpful fact even though it may not apply to every individual thing that the definition includes.

5. Be sure that a definition excludes everything that should be excluded. (The foregoing definition of *bird* did not exclude bats and hence was inadequate.)

6. In writing a sentence definition try to avoid language with which the reader is unlikely to be familiar. The acceptability of whatever language is necessary for the sake of precision has been mentioned; but in a definition, as elsewhere, ordinary language is better than technical language if it will convey your ideas as effectively.

7. In an expanded definition, be sure to point out how the term you are defining differs in meaning from any other term with which it might be confused. For example, if you were defining *toxin* you would probably need to discriminate between *toxin* and the more general term *poison*, and also, perhaps, between *toxin* and the more limited term *venom*. A sentence definition might cover all the facts, but the expanded definition would be written so that all the facts would not only be covered, but would actually reach the consciousness of the reader.

8. Do not forget that you can sometimes make a definition easier to grasp and remember if you mention the root or roots from which the term is derived. For example, *isobar* might be fixed in a reader's mind by a comment on the fact that it derives from *iso*, meaning equal, and *baros*, meaning weight and in this instance referring to the barometer.

TECHNICAL DESCRIPTION

To understand how technical description differs from "literary" description, we need only imagine two descriptions of a room that has been ruined by fire. The literary description would enable us to imagine ourselves in the room—impressed by the fierceness of the fire that had wrought the damage, moved by the half-burned remains of personal belongings, startled to see the sky through a hole in the roof, conscious of the smell of wet, charred wood and the feeling of shattered plaster under foot. A technical description, however, would make no effort to create an imaginary experience nor to arouse our emotions. It would merely tell us, in an objective manner, the facts about the condition of floors, wall, ceiling, and contents—perhaps with the intention of enabling us to consider the need for repairs or to judge what might have been the cause of the fire.

A technical description is sometimes complete in itself, but it is more likely to appear as part of a longer paper. Such a description might deal with the damage done by an accident or a flood, or with the construction, facilities, and condition of a building. It might be written to help us judge the possibilities of remodeling or to decide whether safe working conditions prevailed.

A technical description might also be written to tell us about some newly developed machine, some device that had been used in an investigation, or some piece of equipment the purchase of which was contemplated. Our discussion will deal mainly with subjects of this latter type because such subjects will make the greatest demands on your skill as a writer.

The description of an object may concern the type of object in general or one particular example, but in either event, the basic method would be the same. Indeed, it is often best, in describing some device in general, to describe a single characteristic specimen and then mention the respects in which variation from the chosen example is most common.

The following technical description illustrates many of the points that will be made in this section:

The Greenday Power Mower

A rotary type of lawnmower cuts the grass by means of a blade that rotates in a horizontal plane, moving so fast that it cuts the blades as it strikes them. The power to turn the blade is supplied by either a gasoline or an electric motor. On some power mowers, the motor also supplies the power to move the machine as well as to turn the blade. A characteristic example of the simplest type, however, is the Greenday model described below.

The Greenday X-20 lawnmower consists of four main parts: the chassis and wheels, the handle, the motor, and the blades. Its over-all outside dimensions, exclusive of the handle, are: length, 28 inches; width, 23 inches; and height, 16 to 18 inches, depending on the setting of the wheels.

The chassis covers the blade above and on all sides, and provides support for the motor. It is made of steel and would be a rectangle 17 inches wide and 24 inches long except for two facts. First, a channel 7 inches wide and 4 inches long extends outward at the front right-hand corner to permit cut grass to be discharged; and second, the sides curve outward far enough to leave room for the 20-inch blade to rotate under cover. The top of the chassis is of course horizontal, but the steel turns downward to form vertical ends and sides 3 inches deep. These sides and ends extend all the way around except for the opening through which the grass is discharged.

The wheels are attached to the chassis. The two back wheels and the left front wheel are set at the corners, but in order that the grass may be discharged to the right just behind the front corner, the fourth wheel is located at the center of the right side. The diameter of the wheels is 7 inches and they are made of steel except for their semipneumatic rubber tires, which are 1 inch thick. There are four vertically arranged holes through which each wheel may be attached to the chassis—a feature that makes it possible to raise or lower the machine and thus vary the level at which the grass is cut from 1½ to 3½ inches.

The handle is not essentially different from the type of handle often used in ordinary lawnmowers. It is made of ¾-inch aluminum tubing and is fastened to the chassis just ahead of the rear wheels. It is 3 feet 8 inches in total length and consists of two pieces. One of these, the piece attached to the chassis, is the shape of an inverted U at its upper end but widens enough at the bottom that it can be attached to the outside of the chassis. The other has its two ends as wide apart as the sides of the U, but angles outward enough so there can be a 15-inch straight stretch where the operator holds it to push the machine. The handle is not rigidly attached to the machine, but pivots so that it can be held at any angle from 45 to 90 degrees.

There is nothing unusual about the 3-horsepower four-cycle gasoline motor that drives the blade. It operates on ordinary gasoline, is lubricated with SAE-30 oil, is cooled by air, and has an oil-bath air cleaner. It is started by a recoil type of starter (that is, the rope that is pulled to start it is automatically rewound by a spring, is attached to the motor permanently, and is contained in a compartment on top of the motor). The motor extends 10 inches above the chassis and varies from 10 to 12 inches in diameter. It is controlled by means of a flexible cable that runs from the throttle to a knob mounted on the handle within easy reach of the operator's right hand. It operates at a speed of 2800 to 3000 revolutions per minute. It is mounted in an opening at the exact center of the chassis, where it is held in place by four bolts. The shaft extends downward through the opening so that the blade can revolve under the chassis—which of course has no bottom.

The blade, which is the final part mentioned above, is 20 inches long and 3 inches wide. It is made of hardened steel and is balanced so precisely that it can run at the speed mentioned without causing excessive vibration. Actually, only a 2½-inch section at each end is sharpened so as to do the cutting, for the blade rotates so fast that these end sections sweep through the full 20 inches of the cut many times while the mower is pushed only a few inches.

The total weight of the machine is 50 pounds, so it is reasonably easy to push—though less easy, of course, than a self-propelled model. It does not have all the extra features of more expensive models, but in most respects is the same as they are and does a satisfactory job of lawnmowing.

Description of the Object as a Whole

Though most of the information in a technical description is likely to concern some single part of the object described, the opening section deals with the object as a whole. In this section you should include any of the following materials that are needed: (1) a definition of the object to be described; (2) an explanation of the general manner in which it performs its functions; (3) a general description of the object; and (4) a list of its major component parts, each being preferably a part that performs some particular function. Logic dictates that the first and fourth items in this list be respectively at the beginning and end of the description, but the order of the second and third might often be reversed.

Your definition of the object, if you decide that one is needed, will be sufficient if it merely explains what the reader might be doubtful about. For example, consider the definition, "A demagnetizer is a device for removing the magnetism from hardened tool-steel parts that have been held on a magnetic chuck and thus have become permanently magnetized." The term *demagnetizer* has an obvious meaning, but the writer considered it necessary to indicate that a demagnetizer is used in a certain kind of work and for the purpose of demagnetizing a certain kind of object. His definition was adequate to the occasion and performed a useful function. On the other hand, it would be pointless to write such a definition as, "An electric brake is a brake that is caused to function by electricity."

Sometimes the reader will know without being told what an object is used for, and sometimes the use of the object will be indicated in the definition. There are times, however, when the use of an object will not be apparent unless you make a point of stating it. Such might be the case, for example, if you were writing about a permeameter, a vane borer, or an autoclave. It will always be part of your job, when you write a technical description, to pass judgment on whether the use of an object is obvious or whether it calls for comment, and to include such information if you feel that the reader needs it.

The explanation in the opening section about how a device works may not need to be extensive, but if your reader is to understand a detailed description, he must not be left entirely in the dark about how the object performs its function. He would need to know that an autoclave sterilizes or cooks by means of superheated steam under pressure; that a centrifuge separates different materials by means of centrifugal force; or that the air brakes of a train function when the air pressure between different cars is lowered or released so that the compressed air stored below each car can enter the cylinders and apply the brakes. Even a minimum of such information can make all that follows far more intelligible.

When a person becomes familiar with some object by inspecting it personally, he notices the object in general before he notices the details. Similarly, it is desirable in a description to give the reader an over-all look at the object before presenting him with the information about its parts. He should be told early in the description about the shape and size of the object and also, perhaps, about its finish, its color, and the material of which it consists.

Obviously, however, this information cannot be given about some objects because they are not sufficiently visible. For example, no one could effectively describe the appearance of the hydraulic-braking system of an automobile; and in this instance the appearance is unimportant anyway.

When a reader understands what an object is, what it is used for, how it functions, and perhaps what it looks like, he is ready for a list of its functional parts. This list should not be excessively long. Rather, it should consist of the main functional units, each of which may be broken down into *its* parts, if necessary, when the time comes to discuss it. For example, you might divide an electric washing machine of the nonautomatic type into the tub and gyrator, the wringer, the motor, and the frame. The smaller parts comprising each of these units would not be mentioned until later.

The items in a list of the main parts of an object may be numbered if numbering them seems helpful, and should be arranged in the order in which they are to be discussed. One possible arrangement would be the order in which the parts would be noticed by a person who was looking at the object. A second would be the order in which they perform their respective functions. The latter is usually the best order when the parts function in succession rather than simultaneously. A third possibility might be the order of decreasing importance, for it might be desirable to tell about the important portions of the object at once rather than delaying them while trivial matters are presented.

Description of the Functional Parts

When the main parts or divisions of an object are described, the treatment of each main part is somewhat the same as the treatment of the entire object. That is, it is defined if definition is needed. Its purpose and the general method by which it accomplishes this purpose are made clear. Its general characteristics such as size, shape, and material are indicated. Its position in relation to the object as a whole and to the other main parts of the object is explained. And if it is complicated enough to merit such treatment, it is in turn broken down into its component parts, which are then discussed in the order in which they are listed. This continues until all the functional parts have been described in as much detail as seems necessary.

The Conclusion

Unless the object described is extremely simple, a brief conclusion is desirable, so that the reader's final impression is not limited to the last small detail. No single formula can be prescribed for the conclusion, but its general purpose will be to make the reader visualize the object as a whole, serving its purpose and functioning as it is intended to function. Often, if the object is one that performs some process, the best conclusion is to review one cycle of operation so that the reader can imagine the object in action.

Adaptation to the Reader and Occasion

The reader's knowledge and the demands of the occasion should affect both the contents and the language of a description. The fact that a description of some article is needed does not necessarily mean that all parts of the article must be described in equal detail. For example, electric motors are fairly well known and standardized, and if such a motor is part of a certain mechanism, it should be sufficient to tell the type, the power, and the kind of current it uses.

General Suggestions

1. A technical description, as we have seen, is intended to help the reader to understand an object as well as to picture its appearance. Thus it must include information about parts that may not be visible, and the emphasis is constantly directed to the manner in which the object functions.

2. In actual practice, a technical description is often accompanied by one or more figures. Instructions on the use of figures are given in Chapter 6. It is possible that some Assignments in the writing of descriptions, which appear at the end of this chapter, may be postponed by the instructor until Chapter 6 has been studied.

3. It is often possible to make a description clearer by comparing an object with something that the reader is familiar with. For example, by

saying that an object had the approximate shape of an electric light globe with the socket end down, you might make shape and position clearer than you could ever make them by direct description. Comparison to the shape of letters is especially likely to be helpful, as seen in the phrases *L-shaped, shaped like an H, somewhat resembling an inverted U,* or *having an S curve.*

4. In telling about size, try to avoid general words such as *large* and *small.* To illustrate their vagueness: a cupel, used in assaying, has been called a *small* cup; likewise a crucible, used in the steel industry, has been called a pot for melting a *small* amount of metal. Yet a cupel would hardly hold a teaspoonful of material, whereas a crucible might hold as much as 200 pounds of steel.

5. The positions of various parts of an object must be indicated with care unless the use of a figure makes the position of each part clear. Words such as *above, below, behind,* and *beside* must be used constantly. Information on position must include not only location but also information on such points as whether a cylinder is horizontal or vertical, or whether a hole in the center of a rod is parallel to the axis or across its diameter. Trivial facts should of course be omitted, but whatever is worth presenting at all is worth presenting clearly.

6. The preceding discussion has dealt with objects that function actively. A technical description that deals with such a subject as the characteristics of a building or the condition of a piece of equipment is simpler but not essentially different. First it covers the subject in general and then breaks the subject into its main divisions, continuing this treatment until it provides all the information necessary.

EXPLANATION OF A PROCESS

In discussing the explanation of a process we shall deal mostly with processes that are performed mainly by human action. Some of the suggestions will also apply to processes that occur in nature and processes performed mainly by machinery, but for reasons that will be obvious during the discussion, not all the techniques of explanation are usable for the two latter types.

First, it is necessary to differentiate between explaining a process and giving instructions for performing it. Instructions are written to enable those who may perform a process to perform it properly. The *explanation* of a process, on the contrary, is addressed to readers who may be unlikely to perform the process themselves but want to understand it so that they can judge its reliability, practicality, or efficiency. The manner in which certain tests were performed might be explained, for example, so the reader can judge whether their results were valid. Or again, a method of doing some job might be explained so the reader can judge whether it would be more efficient or less expensive than some other possible method. In such cases the typical reader is a supervisor or executive rather than the worker who performs the process, and the explanation appears in a report, article, or proposal rather than in an instruction manual. In contrast to a set of instructions, it is not worded in such a manner that it gives commands; it tells what actions are performed so that the reader may understand what is, was, or is to be done rather than so that he may do anything himself.

When you explain a process, you will usually find it desirable to follow a fairly well standardized pattern—one that has become standard not because of arbitrary considerations but because it leads to explanations that are easy to understand. This pattern calls for an introduction, an over-all picture including a list of the main steps that make up the process, an explanation of each of the steps listed, and a conclusion if one would be helpful.

The Introduction

The introductions should be limited to information that the reader really needs, and it is unlikely that on any single occasion he will need information on all the points to be mentioned. This qualification should be held in mind as you read the following suggestions. Also, if any of the introductory information applies only to one part of the process, you should feel free to wait until you come to that part before presenting it.

Sometimes the introduction opens with a definition of the process. It indicates why, where, when, and by whom the process is performed. It includes information on the materials, tools, and apparatus needed in performing the process; and if any important apparatus or materials are likely to be unfamiliar to the reader, it identifies them for his benefit. It tells, if necessary, whether those who perform the process need special skills or training. Sometimes, too, it mentions special requirements about the time when the process must be performed, or special conditions that must exist, such as temperature, humidity, freedom from dust, or ventilation. And finally, it sometimes tells about preparations that must be made before the process is performed.

The Over-all Picture

The introduction is followed by any comment necessary about the process as a whole—for example, the theory on which it is based—and by a list of the main steps that make up the process. An effort should be made to hold the main steps to five or six, for if they are too numerous it will be extremely hard for the reader to grasp and retain an over-all picture. The main difference between the treatment of a long, complicated process and a simple one is that the former is subdivided more extensively, not that it includes more main divisions.

The main divisions of the process should be named in chronological order so far as possible. They should be expressed in parallel form and may be numbered if numbering seems likely to be helpful, as it is almost sure to be if the number exceeds three.

Each main division should be based on the completion of a stage of the work rather than on some arbitrary consideration such as place or time. It would be undesirable, for example, to divide a process into work done in the field and work done in the laboratory. Even if the work done in the field comprised one specific task and the work done in the laboratory comprised another, you would give your reader a better picture of the process by identifying that task rather than merely identifying the place where it was done.

The Explanation of Successive Steps

After listing the main steps, you should next take up these steps one by one and treat each of them somewhat as you treated the process as a whole. For each division, a definition is provided if needed, and the facts about time, conditions, apparatus, personnel, and preparations are made clear. Then, if necessary, the parts of which the step consists should be listed.

When nothing would be gained by further subdivision, you can begin to tell what is really done when the process is performed. In telling what is done, you should emphasize the results that the acts performed are supposed to accomplish rather than the actions themselves. The effect of this emphasis may be seen by comparing the following examples:

> First, the form is filled with mix and then the mix is tamped with a ½-inch rod 25 times, which leaves room for more mix. Again, and finally a third time, the process is repeated, the result being that all samples are compacted to the same degree.

> In order to compact all the samples to the same degree, each is tamped in the same manner. First, the form is filled with mix, and then the mix is tamped. . . .

The important fact here was that the samples had to be uniformly compacted. The tamping was performed in a certain manner only because it produced that result. Yet in the first example, the result aimed at seemed added as an afterthought, and the reader was expected to follow a series of actions the purpose of which had not been indicated. The difference between the two methods may seem small when observed in a brief specimen, but in a longer paper it can mean the difference between understanding and confusion. As a reader reads about an action, he should know what that action is intended to accomplish; and when several successive actions are all performed in order to accomplish a single result, that result should be indicated at the beginning of the passage. Otherwise, the reader will soon be lost in a maze of details.

As your explanation progresses from step to step, you should keep the reader aware of his progress. When you take up a new step you should point out that you are doing so, using the phraseology and the numbers, if you used any, that you employed when you originally listed the steps. Special care is necessary when the steps do not follow one another in a regular, chronological order, as when two steps are performed at the same time by different people. By careful use of transitional material, however, you should be able to keep the reader oriented and constantly aware of the process as a whole and of where he stands at any given moment in his reading.

In the explanation of a process, as in any other writing, you will have to decide how much detail is necessary. There is no reason that all parts of a process must be covered in equal detail. Suppose that one step of a process consists of some test which the reader already understands or which is a recognized, standard procedure. It would probably be sufficient merely to say that this test is performed. Yet some other portion of the process might involve unusual procedures that would call for detailed explanation. Thus, in regard to each portion of the process as well as in regard to the process as a whole, it is part of your job as writer to include the material that serves a purpose and to omit what can be omitted without loss.

The Conclusion

There are many occasions when the explanation of a process does not need a conclusion—especially when the process was performed on some specific occasion and the explanation is part of a longer paper. When you feel that a conclusion is desirable, however, you need not hesitate to add one. Your conclusions might summarize the process, perhaps restating the main steps so that the reader's final impression will include the process as a whole rather than only one small part. It might evaluate the process or the results of the process. It might comment on why the process is important or indicate how it fits into some larger process of which it is a part. But unless any of this material fits the occasion, your explanation should probably end with the final remarks about the last action performed.

Explaining a Process Performed by Machinery

When a process is performed mainly by machinery that functions to some extent automatically, explaining it involves telling how the machinery functions. This creates a problem very much like the problem of writing a technical description. The difference is primarily in the points about which details are numerous and the facts that are emphasized. The technical description emphasizes the facts about the machine and tells, incidentally, how the machine operates. The explanation of a process emphasizes what the machine does as it operates, and makes the actual description of the machine incidental.

One possibility of handling the job is to tell first what actually is done by the machinery, organizing the information if possible on the basis of stages of the work as we would do if the work were performed by human beings. The next step is to tell what it is necessary to know—no less and no more—about the machinery that does the job—what it is like and how it functions.

Sometimes this treatment can be varied. If what is said about the machinery falls naturally into divisions that are basically the same as the main divisions of the process—that is, if each separate and distinct part of the process is performed by a separate and distinct part of the machinery—it may be advisable to open with an over-all picture of the process and then combine the discussion of each part of the process and the necessary information about the machinery that performs that part. Discussion of human action can be limited to information about how many people are involved and what abilities they need.

One might summarize by recommending the following general method. First, use an introduction consisting, so far as it would be appropriate, of the same kind of information you would use in explaining a process performed by human action. Next, give an over-all picture of the process by telling its main divisions. Then tell what is needed about each of the divisions, placing emphasis in descending order on *what* is done, *how* it is done, and the kind of machinery that does it.

Some of the processes that this technique would clearly apply to are:

> Feeding cattle by automated machinery
> The manufacture of paper
> Crushing ore
> The extraction of minerals by the flotation process
> Manufacture of steel by the oxygen process
> Harvesting by means of a combine
> Cracking petroleum
> Extinguishing a fire in an oil well
> Killing brush with a machine that applies chemicals
> Treating water with various kinds of water-softening equipment

Explanation of a Natural Process

The introductory information for the explanation of a natural process obviously cannot include some kinds of information used to introduce a process performed by human action, but it might call for the following: a definition which may either tell the meaning of the term that identifies the process or clarify the exact nature of the process; a brief statement of the scientific facts, principles, or theories that cause the process to occur; and possibly the conditions under which the process occurs.

This introduction may best be followed by an over-all picture of the process indicating the stages in which the process occurs. If possible, the stages should be so presented that there will be no more than five or six main divisions, just as is the case with processes of other types; but such a limitation may be prevented by the facts.

When the general, over-all picture of the process has been completed, each stage should be explained, in chronological order. The explanation of a stage would consist merely of telling what happens, and, if possible, why it happens, unless the reason is common knowledge among the readers addressed or has been covered in the introduction. Obviously, the insistence on emphasizing purpose and stressing the point that actions are merely a means to an end does not apply, but we can apply the principle that single incidents are significant mainly because they show how major developments occur. That is, a natural process in which twenty or thirty happenings occur need not be treated as twenty or thirty distinct happenings. Rather, the happenings can be grouped together as they combine to produce the major developments, so that we conceive the process as occurring in a reasonable number of stages.

The explanation of a natural process may or may not call for a conclusion. The suitable kinds of conclusion materials might be a summary of what has preceded, information about the significance or importance of the process, or both. In the last analysis, however, the use or omission of a conclusion should probably depend upon whether the explanation of the process is an independent piece of work which for psychological reasons should not end abruptly, or whether it is a part of some larger piece of writing and leads naturally into whatever follows.

The following explanation of a process is a typical example.

Crossing Strawberries [2]

Crossing is the process by which the geneticist or plant breeder combines the genetic characteristics of one plant with those of another. He does this, of course, in the hope of obtaining a new individual that will maintain as many desirable qualities of both parents as possible and will be free from a maximum number of undesirable qualities. The person who performs the process must have access to a greenhouse in which to grow the breeding stock and to a plot of truck ground in which to raise the seedlings. The only equipment needed in addition to what is ordinarily available in a greenhouse and garden is a pair of very sharp long-nosed tweezers for use in emasculation. Also needed, of course, is a supply of the

---

[2] Courtesy of DeLance Franklin, University of Idaho Experiment Station, Parma, Idaho.

desired varieties of plants for use as parents. The crossing involves three fundamental operations: (1) cross-pollinating, (2) growing the progeny, and (3) selecting the desirable individuals from the progeny.

In the cross-pollinating the breeder's first task is to prevent self-fertilization by emasculating, in the greenhouse where they have been raised, a number of flowers from all the plants that are to be used as female parents. With this purpose in mind he selects primary and secondary flowers that are just beginning to unfold and uses the tweezers to remove all the stamens of each flower selected. Then, in order that the flowers chosen may be easily distinguished from any flowers that may open later, he again uses the tweezers to remove the corolla and calyx from each of them.

When all the flowers to be used as female parents have been thus emasculated, the breeder picks from the desired male parents a suitable number of flowers that have unopened, pollen-bearing stamens. One such flower is usually sufficient for four to six pollinations. He allows the picked flowers to wilt until anthers dehisce (burst open). He then does the actual pollinating by holding a male parent against the pistils of a female parent and twirling it, making sure that it touches the stamens so that the pollen will reach the stigmas. Since casual cross-pollination by insects is not a danger when the work is done in a greenhouse, it is not necessary to bag the pollinated flowers as would be done if the operation were performed out of doors.

When the berries have matured on the crosses, the breeder can grow the progeny. The first step is to separate the seeds from the pulp. This he accomplishes by mashing the berries into a container of fine, clean sand. Later, he sows the mixture into pots or flats of good soil, covering the seeds with a one-eighth inch layer of the sand. The seedlings are raised at a temperature that is held between 65 and 85 degrees, and the seedbed is never allowed to dry out. When the plants are large enough that they can be handled conveniently, they are transplanted into thumb pots or flats—in the latter case being placed 2 inches apart. Within two to four weeks they are again transplanted, this time into the outdoor truck plot.

When the berries first show signs of ripening, the breeder begins the process of selecting desirable individuals by first pulling up and discarding all the plants that show disease or weak growth. As the berries ripen further, he discards all the plants that are obviously below the standards he has set for them. These two steps result in the elimination of all but about five per cent of the plants that have been raised. He compares the plants that remain with the best of the already-existing varieties, and saves only the choicest individuals. From these he propagates new plants asexually (usually from runner plants) to obtain enough specimens of each hybrid that he can test them more critically throughout the range of conditions he may require for proving or disproving the merits of each.

By means of this process, the breeder may accomplish his objective. That is, he may obtain resistance to disease, insects, drought, or extremes of temperature; he may obtain the qualities that are specially desirable for a specific use such as canning or freezing; or he may obtain berries that are firmer or taste better than other varieties.

INSTRUCTIONS

A piece of writing giving instructions has much in common with the explanation of a process, but it is addressed to a different reader and serves a different purpose. The reader is someone who may be expected to perform the process, and the purpose is to enable him to perform it properly rather than just to understand it. In one sense of the word, instructions seem to mean the same thing as orders; but there is a difference between ordering a person to do something and telling him *how* to do something. The two possibilities are not mutually exclusive, and both may be called for on some occasions. In our context, however, giving instructions means giving information rather than giving orders, even though such information may sometimes be expressed in the imperative form.

In technical writing giving instructions is usually a matter of telling how to perform some physical process such as assembling, using, inspecting, or repairing equipment, performing a test, or doing some job in a laboratory. Such instructions are given by manufacturers to dealers who sell and service their products and to consumers who use them; they comprise the bulk of the contents of laboratory manuals; they are produced, in the form of instruction manuals, as a result of enormous labor, by the multimillion-dollar industries that serve the armed forces. But in spite of the variation in complexity that these extremes represent, it is possible to offer a good many general suggestions that should be helpful.

Introductory Material

The same kind of introductory material used in explaining a process may be called for in giving a reader instructions for performing a process. That is, the term used to identify the process *may* call for definition. The purpose of the process may need to be stated. Other useful information might concern equipment needed, conditions that must exist, skills necessary, and preparations to be made before the job itself is begun. It would be wrong to assume, however, that every item in the list is always to be covered. On the contrary, the introductory information should be limited to what will be useful on the particular occasion.

How Much to Include

When the introduction is complete and the actual instructions begin, one question that always arises is what to include and what to omit. For example, should purposes be explained or should the contents be limited to the actions called for? It is certainly true that instructions are grasped more easily, remembered better, and carried out more intelligently if the reader understands the reason that he is told to do things in a certain manner. But such explanations are a means to an end and should be kept distinct from the instructions proper so that the latter will stand out sharply and be easy to identify. This result can often be accomplished by a simple change in manner, as shown by the following examples.

> . . . To charge the expense of a machine against production for a short period would be extremely complicated. Therefore an hourly rental rate period has been set up for each type of machine. It is to be applied as follows:
> 1. Keep an accurate record of the time a machine is used on each job that has a separate account number.
> 2. Charge the job account with the amount arrived at by applying the rental rate.
> 3. Charge the time lost for minor repairs and service to the job on which the machine is working.
> 4. Charge major repairs or overhaul against operating accounts 700 to 799.
>
> OR
>
> 1. An accurate record shall be kept of the time the machine has been used on each job that has a separate account number.
> 2. The job account shall be charged with the amount arrived at by applying the rental rate.
> 3. Minor repairs and service shall be charged . . . etc.

Use of Numbers and Other Mechanical Devices

Numbering the items is almost always useful in giving instructions—though it is no substitute for careful, systematic arrangement and organization. Sometimes a single sequence of numbers is adequate, but if the subject matter is at all complicated it may call for a system of numbers and letters comparable to the system used in an outline. That is, a major order (A. Assemble the blower unit) might be followed by a numbered list of specific acts involved in the assembling. The basis for treating several actions as a single larger unit should practically always be the fact that they combine to produce a single result, or that they concern a common problem.

In addition to numbers, other mechanical devices are useful in giving instructions more frequently than in most kinds of writing. Figures (in the sense of illustrations) may be almost essential. Other possibilities are extra-wide margins, parentheses, explanatory notes—either footnotes or notes labeled as such and inserted in the text—and variation in the style of lettering (different type faces in printed matter, and the use of capital letters and underlines in typewritten copy).

These devices are useful mainly because they permit the writer to use inserts that clarify the meaning of terms and give warnings yet still make the instructions proper stand out so that they cannot be missed. It is possible, of course, to overdo these devices, and thus produce a cluttered-looking paper; but judiciously used they make it easier for the reader to focus his attention mainly on the parts that tell the essential action and to recognize the other material for what it is.

Special Elements

In writing instructions it is often necessary to emphasize something that is not part of the instructions proper. For example, in giving instructions on the use of an insecticide it may be necessary to warn against letting it get onto the skin or into the eyes. In giving instructions about using a poisonous substance it may be necessary to tell what antidote is most effective. Such material should be placed under conspicuous headings and inserted wherever it applies. These special headings not only secure for it the attention it deserves, but also make the instructions proper easier to follow.

Less vital than warnings against damage or danger are special instructions that apply in exceptional circumstances. It might be necessary, perhaps, to tell about a special procedure to use in extremely cold weather, or what substitute can be used if material that is normally used is unavailable. Here again the main consideration is to make the information easily available without letting the instructions proper become so cluttered with *if*'s and *when*'s that it is needlessly hard to discover what to do under normal circumstances. The exceptional circumstance can sometimes be provided for by the simple expedient of a parenthetical insertion at the appropriate place. Much of the time, however, the best method is to present the instructions that apply under normal circumstances without interruption and then cope with the variations by adding what is necessary, suitably headed or introduced. A suitable introduction might be somewhat as follows: "Though the preceding instructions can ordinarily be followed as they have been given, it may be necessary, under special circumstances, to modify them as follows."

Style and Tone

Because anyone who writes instructions tries to make them simple and easy to follow, and because this involves breaking down whatever is complex into its simplest elements, the sentences used in instructions are likely to be extremely short. And since a person who reads instructions expects them to consist of a series of separate actions, preservation of continuity is less important than in most kinds of writing. This does not mean that gaps in thought are permissible, but merely that connective words and phrases showing thought relationship may be used sparingly, because the relationship among the items is already understood to be that of separate elements in a series.

In keeping your sentences short and simple, you should not ordinarily try to save words by departing from normal language. Unless space is artificially limited, as, for example, on a package, a cookbook style is not desirable. (A characteristic example of the cookbook style is the sentence, "Place 8 ounces water and three pellets in jar and shake until dissolved.") Not enough space is ordinarily saved by the omission of a few words to compensate for the loss of naturalness and readability.

As for tone, sometimes, as in a maintenance manual or a laboratory manual, it calls for little consideration because the situation is entirely impersonal. There are times, however, when a pleasant tone is an asset. If you compare the booklet that an automobile manufacturer prepares for a purchaser with the repair manual prepared for mechanics, you will see that the automobile industry recognizes the desirability of addressing the user of its products in a manner that develops good will. Often, instructions addressed to subordinates also will get better results if they are given pleasantly and courteously with a view to securing willing cooperation. Most of the effort to create a pleasant tone is expended in introductory and explanatory passages rather than in the instructions proper, which can thus be kept clear of everything except the bare minimum necessary to cover the action.

Conclusion

Writing instructions that will be clear to the reader involves, first of all, asking yourself who the reader will be, what he knows already, how much detail he must be given about the action, and how much explanation about reasons he must be given in order to persuade him to do things as they are supposed to be done. You will need to use your imagination in order to foresee the possibilities of errors and misunderstandings, and to provide for every likely contingency. You will need to use good judgment in deciding how simple your over-all organization can be. You may usually feel free to sacrifice some of the niceties of style (for example, primer style is often effective) when clarity demands such a sacrifice. And you should often use illustrations and mechanical devices such as headings, notes, and variations in lettering to help your reader see how everything he reads is related to what he is expected to do. If you handle your instructions in this way—and, of course, if you have reasonable skill in writing—you will probably find that your readers can understand your instructions well enough to comply with them.

The following specimen shows how the recommendations for writing instructions work out in practice. The form is that of a memorandum.

To: Superintendents of Branch Plants

From: Report Writing Department

Subject: Writing the "One-page" report   Date: June 26, 196_

As you know, this department has been asked to issue a standardized set of instructions for writing the "one page" report and preparing it for reproduction. These instructions are presented below. We
would appreciate it if you would have those who work in your plant follow the procedures recommended.

1. Suggestions for Writing

a. Detailed information shall be held to a minimum. One-page reports shall include only general material such as reasons that tests
were conducted, conclusions, general methods (unless these are established routine), and principal results.

b. If no major report is to be made later on the subject concerned,
additional photographs and data may be filed with the original copy of
the one-page report, and a note to that effect shall be made in the report itself.

2. Illustrations and Curves

a. When photographs are selected for reproduction on the back of
one-page reports, care shall be taken to select clear prints, especially
when reduction in size will be necessary. Four photographs is to be the
maximum number reproduced on the back of the one-page report.

b. Curves are to be drawn on the back of the graph paper instead
of on the side bearing the cross-section lines. (As many as six curves
can be reproduced on the back of one report if this is done and if the
explanatory lettering is large enough.)

3. Corrections

After a report has been typed by the Report Writing Department on
vellum, it will be returned to the writer for correction before it is
reproduced. When corrections are made, the following suggestions should
be followed:

a. Corrections may be made either on the vellum sheet, on separate
sheets, or on tissue overlay sheets.

b. If corrections are made on the vellum sheet, they must be made
very lightly, and preferably in blue pencil. (Heavy pencil corrections,
ink corrections, and especially corrections made with colored pencils
are difficult or impossible to erase from the vellum sheet from which
the prints are made.)

We feel confident that if full cooperation can be secured in this
effort to improve reports, your plant as well as all other divisions
of the company will benefit.

ANALYSIS

Analysis, as viewed in the context of technical writing, consists of the process of examining something to distinguish its component parts or elements either separately or in their relation to the whole. Situations in which it is necessary to analyze something and present the results in writing are likely to confront anyone in a position where technical writing is called for. It would be impossible to name everything that those who use this book will be called upon to analyze, but the list would include conditions, causes, results, trends, and problems of every kind.

The nature of a written analysis can be made clearer by recalling some of the analyses that all of us encounter in our normal reading. We read analyses of business conditions or the conditions of some particular industry; analyses of the causes of increase or decrease in production; analyses of the manner in which funds have been distributed or the areas in which expenses have increased; analyses of the results of new technology or legislation; analyses of the shift of industry from one region to another; analyses of problems such as the detection or prevention of defects in materials or the design of better products.

For a concrete example, let us see what was involved when an analysis was made of the suggestion that colleges introduce new programs designed to prepare students to do technical writing as a full-time occupation. Some of the questions that arose were as follows:

What existing courses would the program include?

Could these courses accommodate the increased enrollment?

If new courses were needed, would qualified instructors and acceptable textbooks be available?

Would any existing department be prepared to administer the program?

If not, would a new department of Technical Writing offer enough work of its own to justify departmental status?

Would students enter such a program if it existed?

If so, from what existing programs would they be diverted?

If students completed the program, would they enter the vocation it had trained them to enter?

Would the program assist industry if those who entered it were diverted from other fields where there is as acute a shortage of manpower?

This list could be expanded, but it is long enough to show that analysis of the suggestion demanded consideration of the content, staff, administrative organization, students, value, and expense of the program. In short, analysis showed the numerous points into which an apparently simple suggestion had to be broken down before it was possible to see all that was involved.

In actual practice, of course, many an analysis can follow a pattern established in previous analyses of the same or similar matters. But when there is no established pattern to rely on, one must often use considerable imagination in order to discover what facts might be significant. An analysis of the unemployment situation, for example, would obviously include the total number and percentage of employable persons out of work, but would also need to tell such facts as the geographical distribution of the unemployed; their distribution in towns and cities of different sizes; their distribution as to age, sex, and race; their education and their training in vocational skills; the number in various brackets based on length of time since last employment; the changes since previous figures were released; the effect of the season or of special causes (strikes, for example) on increase or decrease; and the specific industries with which the unemployed might be connected. All these facts and of course many more might affect the validity of any generalizations upon such points as the seriousness, the causes, and the possible means of improving the situation.

Unemployment is of course a vast and complicated subject, and an analysis of it on the scale described above would probably be produced in order to make available all the facts anyone might need for his own special purposes. Most of the time, however, the person who writes an analysis, like the person who writes anything else, should not exhaust the subject but should bear in mind the specific function his product is designed to perform. He should take into consideration the question of who his readers will be and why they need an analysis of the subject. The entire approach to the job of analyzing, the organization, and the amount of detail and emphasis on various aspects of the subject can be determined more intelligently if the reader and purpose as well as the subject receive constant attention.

This brings us to the question of how one goes about the task of writing an analysis. The following method is suggested.

First, concentrate on the question of who will read the finished product and why. Will it be read by those who need information only so as to understand the subject, or will it form a basis for decisions and action? To illustrate the latter possibility—a reader might want an analysis of competing products in order to decide which one to buy; he might want an analysis of expenses so as to decide upon the areas in which to economize; he might want an analysis of the probable side effects of a change in the design of some product in order to decide whether these would offset the benefits; he might want an analysis of the demand for heat and power that would result from some enlargement of operations so as to know whether existing sources would be sufficient.

Next, bearing the function of the analysis firmly in mind, begin to list the points, large and small, on which information will be needed; and as information becomes available, decide upon an appropriate pattern for presenting it. Perhaps the key question in organization is whether to weave together the facts on different aspects of the subject or whether to keep each aspect separate from the others. In an analysis of a record of accidents, for example, facts might be presented on such different matters as the number of accidents in different kinds of jobs, the number in different shifts, and the relative number for workers with different amounts of experience. It would be possible to create a pattern in which these matters comprised respectively, main points, subpoints, and sub-sub-points; but it would also be possible to handle each of them separately, subdividing it if subdivision seemed desirable.

When an analysis is made for what might be called random use rather than for specific application, the general method suggested for making an outline (see Chapter 3) would be hard to improve upon as a method of starting the job. This consists basically of jotting down rough notes and creating a plan by grouping together related material. When an analysis is made for a specific application—that is, because it is needed for a pre-determined purpose—the writer's understanding of what is needed permits him to narrow down his approach and concentrate attention on what is significant in view of the particular occasion. For example, an analysis of the quality of some curriculum in a specific university might be different if made for the general purpose of accreditation than if made by the personnel department of a corporation as a basis for recruitment.

The actual writing of an analysis poses no unusual problems. A brief introduction is usually sufficient to cover, so far as circumstances demand, such points as the purpose for which the analysis has been made, the basis on which the major divisions rest and perhaps the reasons for their choice, the source of facts included and the scope and limitations of whatever investigation was made, and the assumptions, if any, on which the interpretation of the facts is based. To these points may be added individual facts of special importance and general conclusions that are specially significant.

When the bulk of the material in the body of an analysis consists merely of objective facts for their own sake, the main problem in presenting it is the avoidance of monotony. Unless a writer has a natural gift for interesting style, there is not much that can be done about this except to break the prose with informal tables—which would probably be desirable for the sake of clearness even if monotony were not involved.

When the objective facts call for interpretation, the main consideration is to make the relationship of facts to each other entirely clear and to explain the processes of reasoning involved in deciding upon their significance.

An analysis may or may not call for a general conclusion. Sometimes, merely breaking down the total subject into its component parts is all that is necessary. Yet, as mentioned earlier, an analysis indicates parts of something either separately or in their relationship to the whole; and when their relationship to the whole is important—when the analysis is made to provide a basis for decisions and action—a recapitulation of the major facts, a reenforcement of whatever has been said about their significance, and an application of the analysis to the unsettled issues become a practical necessity.

Many people who write analyses do not think of them as being a distinct type of writing, but most of us can obtain better results if we recognize what we are doing. And skill in writing an analysis is well worth while because an analysis may not only exist independently but is often an important part of a report, a proposal, an article, or any other kind of technical writing.

The following specimen shows how systematic analysis makes it possible to grasp the significant facts about the use of water in an industrial plant.

Specimen Analysis

The use of water, when the plant is in full operation, is almost 190,000 gpm; but the re-use can cut the amount that must be supplied to about 110,000 gpm. (The extent of re-use varies because the supply available varies, and there is no need for maximum re-use when the supply is ample.)

Water is distributed in four systems, called (1) Domestic, (2) Boiler, (3) Treated, and (4) Untreated. The first two use trivial amounts compared to the latter two.

The Domestic system is used for purposes obvious from its name. Its water comes from deep wells and is chlorinated. The average demand is 650 gpm. The waste is given complete sewage treatment and the effluent after such treatment—260 gpm—is of good enough quality that it can be added to the water used in the untreated system.

The Boiler system uses only 1200 gpm of new water. Like the water in the domestic system, the boiler water comes from deep wells; but it is treated by the zeolite process to remove hardness rather than purified by chlorination. None of it is re-used in other systems.

The Treated water system supplies water for steam condensing, furnace cooling, and heat exchange. The quantity used is very great— 160,000 gpm. Of this amount 90,000 gpm is used at the power house and 70,000 in the coke plant and rolling mills. Its source is the White River. It is pumped from the river into a 300-acre reservoir, into which the portion available for re-use is also pumped. The amount available for re-use is 65,000 gpm, but its heat and quality create a need for chemical treatment—primarily the addition of sulfuric acid—in the reservoir.

The Untreated system uses water from shallow wells and surface drainage. This water is untreated in the sense that no chemical treatment is used, for quality is not so important as in the other system. The water is used mainly to catch dust from the blast furnace and in the descaling and cooling facilities in the rolling mill. The amount demanded is 26,000 gpm, of which as much as 12,000 gpm may be re-used. Though untreated chemically, all the water in this system is pumped into settling basins, where it is clarified before its first use and before its re-use (or its discharge when an ample supply of new water makes re-use unnecessary.)

All in all, the plant's normal operation may call for a supply of about 110,000 gpm of new water, of which 1600 gpm comes from deep wells, 95,000 gpm from the river, and 14,000 gpm from surface sources. The total use, as mentioned, is almost 190,000 gpm, of which about 36 per cent is re-used and 64 per cent is new. And by far the heaviest use is the use of river water for steam condensing, furnace cooling, and heat exchange.

TECHNICAL ARTICLES AND PAPERS

Many students may not expect to write technical articles. The chances that they will do so—or at least profit by doing so—are greater than it might appear. Hundreds of technical periodicals roll steadily from the presses, and the students of today will be called upon to fill their columns in the future. Writing for scientific and technical periodicals is one of the methods by which a technical man can build a reputation among his colleagues and improve his chances for advancement.

The term *technical article* or *technical paper* is actually an oversimplification, for such articles and papers vary a great deal in the extent to which their substance and style are technical. At one extreme is the article published in a scientific journal with a highly specialized circulation, presenting scientific information and theories far beyond the grasp of anyone but a specialist in the field concerned. At the other extreme are articles, for example some of the articles in industrial periodicals, that are sound in content and include material that is interesting and understandable to a reasonably well-informed layman.

The vast difference between these articles does not mean that one kind is better than the other; any type can serve a useful purpose. Exchange of ideas and information is important whether the material happens to be in the most advanced reaches of pure science or whether it concerns the practical application of scientific principles that have long been recognized. But a technical article of any kind differs from a popular or a journalistic article. The technical article is written by someone whose professional work is related to the subject. The popular article, on the contrary, is often the work of a man whose main occupation is writing and who makes no pretense at being a specialist in the field he writes about. Hence its main appeal is to readers whose interest in the subject is incidental, not professional. It places entertainment higher in its scale of values, tries harder to be colorful, and is less likely to be organized with care and written with objective restraint.

Choice of Subjects

The first essential in writing a technical or semitechnical article is to choose an appropriate subject. Although it would be a waste of time to classify subjects merely for the sake of classification, there is no better way to increase your resourcefulness than by becoming familiar with the types of subject that are actually used in periodicals. Most articles belong to one of four types: (1) the article that presents a genuinely new subject; (2) the article that provides new information on a subject that has been written about before; (3) the article that concerns a subject made timely by some recent event; and (4) the article that purposes to establish some special conviction on a particular question.

Some articles of the first type are written to present information on new scientific discoveries, which, of course, are constantly being made at the present time. Yet basic research is far from the only possibility. A new product, the opening of a new mineral deposit, the outbreak of an unidentified plant disease—anything of the sort may be a subject that can be regarded as new.

More numerous, however, are the articles of the second type—those presenting new information on subjects previously written about. In every kind of technical activity, new information on old subjects is constantly being developed. Most of the discoveries made in research laboratories are related to subjects that are not entirely new. New methods of performing old tasks and new developments in established fields, familiar processes, or existing machines can be written about.

Extremely numerous, also, are the articles of the third type—those brought into the focus of attention by some new event. For example, in a year when tornadoes were especially frequent, many writers who understood these phenomena produced articles about them. Most of the information was not new, but a minimum of new ideas about an old subject was sufficient to motivate the articles when the subject of tornadoes was timely. Similarly, an outburst of articles is often produced by the enactment of new legislation in Washington, or by the announcement of an important decision by some regulatory board such as the Federal Communications Commission. Accordingly, when you are looking for a subject, you can do worse than scrutinize external developments affecting your area of interest. There is always a likelihood that one of them will revive interest in a subject that has recently been dormant.

The fourth type of article, the one that aims at establishing some particular conviction, may concern either a new subject or an old one. It is obvious, however, that though the subject may be old, the conviction to be established must be either new or unusual. An article written to express an attitude that has been widely expressed already, or to prove a point that no one will dispute, has no excuse for being written. If it expresses a new point of view, however, the article can be stimulating and valuable. Such an article is well worth writing, for every profession should unceasingly scrutinize the attitudes it has come to take for granted if it hopes to keep pace with a changing world. The simplest method of thinking of such a subject is to ask yourself, "Do I agree with *every* attitude that is conventional in my profession? Do I have *any* ideas of my own?" Many a person has within himself the germ of an article if he would realize that it lies in the unorthodox remarks he makes in private conversations.

Adapting the Article to the Periodical

Even when you write an article as a class assignment, you should proceed as if you intended to submit it for publication. Surely you will hope to publish any article you write after graduation; and accordingly, as a student, you should have in mind one or more outlets for which your article might be suitable. Any experienced writer will tell you that it is futile to write an article first, and try to figure out later where to send it.

To adapt your article to a periodical you will need to examine the periodical thoroughly. Thus you can see what kind of readers you should address, and can make the length of your article, the style, and the language appropriate. If you see, for example, that most of the articles in a publication are no longer than 2000 words, it is useless to submit an article of 4000 to 4500 words. The best you can hope for if you do so will be an invitation to reduce its length and submit it again.

The opening of your article should be similar to the openings of those published in the periodical; the same is true of the length of your paragraphs. To be sure, you cannot be expected to surrender your own sense of values, your own judgment as to what is accurate and important; however you should try to follow the example of the free-lance writer who "slants" his article to the periodical.

In this connection, it is best to forget about magazines with immense and general circulation. Their authors are almost without exception professional writers or well-known names. The writing you do in your profession, if intended for publication, will be sent to periodicals devoted to special interests and read by a special group of readers—or will perhaps consist of technical papers originally read at some meeting and then adapted for publication in the type of periodical mentioned. The present instructions are not intended to apply to writing for any publications except those that professional men read in an effort to keep abreast of developments in their professions.

Writing the Article

The actual process of writing an article is not essentially different from the process of writing in general. Consequently, no special instructions seem necessary except perhaps the reminder to apply what you have learned from the earlier chapters about organization, effectiveness of style, and all other points that have been covered.

It may be desirable to devise a title that will attract attention and an opening that will secure interest. Certainly you should try to secure interest by concreteness and vivid language. The article should contain few if any internal headings—at the most, no more than enough to indicate your main points. The headings that you see in many articles have been inserted by the editor mainly to break up formidable columns of type, and should not be confused with the systematic topic headings that show the organization of a report or of a chapter in a book.

The question of illustrations calls for special consideration. The use of figures will be covered in more detail in Chapter 6, but it should be mentioned here that illustrations can be a fundamental part of a technical or semitechnical article. Accordingly, you should notice the extent to which illustrations are used in the articles printed in the periodical for which you are writing.

If you utilize all these suggestions, and if you have a reasonable aptitude for writing, it is altogether possible that in later years you can produce articles that will be of value to others in your profession while at the same time you improve your professional reputation, catch the attention of those whose good opinion is valuable, and thus further your own career.

Because it seems advisable that each student familiarize himself with articles in the magazines of his own field, no example of an article is presented.

EXERCISES

Exercise 1

Indicate the genus under which you would place each of the following terms if you were defining it in a sentence definition. Be sure that your decisions are accurate, and try in each case to choose a genus that limits the term as much as is practical so that the differentia would not need to be unnecessarily long and complicated.

(*Note:* In this and the other exercises concerned with definition, most of the terms involved will be familiar to you, so that you will not have to rely on a dictionary to such an extent that independent thought would be reduced to a minimum. The exercises in writing definitions are not intended to test your knowledge; they are designed to demonstrate the need of making sure that you do not accidentally omit essential facts that you know but do not think about, the need of checking upon facts you are not sure about, and the need of expressing all the essential facts in a precise and orderly manner.)

asbestos	chlorophyll
peanut	polymer
thermocouple	to crack (in the sense of cracking petroleum)
brazing	to distill

Exercise 2

It is often necessary, in a definition, to discriminate with special care between the term to be defined or the referent that the term stands for, and one or more other terms or referents. For example, if you were defining *tree* you would need to discriminate between *tree* and *bush*. If you were defining the following terms, what other terms would call for this special discrimination? (Choose five to answer.)

sleet	berry	allergy	cellophane
cement	dacron	gravel	diesel motor
tympani	hypnotism	metal	bush

Exercise 3

Indicate the faults that you find in the following sentence definitions:

(*Note:* The function of a single definition is merely to tell what the term means in one legitimate use rather than to cover all the possible meanings. For example, a definition of *lock* would not need to cover the meaning of the term as used in *lock of hair, lock in a canal,* and *lock on a door.* The following definitions are faulty not because they fail to include all the different meanings the term may convey but because they fail to express satisfactorily the single meaning obviously intended on the particular occasion.)

1. Fusion is when different materials are caused to join together by a process that involves melting.
2. A diesel motor is an internal-combustion motor in which a light oil known as diesel oil is used as fuel.
3. A shingle is a thin piece of wood—thinner at one end than at the other—used as the outside material on the roofs of houses.
4. Sleep is a condition in which sensation, thought, and feeling are diminished to such an extent that a person is entirely or almost entirely unconscious.
5. A salamander is a small, amphibious lizard with a soft, moist skin.
6. Silk is a strong, lustrous fiber or the fabric made of that fiber.
7. Nylon is a synthetic fiber or fabric that in many respects resembles silk.
8. Sugar is a substance, usually white or colorless if pure, that because of its sweet taste is used to sweeten food.
9. To synthesize a substance is to produce it by a process of synthesis.
10. A dolphin is a fish that is usually from 6 to 8 feet long and that has a snout long enough to look like a beak.

Exercise 4

Write sentence definitions of five terms from the following list. None of your definitions needs to cover more than one meaning of the term chosen, and each may be limited, if necessary, to a special point of view.

pathogen	infection
agate	plywood
heat pump	beneficiation (as of an ore)
flotation process	clay
microcircuit	peat
drift (as used in mining)	thermoplastic (noun)
survey	vein
outcropping	astigmatism

antibiotic (noun)   anaesthetic
cybernetics   triangulation
computer   allergy
calculus   fertility
isotope   two-cycle motor

ASSIGNMENTS

The following assignments cover all the writing problems discussed in the chapter. In almost every case a list of possible subjects is provided. These lists call for comment. *First:* Some of the subjects may impress you as not being especially technical, but there are valid reasons for their inclusion. This book is intended for the use of students in a wide range of fields; and the more technical and specialized a subject is, the smaller would be the percentage of students who could use it. Because it would be impossible to suggest several highly technical subjects in every conceivable field of specialization, a good many subjects have been included that can be handled without specialized knowledge.

It is not necessary to discuss a highly technical subject in order to profit from doing what an assignment calls for. It is entirely practical to learn the technique of handling a technical subject by writing about a subject that is not technical. For example, you could improve your ability to describe any machine by attempting to describe an electric dishwasher, even though you do not need a technical education to learn the facts about one.

Second: In choosing a subject for any assignment you may find it helpful to look over the lists for other assigments also. A certain mechanism, for example, might be listed as the subject for a technical description; but it might also be possible to base an explanation of a process on the way that it functions or to write a set of instructions for using it or repairing it.

Third: As you look over the lists, use your imagination. The lists may be helpful in stimulating you to think of additional subjects for yourself.

It would be ideal if every paper that you write could concern a technical subject related to your chosen profession, and it is recommended that you use such subjects when possible. There is no reason, however, that you cannot acquire the writing skill an assignment is intended to teach you even if the best subject you can think of, as you look over the suggestions, is not very technical and lies outside the field in which you are most interested.

Assignment 1

Write one or more expanded definitions of terms listed in Exercise 4, or of other terms if permitted by the instructor. Each definition should be from 100 to 400 words long. (Some of the terms, of course, may not present enough problems to call for an expanded definition.)

Assignment 2

Write a technical description of one of the following objects or of some other relatively simple object with which you are familiar. Aim at a length of 400 to 800 words, adjusting the degree of detail so that the paper falls within these limits. Do not attempt to describe anything so complicated that you cannot do justice to it. (This assignment may or may not be accompanied by one or more figures, as the instructor directs. If figures are used, it may best be postponed until after the chapter on tables and figures has been studied.)

a pressure-spraying device (for killing weeds or insects)
a slide rule
a wind-measuring device
a spinning reel
some specific kind of musical instrument
an automobile muffler
a lawn sprinkler (the type that turns or oscillates)
an electric grass-edger or hedge-trimmer
a tent
a fire extinguisher
a shock absorber
a charcoal broiler
a device for spraying with paint
an appliance for removing an automobile tire from the rim
an electric dishwasher
a hydraulic jack for raising one end of an automobile
a rototiller
a milk cooler
an incubator
a gasoline stove or lantern

Assignment 3

Write an explanation of one or more of the following processes, or of some other relatively simple process with which you are familiar. It is suggested that you explain a process that you can cover in 400 to 800 words. If you would like to explain a process that cannot be covered within this length, you may be able to reduce its size by covering only some one part of it. List A includes processes performed mainly by persons, and list B includes processes performed mainly by machines.

List A

1. Tuning an automobile engine.
2. Patching breaks in an asphalt road.
3. Grafting a branch onto a tree.
4. Testing milk for butter fat.
5. Preparing a transparency for reproduction.
6. Preparing a slide for microscopic examination.
7. Solving one of the various transit problems used in surveying courses.
8. Performing some type of welding or brazing process.
9. Checking some type of equipment to determine the cause of failure.
10. Producing a casting by pattern molding, using a sand mold.

List B

1. How an electric dishwasher operates.
2. What happens when the thermostat turns on an automatic furnace.
3. How cement is manufactured.
4. How a mimeograph or some other kind of duplicating machine functions.
5. How a milk separator performs its function.
6. How a water softener performs its function.
7. How some other process of water or sewage treatment is performed.
8. How a traffic counter performs its function.
9. How a polaroid camera performs its function.
10. How some piece of agricultural equipment performs its function.

Assignment 4

Write a set of instructions for performing one of the following processes, one of the processes mentioned in list A of Assignment 2, or a process of your own choice that you know how to perform.

1. Assembling, tuning, or operating a power lawnmower or some comparable piece of power equipment.
2. Pruning a tree.
3. Operating a mimeograph machine or some other kind of duplicating machine.
4. Performing one of the various processes connected with photography.
5. Starting a thermostatically controlled gas furnace.
6. Performing the slump test on concrete.
7. Protecting the basement of a house against water by providing drainage and waterproofing the concrete.
8. Starting a new lawn.
9. Operating a motion-picture projector.
10. Operating a tape recorder.

Assignment 5

Write an analysis of one of the subjects listed below or of a comparable subject about which you can obtain information.

1. Analyze the contents of this book: the kinds of material—such as discussion, exercises, specimens, etc.—and the subjects covered.
2. Analyze the requirements you must meet in order to earn the degree you are working for.
3. Analyze the composition of the student body of your school or of some unit within your school.
4. Analyze the kinds of positions that are available to students who graduate in your field. (This may involve not only the names attached to the jobs, but the opportunities, the kinds of employer, the locations where work is done, etc.)
5. Analyze the use of space in some technical magazine as judged by at least three issues. (This may or may not include advertisements, as necessary to provide material for a paper of suitable length.)
6. Analyze the actual significance and value of the "guarantee" offered by the manufacturer of some product such as an automobile, a watch, a battery, a tire, a vacuum cleaner, or a kind of paint.
7. Analyze the good and bad qualities of some variety of a specific crop such as wheat, apples, or potatoes.
8. Analyze the effect of a new regulation or a change in regulations in something such as zoning, traffic control, or the sale of some product. (This may be the effect expected if the change is merely contemplated, or the actual effect if the change has been in effect long enough for the result to be apparent.)
9. Analyze the significance or lack of significance of the claims made for some make of oil or gasoline.
10. Analyze the use of first-floor space in some selected area (the property on the two sides of some one street or a few chosen blocks) in a city or town where it is possible for you to make the necessary observations. For example, what kinds of business establishments

operate? How much space do they occupy? Where are those of each kind concentrated if any concentration exists? What kinds of customer (if, for example, they include bars or restaurants) do they cater to? For the purposes of this assignment, reasonable estimates of distances and areas may replace actual measurements.

11. In an area such as the one referred to in number 10, analyze the way in which curb space is used for such purposes as public parking, delivery zones, entrances to service stations, etc. Include off-street parking area if you wish.

Assignment 6

Make an outline for a semitechnical or technical article. After the outline has been approved by the instructor, write the article. When you hand the outline and article to the instructor, you should name at least one periodical to which you feel the article might be submitted. Your choice of subject and the nature of the article should result from a previously acquired familiarity with the periodical. The article should be a length that is approved by your instructor and is appropriate to the periodical you have in mind.

6

TABLES AND FIGURES

It is almost impossible to imagine technical writing that does not make frequent use of figures and tables. This is true because some kinds of information—for example, statistical data or the shape, arrangement, and size of objects—are difficult if not impossible to convey by the use of words alone. Hence it is important to know when and how to supplement words by using figures and tables, and how to use words in order to point up the significant features of the figures and tables used.

This chapter will call to your attention the main conventions that govern the use of these nonverbal forms, but there is only one way in which you can really learn to use them to the best advantage. That is, to notice what you see done in the books and articles related to your studies. Not that everything done is desirable; but systematic observation will increase your resourcefulness and will help you to form an intelligent opinion about whether something you are contemplating is done often enough that it will not strike your reader as strange.

TABLES

Of all the nonverbal devices, tables are used most frequently. Usually their function is to enable a reader to compare statistical information more easily. They often take considerable time to compile, and you may often be tempted to take the easy way out and present your statistics in ordinary text, but there are times when it will be almost hopeless for the reader to grasp your information unless he receives it in tabular form.

Though tables usually consist of numerical data, resourceful writers use them to present other kinds of information also. A consumers' magazine uses them, for example, to present the facts about different makes of automobile. It names the different makes of car in the column headings, lists the feature being compared—such as brakes, visibility, steering mechanism—at the left, and indicates the facts about each car in the column under its name. This enables a reader, with equal ease, to check up on all the features for any make of car covered or to compare each make to the others in any particular feature. This same type of table can be used for numberless other types of comparison—the characteristics, for example, of different kinds of apples; the identification of insects that damage crops and the measures for controlling them; the results of using different quantities of fluoride in water to reduce tooth decay.

Because tables can be used for so many purposes, a technical writer should always be on the alert for opportunities to utilize them. Also, he should realize that when the construction of a table seems extremely complicated, he can often serve his reader's best interests as well as his own by dividing the material into two or more simpler tables.

For your assistance in using tables, the following suggestions are offered:

1. At the top of every table there should be a title—preceded by a number if more than one table is used. Numbers of tables are sometimes Roman numerals but more frequently Arabic.

2. Unless a table is merely supplementary and is placed in an appendix, it should be referred to in the text so that the reader will know when to give it his attention. Reference to a table *may* be desirable even if the table is in an appendix.

3. Each table (unless tables are relegated to the appendix) should be placed where it is conveniently accessible at the proper moment. Ideally, a table should be placed shortly after the point where it is first referred to—always on the same page if there is room for it. Under no circumstances should a table be placed very far in advance of the point where it is referred to or discussed.

4. The form of tables varies in detail as necessitated by the material to be presented. Examples will appear later in the discussion.

5. Regardless of other details of form, each column should have a head-

ing that shows accurately the nature of the contents below. When necessary, this heading should designate the units in which quantities below are expressed. If there is not enough room for the essential information in a column heading, part of it may be added to the table in notes, as described in rule 10.

6. A table should indicate all the factors that affect the data it contains. (For example, the size of pipe used would affect data on the performance of a pump.)

7. Standard symbols and abbreviations may be used to save space.

8. Figures in columns are usually aligned under similar digits—ordinarily the right-hand digit.

9. Fractions should be expressed as decimals unless decimals are not customary for data on the subject concerned, or unless they would misrepresent the degree of accuracy achieved.

10. When a note is needed to explain some part of a table, its presence is indicated by a lower case *letter* raised half a space above the line at the point where the note applies. The notes applying to a table are placed at the bottom of the table, rather than at the bottom of the page where they might be confused with ordinary footnotes.

11. A table should not break into the normal margins of the page. If necessary it may be placed so that it extends across the length of the page, with the top of the table toward what would normally be the left side of the page.

12. Do not use needless lines, especially solid lines, between columns of data, between lines, or at the bottom of the table.

13. No table should continue from one page to another unless continuation is unavoidable because the table is more than a page long. When such is the case, *continued* or *ctd.* should be used at the bottom of the first page to indicate that the table has not been completed, and at the top of the second page to indicate that part of the table has preceded. Column headings must be repeated on the second page. If totals are to be indicated at the bottoms of columns, the subtotals should be at the bottom of the first page and at the top of the second page. The word *forward* should be used at the left side of the subtotals, to show that they are not final totals.

14. A table from an outside source must be acknowledged, as one would acknowledge any other borrowed material. This may be done by naming the source in parentheses after or under the title, or by use of a footnote. If the footnote is used, its presence is indicated by a number raised half a space above the line. If the number and title of the table are on one line, the footnote number follows the title; if they are on separate lines, the number of the footnote follows the number of the table.

Table 2.   Average Daily Emission (in tons) of Atmospheric Pollutants

Source	Hydrocarbons and Hydrocarbon Derivatives		Aerosols	Sulfur Oxides	Nitrogen Oxides
	Hydrocarbons	Hydrocarbon Derivatives			
Automotive[a]	1100	150	35	35	775
Petroleum Marketing	70	0	0	0	0
Petroleum Refining and Production	160	2	5	45	45
Solvents and Coatings	210	150	0	0	0
Totals	1540	302	40	80	820

[a]These figures are now being revised to incorporate later data.

Table II

Average Daily Emission (in tons) of Atmospheric Pollutants

Source	Hydrocarbons and Hydrocarbon Derivatives		Aerosols	Sulfur Oxides	Nitrogen Oxides
	Hydrocarbons	Hydrocarbon Derivatives			
Automotive[a]	1100	150	35	35	775
Petroleum Marketing	70	0	0	0	0
Petroleum Refining and Production	160	2	5	45	45
Solvents and Coatings	210	150	0	0	0
Totals	1540	302	40	80	820

[a]These figures are now being revised to incorporate later data.

Figure 2.   Specimen Tables.   The forms shown, unlike most forms seen in print, can be produced on a typewriter. They may be altered as necessary to accommodate different materials. The numbers at the left are not part of the tables but are added in order to indicate vertical spacing. Additional forms and uses of tables should be observed in publications dealing with your intended profession.

The preceding suggestions are modified when a writer uses a form that cannot strictly be called a table. The term *table* means something more than a mere list, or two or three lists placed side by side. If you examine the work of experienced writers you will find that they rarely

Table 6. Performance of Self-Polishing Wax on Linoleum

Test	Nukoat	Florglo	Waxeeze	Hygrade
Ease of Application	Excellent	Excellent	Fair	Good
Original Appearance	Good	Good	Excellent	Good
Resistance to Scuffing	Good	Fair	Fair	Poor
Resistance to Scratching	Good	Good	Poor	Poor
Resistance to Water Spotting	Fair	Fair	Poor	Fair
Response to Rebuffing	Fair	Fair	Good	Good

Figure 3. Specimen Table Showing Tabular Presentation of Nonstatistical Information.

call anything a table unless it not only has headings at the top of its columns, but has a left-hand column that also consists of headings. This is illustrated in the following extremely simple example, as well as in the other specimens.

TABLE 1. COMPARISON OF DIFFERENT BRANDS OF PAINT

Quality	Brand "A"	Brand "B"	Brand "C"
Ease of application	Good	Fair	Good
Appearance	Fair	Fair	Good
Durability	Good	Poor	Poor

Well-informed people sometimes call material that does not meet the preceding specifications "informal tables." But they do not use the word *table* before the title of such material, nor refer to it as a table in their text. These "informal tables" are not numbered and need not be referred to specifically in the text because, unlike a true table, they are actually part of the text in substance if not in form. This is not to discourage the use of this form, but the writer who treats it as he would treat an actual table makes his work look both stiff and amateurish.

Forms that may be used for tables are illustrated in Figures 2 and 3.

FIGURES

In the following discussion, all forms of illustrations are referred to as figures. Examination of technical books and magazines will justify this terminology.

To the technical writer, figures are functional rather than ornamental. Though in other kinds of writing they are frequently used merely to arouse interest or improve the appearance of a page, in technical writing they serve primarily as a means of giving information. If they also happen to catch attention or make a page look more attractive, so much the better; but that is not the main reason for their use. On the rare occasions when a technical writer must use figures mainly for the purpose of arousing interest, he will disregard many of the rules for use of figures in technical writing.

Whatever types of figure one may use, the following suggestions should be helpful.

1. *Number and title.* Every figure should have a title, which should be preceded by a number (usually Arabic) if more than one figure is used. It is usually best to use a single sequence of numbers even when figures differ in kind. The number and title are normally placed underneath a figure but may be placed in a convenient location on the figure itself. (This is likely to be desirable on a graph because of the lettering at the bottom.) A title is ordinarily phrased as a topic (see page 190 for definition of *topic*); but sentences are sometimes used for figures appearing in magazine articles.

2. *The legend.* In addition to a title, a figure may also have a legend if it needs one. The term *legend* applies to the additional lines, often in smaller type if printed, that follow the title and explain the figure or identify its parts. If a legend follows a title that is phrased as a sentence, the two blend together so that in appearance they constitute a single unit.

3. *Spacing of the title and legend.* When the title is underneath the figure, there should be at least a double space between the figure and the title. However, the title, and the legend if one is used, should be closer to the figure than to the text that follows, so that they will be identified with the figure, not with the text.

4. *Reference to the figure.* Every figure, unless it is purely supplementary and is placed in an appendix, should be mentioned in the text. (It *may* be referred to even if it is in an appendix.) The reference to the figure is placed in parentheses unless it is part of the sentence where it occurs. Note the following examples:

As can be seen in Fig. 4, the dimensions . . .

The arrangement of the equipment (see Fig. 5) is planned so as
to . . .

If a figure is related to a long stretch of text, it should not be referred to
more frequently than is necessary to keep the reader reminded of its
bearing on the discussion.

5. *Placement of the figure in the text.* Any figure in the text should be
placed, if possible, almost immediately after the point where it is first
mentioned. Certainly it should not come very far ahead of that point,
for if it does, the reader may either study it too soon or else, having
passed it, may neglect to turn back to it. When possible, you should place
a figure on the page where you discuss it.

6. *Partial lines of type.* If a figure is narrow enough to leave room for
partial lines of type, the type should be placed on the left and the figure
on the right. (This suggestion applies to material typed on only one side
of the sheet and therefore regarded as the right-hand page of a book.
On a left-hand page, the figure is placed on the left.) However, if two or
more figures are placed on one page, the layout may be designed in any
manner that gives the page a good appearance and places each figure
where the reader can consult it conveniently.

7. *Drawing the figure.* Full instructions for drawing figures are beyond
the scope of this text. It should be mentioned, however, that figures
should be drawn in India ink, that they should be no larger than is necessary for clearness, and that each figure should be placed within a border
unless its own shape creates a natural border. The figure should not extend into the margins of the page.

8. *Self-sufficiency of the figure.* A figure should be self-sufficient so
that the reader for whom it is intended may study it without being forced
to consult the text. Every part of a figure that cannot be identified from
its appearance should be labeled or else identified by use of a key. The
key may appear on the figure or may be a legend under the title.

9. *Lettering on the figure.* The lettering on a figure should be placed,
when possible, so that it can be read with the bottom of the figure down.
Lettering that must run at a right angle to the bottom of the figure should
read with the right side of the figure down.

10. *Sidewise figure.* If a figure must be turned sidewise on the page,
it should be drawn so that the bottom of the figure comes on what is
normally the right side of the page. (This can sometimes cause lettering
to appear upside down when the page is in normal position.)

11. *Acknowledgment of source.* If a figure is taken from an outside
source, the source must be acknowledged. The acknowledgment may be
placed in parentheses after the title, or after the legend if you use a
legend from the same source. Acknowledgment may also be made by
means of a footnote.

12. *Mounting a photograph.* If a photograph or clipping is used as a figure, it should be mounted neatly, preferably by use of rubber cement, unless copy is being prepared for printing.

13. *Preparation of figures for printing.* If copy is to be printed, figures must not be fastened to the pages of the manuscript. The figures and captions are separately prepared and numbered, and the manuscript is marked to show where the figures should be placed. The figures should be drawn larger than they will be on a printed page—perhaps twice the size. Figures for offset reproduction should be drawn, usually, in the size that they will appear in the reproduction. The full planning of layouts for display printing is beyond the scope of this book.

The preceding instructions indicate that a table or figure should be referred to in the text. This does not imply that a mere mention is the only attention it receives. Often the text will discuss a table or a figure in considerable detail, so that the reader can understand it as easily as possible. The text may direct the reader's attention to the points that are most important, or may explain the table or figure in sufficient detail to make sure that its full significance and implications are not overlooked. One test of your skill as a technical writer—a test often overlooked in this kind of discussion—is your use of the text to help the reader benefit from tables and figures, as well as your use of tables and figures to assist the text.

Thus far, all that has been said about figures applies to figures of every type. Some of the common types call for individual attention. Before they are discussed, however, it should be re-emphasized that no amount of discussion can eliminate the need for constant observation of the figures in technical books and magazines.

Bar Charts

One of the simplest and most useful types of figure is the bar chart, with which every reader is familiar. The type of information it presents might also be presented in a table. In fact you may often first make out a table and then convert it into a bar chart to make differences in quantity instantly and unavoidably *visual*. For example, a reader might see numbers such as 841,654 and 418,543 arranged in columns, along with several other numbers, and yet fail to become aware of the relative quantities until he had given the table close attention. If such numbers were presented as bars, one of which was more than twice the length of the other, the relative amounts, being clearly visible, could hardly fail to be perceived.

The bars in a bar chart are sometimes vertical (see Figure 4), sometimes horizontal (see Figure 5). They may be shaded differently in different portions of their length so as to permit comparison of parts as well

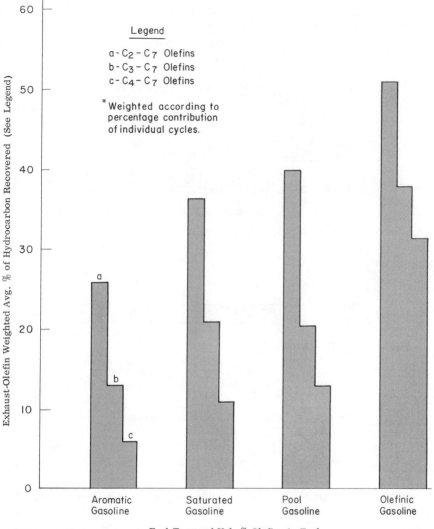

Figure 2. Olefin Content of Exhaust Hydrocarbons from Several Gasolines.

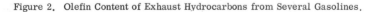

Figure 4. Bar Chart with Vertical Bars   (Courtesy of Air Pollution Control District, County of Los Angeles).

as of the whole. For example, the different bars in a chart might represent the total expenditures of different divisions of some organization, and each bar might be shaded differently in different sections of its length so as to show what amount of the expenditures went for specific expenses such as wages, raw materials, power, and overhead.

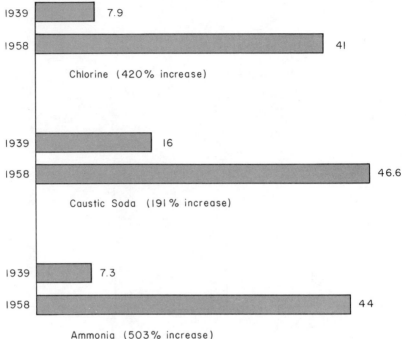

Figure 11. Increase in Per Capita Production,
in Pounds, of Representative Heavy Chemicals.
(1/16 in. equals 1 lb.)

Figure 5.   Bar Chart with Horizontal Bars.

There are variations of the bar chart such as the drawing of pictures to represent quantities. For example, the increase in the number of passengers carried by an airline might be suggested by pictures of men, or the increase in the production of a metal by pictures of ingots. This pictorial treatment is used primarily when an effort is being made to popularize the material. It is intended to arouse interest as well as give information. Properly handled, it may be a useful device. Often, unfortunately, it is not properly handled. Instead of drawing, let us say, three times as many men to show that one airline carried three times as many passengers as another, a writer may draw one man for each line but make the second man three times as tall as the first. This is confusing, for in *area* the large man is *nine* times the size of the small man—and a reader forms only a vague or even erroneous impression until he studies the exact figures.

All in all, since a bar chart fails to perform its major function unless it uses visual methods to create a clear and accurate impression of the facts, it is best to use ordinary bars or lines, so that no dimension varies except length, or else to show the variation of quantity by varying the number, not the size, of pictures. These methods are the most honest and accurate, and are also the clearest to the reader.

Graphs—Curves

Like the bar chart, the graph or curve is a means of presenting data that might also be presented as a table. In fact it is hardly possible to construct a graph without having constructed a table first. The extra work that it takes to convert a table into a graph is often justified, however, by the fact that a graph makes it much easier for the reader to grasp the information.

Suppose you wished to show how the price of a commodity varied from month to month over a period of one or two years. To learn the low, the high, and the general trends from a table your reader would find it necessary to study the data at length. Yet all these points would be perceptible at a glance if the table were converted into a graph. If the data concerned three or four commodities, the use of curves would be even more advantageous. It would enable the reader to grasp the situation in a moment, whereas he would have to read and compare dozens of figures to get the desired information from a table.

The graph or curve differs from a bar chart in that the graph always shows changes in two values. It shows how one varies as the other varies —for example, how employment increases or decreases as the year progresses. One of these elements is frequently the passage of time and the other is an amount or quantity. When this is the case, the passage of time is usually shown on the horizontal scale and the variation of quantity on the vertical scale.

A graph always has a horizontal and a vertical scale, the horizontal usually indicating what might be called the independent variable, such as time, and the vertical indicating the dependent variable. Full information about the scales must appear as part of the graph. The specimens shown illustrate the placement of this information. The vertical scale, ordinarily placed on the left, may be placed on the right side too if the graph is so large that it is needed there.

Sometimes more than one curve appears on the same graph. In this case, if there is room, each curve should be identified by a short title lettered above it. If room does not permit this lettering, a different kind of line may be used for each curve, and a key identifying the lines can be shown on some unused space on the face of the graph. Other means also —for example a legend under the title—may be used for identification.

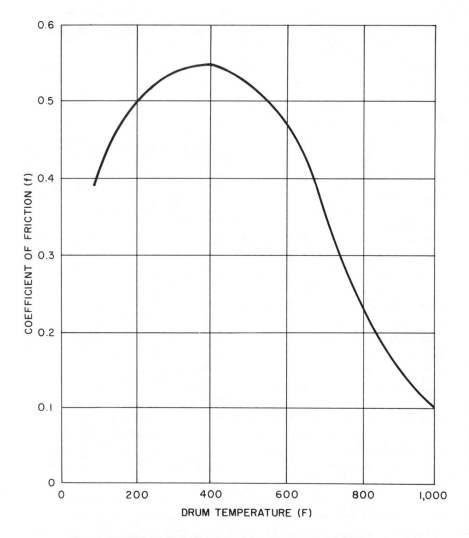

Fig. 2–EFFECT OF TEMPERATURE ON LINING COEFFICIENT. In a typical plot of temperature versus brake lining coefficient of friction, the coefficient gradually rises, peaks out, then falls rapidly as temperature is increased. The rapid fall is referred to as brake fade.

Figure 6.   Specimen Curve   (Courtesy of General Motors Corporation).

Be sure that when you make a graph you choose the scales, both vertical and horizontal, in such a manner that the visual impression the graph conveys is justified by the facts. When a line goes up or down at a sharp angle, a reader infers that the rapidity of change is highly significant. If it climbs or falls at a slight angle, he interprets the change as insignificant. Yet the angle at which the line goes up or down is dependent on

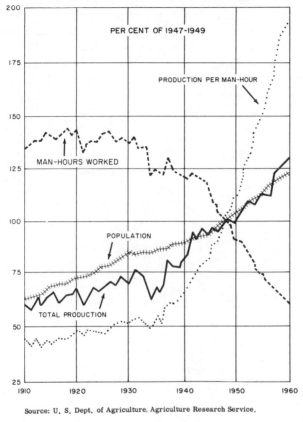

COMPARISON OF AGRICULTURAL PRODUCTION
WITH PRODUCTIVITY AND POPULATION

Source: U. S. Dept. of Agriculture, Agriculture Research Service.

Figure 7.   Specimen Curve.

the scales selected. It therefore becomes a matter of mere honesty for a writer who makes a graph to work out his scales so that if a change is important the line climbs or drops at a sharp angle, and if the change is not important the line goes up or down slowly.

Figures 6 and 7 are examples of curves.

The "Pie" Diagram

Another widely used device is the "pie" diagram, consisting of a circle divided into segments. This form is used to make visual the relative percentages of a whole. For example, it might show what percentages of a corporation's income were allotted to various expenses, dividends, and capital gains. More than any other device it permits comparison of parts to each other and to the whole at the same time.

Like any other drawing, it should state amounts as well as illustrate them. These amounts should often be the actual quantities as well as the percentages.

One difficulty in making such a diagram is the problem of making the letters identifying the segments all run in the same direction. If there are too many segments and if they are too small, this difficulty may become insuperable and make it inadvisable to use the form.

A characteristic pie diagram is illustrated in Figure 8.

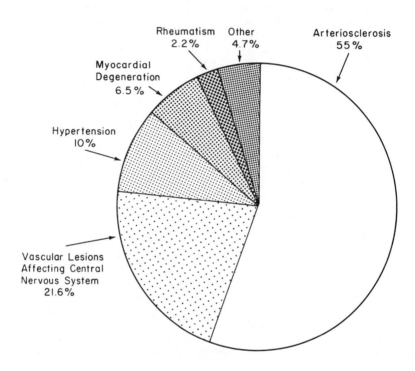

Figure 17. Distribution of Deaths Caused by Cardiovascular Disease. (Source of Information: U. S. Dept. of Health, Education, and Welfare)

Figure 8. Pie Chart.

Organization Charts and Flow Sheets

Unlike the figures discussed above, the organization chart and the flow sheet are not concerned with statistical information. The mere name *organization chart* shows the kind of information it presents—divisions of an organization, which are represented by circles or rectangles so arranged and connected by lines that authority, relationship, and responsibility are easily seen. Such a chart is far more effective than words in presenting this information. Indeed, many a body has been induced to

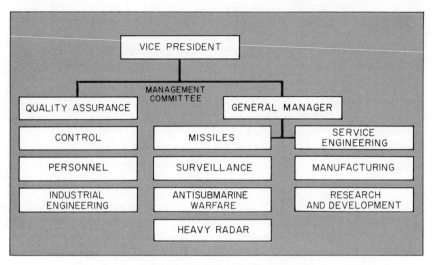

Figure 12. Apparatus Division Organization Chart

Figure 9.   Specimen Organization Chart   (Courtesy of Texas Instruments Incorporated).

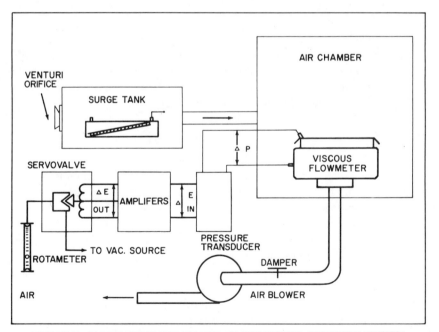

FIGURE 7. CALIBRATION SET-UP FOR PROPORTIONAL SAMPLING SYSTEM

Figure 10.   Specimen Flow Sheet   (Courtesy of Air Pollution Control District, Los Angeles County).

improve its own organization when an organization chart revealed confused or illogical relationships.

The flow sheet is very similar. Its typical use would be to indicate the method by which some process is carried out. The machines used are sometimes indicated by the conventional circles or rectangles, and sometimes by simplified drawings suggesting their actual appearance. The main difference between the flow sheet and the organization chart is that the flow sheet indicates actual physical movement of materials. The direction of such movement is shown by arrows wherever necessary.

Figures 9 and 10 illustrate an organization chart and a flow sheet.

Photographs

In technical writing you may need to use photographs for either of two main purposes: to assist verbal description, and to prove the truth of assertions. Photographs would be helpful, for example, in showing characteristic fractures of metal that might result from different causes, or in identifying insects or plant diseases. They might also illustrate the condition of equipment that had not been maintained properly, the breaks that had developed in a pavement or the lining of a canal, or the crowded condition of a factory. Sometimes, as mentioned, the purpose of the photograph might be merely to give information; but often a photograph can be used to prove the truth of an assertion by letting the reader see for himself. For this latter purpose, it has no equal.

The photograph is limited, however, by the fact that it can show only the surface and that it may sometimes unavoidably present both significant and nonsignificant facts of appearance with equal emphasis.

Figure 11 is a photograph used in a typical manner.

Diagrams and Drawings

There are many occasions when diagrams and drawings can help to illustrate the text. For example, electrical wiring plans, schematic diagrams showing how any type of equipment operates, or drawings intended to illustrate actual appearance are constantly used by those who write on technical subjects. The shape and relative location of objects as well as the manner in which equipment functions can often be shown better by a diagram than by any other method.

Also, unlike photographs, drawings can picture the interior rather than just the surface of an object. They make it possible to omit what is not significant and to emphasize what is important. As you read the technical writing of others, you should make it a point to observe the manner in which drawings are used; and as you plan your own writing, you should constantly be on the alert for opportunities to make your work more effective by means of drawings.

Close-Up of Oscilloscope Showing Data-Trace Presentation

Figure 11.   Specimen Photograph   (Courtesy of George A. McKean, University of Idaho Engineering Experiment Station).

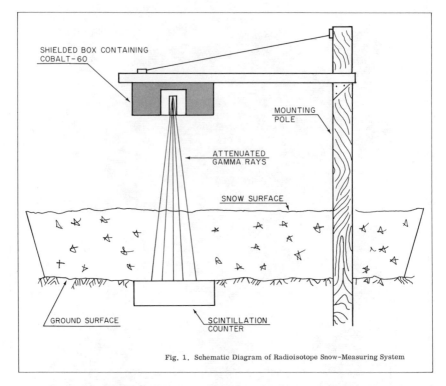

Fig. 1. Schematic Diagram of Radioisotope Snow-Measuring System

Figure 12. Specimen Diagram (Courtesy of Calvin C. Warnick, University of Idaho Engineering Experiment Station).

A characteristic use of a drawing is seen in Figure 12.

ASSIGNMENTS

Papers in which tables and figures are used can be based on Assignments 2, 3, and 4 at the end of Chapter 5.

Part Two

REPORTS
AND
PROPOSALS

7

REPORTS—
DEFINITION,
IMPORTANCE,
AND
QUALITIES

DEFINITION

Anyone who has seen reports from varied sources has noticed that they differ widely in form, length, and many other respects. This gives rise to the question, "What is it that causes reports to be considered a distinct species of writing?" The answer can be found in the following definition: a report is a communication in which the writer (or speaker, if it is an oral report) gives information to some person or organization because it is his responsibility to do so.

As this definition indicates, the common element in all reports, which sets them apart as a distinct species, is the element of responsibility. A report may be made by a committee to its parent organization. It may be made by a consultant to a client. It may be made by the man on the job to his superior. It may be short, simple, and intended for a single reader or it may be long, elaborate, and printed at great expense—for example, the report of a great corporation to its stockholders. But regardless of all these differences, the term *report*, at least in the context of technical writing, should not be applied to a piece of writing unless the writer is responsible for reporting to the reader or readers.

IMPORTANCE

In any large organization, reports perform an indispensable service. They enable those in positions of authority to keep track of normal operations, to learn about unexpected developments, and to judge whether progress is satisfactory on new projects. They enable the executive to base his decisions on the advice of specialists. They are the link between research and the practical utilization of its discoveries. They often provide the basis for the writing of proposals and specifications. They sometimes are the only tangible result of long and expensive work. In general, they comprise one of the most important parts of the process of communication that is vital to efficient operation in government and industry.

DIFFERENCE BETWEEN PROFESSIONAL AND SCHOOL REPORTS

Before a person begins to write reports in his professional career, he is almost certain to have written reports in the classroom. Many of the qualities that are desirable in the classroom reports are also desirable in reports written on the job, but there is one important difference. The value of a report written on the job depends mainly on the answer to one question: how well does it meet the needs of those who receive it? Whatever good qualities it may possess are good only because they help it to meet this one test of excellence.

In the classroom, this test does not ordinarily exist. The instructor assigns a report not because he needs or will use the information it contains, but because the student will profit by acquiring that information and perhaps by reporting it. As a result, the student does not form the habit of constantly asking himself, "Does the man I am reporting to need these particular facts?" When at some later date he writes reports on the job, he is likely to include information that is not needed just because it is available and he himself is intensely interested in the subject.

A case in point is the laboratory report. Many instructors insist that a laboratory report contain information on theory and procedure—because one purpose of the report is to show whether the student understands these matters and can explain them. But in industry, it is usually taken for granted that the writer understands the theory on which his work is based and has used an accepted procedure. And since the reader will usually know about these matters already or else will not need to know, he will be just as well satisfied if they are omitted, *unless they involve something new and significant.*

A person who realizes, at the beginning of his career, the difference between what is desirable in reports written on the job and the reports he has written in school has taken an important step toward becoming a good report writer.

QUALITIES TO STRIVE FOR IN REPORTS

Like any other kind of writing, a report must be considered good or bad mainly on its success in performing its function: to affect the readers as it is supposed to affect them. What specific qualities will help it to produce that result?

Some of these qualities have already been discussed because they should be cultivated in other technical writing as well as in reports. These include accuracy, adaptation of the contents and organization to the needs and abilities of the reader, and effective style. But a report makes additional demands. The key to these lies in a single word: *imagination.* As a report writer you will need to visualize what will happen after your report is submitted, and face such questions as: Whom will it reach? How much do the probable readers know about the subject already? How much do they want and need to know? How busy are they? What is the relative importance of the report at the level that the readers occupy? How much time will they give to it?

The following discussion will touch upon several specific qualities. Some of these re-enforce each other, but there are times when an excessive effort to achieve one quality will mean the sacrifice of another. Thus in considering the question of how vigorously to cultivate any of them on a specific occasion you will need to foresee the circumstances that will probably prevail when your report is actually used, and decide what the report must be if it is to perform its function under those circumstances.

Self-Sufficiency

A report should be self-sufficient. That is, anyone who is likely to read it should be able to do so without having to rely on his memory or consult his files for extra information.

To make this possible, you may need to include facts that could otherwise be omitted. For example, instead of assuming that you may omit facts you originally received from the person to whom you are reporting, you might well remind yourself that details that were fresh in his mind at an earlier date might be hard for him to recall after the passage of considerable time. Also, it is well to remember that the person you are reporting to may pass the report on to others who lack his own familiarity with the subject. In view of these facts, it is best to make sure that whoever the reader might be and whatever circumstances might exist at the time when he reads, a report should provide what is needed for full understanding.

The material that makes a report self-sufficient comes mainly at the beginning. The opening should make clear the function of the report and the circumstances that called for its preparation so that the question, "What's this all about?" is not lurking in the reader's mind as he plunges into its contents.

Interest

It is natural for a person who concentrates a great deal of attention on anything to become so interested in it that he assumes it is interesting to others. Applied to reports, this is a dangerous assumption. Those who read our reports are busy men. Many matters—probably many reports—compete for their attention. Whether your reports get the attention you hope for will depend in part on whether they make an immediate bid for interest.

Many a report, especially if it does not concern a colorful subject, will have a better chance of arousing interest if it is based on a principle that is a commonplace in sales work: a person often buys something not because he wants what he buys but because he wants the results of possessing it. He buys a grey flannel suit, for example, not because he especially wants the suit but because he wants to be identified with the kind of people who wear suits of that kind. A report writer can attempt to arouse interest in his report by quickly showing that it offers a prospect of producing results that the reader already desires: a better product, for example, or economy of operation or saving of time.

This does not mean that a report should resort to sensationalism in its bid for attention, or that its appeal should be specious. It means only that the interest in reports stems primarily from their practical value, which should therefore be pointed out without delay.

How can this result be accomplished? At least two concrete suggestions can be made. First, organize the body of the report so that the reader discovers as early as possible what benefits may result if your report receives attention. Your skill in organizing in this manner yet at the same time making your plan logical and coherent will be one of the decisive factors. Second, in one or another of the preliminary parts—the letter of transmittal, the covering memorandum, the introduction, or the summary—provide a sentence or two deliberately calculated to arouse interest by foreshadowing the significance of the full report. These sentences should be specific and concrete. Just to say, in effect, "This is interesting and important" is a waste of space.

Whether you can retain interest once you have aroused it depends to some extent on the effectiveness of your writing style. The likelihood that style in itself can *create* interest is slight, for readers read reports for the value of their contents, not for enjoyment. But readability, conciseness, and the color and vigor that can be obtained from concreteness will most assuredly help to retain or increase the interest, and a dull, wordy, obscure style will force interest to engage in a desperate struggle for survival.

Thoroughness

It goes without saying that thoroughness is desirable in a report as elsewhere; but whether this quality is achieved depends in many cases on whether the writer uses his imagination. There are always some obvious questions that a report must answer. But answering the obvious questions is not always enough. For example, an increase or decrease in the number of people taking a training course in two successive years might seemingly point to a conclusion about the success of the course. But difference in weather, the existence of an influenza epidemic during one year, or a change in the makeup of the working force could also affect the number; and the possibility of such outside forces could not safely be overlooked.

There are other factors to be considered for the sake of thoroughness. Assuming that you have demonstrated that the action you recommend would definitely produce the result desired, might there be other and possibly better ways of producing that result? Also, is it possible that the actions you recommend would not only produce the desired result, but would also produce undesired side effects that you have overlooked? For example, you might prove that leaving stubble in the fields rather than burning it would prevent erosion, yet overlook the possibility that leaving it would permit harmful insects to multiply. Or again, a program to destroy predatory animals might succeed in reducing the number of predators but in doing so permit an increase in the population of crop-destroying rodents.

Obviously, if a report is to be thorough, its writing must be preceded by a thorough job of gathering information; but many a writer who has answers to all the essential questions, the less obvious as well as the obvious, fails to include them. He makes the mistake of assuming that because he knows all the necessary questions have been considered, he need not answer them all. He overlooks the fact that the reader will not share his confidence unless he, the reader, is told enough to be sure nothing has been overlooked.

How much detail about secondary questions should a report include? There is no formula that provides an answer to this question, but at least we can realize its existence and use our judgment about whether we have given the reader not only the information he will actually use, but also the extra information that will free him from worry about whether something has been overlooked.

Omission of Unnecessary Material

Like any other desirable quality, thoroughness can be carried too far. We need to ask ourselves not only, "Am I overlooking anything that should be included?" but also, "Am I including anything that could be left out?" If we do not consciously guard against including too much, we are almost certain to err in this direction.

It is not surprising that this should be true. It is natural for a person who devotes a great deal of time and attention to any subject to overestimate the extent to which it will impress others as important. And when we report to those above us, it is easy to forget that something which is a major element in our own area of activity may be a much smaller fraction of the area in which those farther up the line are involved.

The danger of including too much is increased by the fact that, as we gather our material, it is almost impossible to gather exactly what we need and no more. In fact we cannot be positive just what will ultimately be needed and what will not. And since it is painful to see facts and ideas go to waste—facts and ideas that we have worked hard to obtain—it is a temptation to include them just because we have them.

Unfortunately, their inclusion sometimes does more harm than good. A reader is less likely to grasp and remember the facts of real importance if he must separate them from material that he does not really need.

The temptation to include unnecessary material is especially strong when a report leads to negative conclusions and recommendations. To see why this is true, consider the following situation. The question of whether to handle a crop of some kind by a different method is being investigated. The decision rests upon answers to such individual questions as the cost of buying and operating the new machinery, the quality of product it turns out, the skills it demands of its operators, and its reliability. Suppose that the investigation of its reliability shows it to be subject to frequent breakdowns; and since a breakdown at a critical time during harvest would mean a heavy loss because of spoilage, this single defect is enough to bring about a negative decision. If you were reporting on the investigation you would be tempted to tell all you had learned on each aspect of the study. But if you were the reader, you would not wish to waste your time on details about cost of operation, quality of product, and operator skills only to learn later that the machine was not reliable enough to use. You would probably want full facts about the unreliability because those facts would be the basis for a decision, but would want only a minimum of information on the other questions.

Writers of reports or of any other kind of communications will always have to encounter the question, "How much should I say?" And there is no better way to answer this question than by using your imagination— by trying to visualize the moment when those who will read your report pick it up, pressed as they will be for time, and start to read. With this picture in mind, scrutinize the contents of your report and ask yourself constantly, "Would the report perform its function just as well if I left some of this out?"

Freedom From Bias

A person who must investigate a subject and report his findings often starts work with a strong expectation about the probable outcome. When this expectation is based upon sound previous knowledge and experience, it is entirely natural and unobjectionable. When it is based on mere prejudice, however—or even worse, on self-interest—the case is different. There is no surer way to lose a reader's confidence than by letting him gather the impression that you have been swayed by an eagerness to reach a preconceived conclusion.

To be sure, some so-called reports fail to meet the requirement of impartiality. Protagonists of conflicting interests, in preparing reports to use in a controversy, usually present matters from their own point of view. But these reports are not suitable models for a person entering a technical profession. A bona fide technical report is not begun with the purpose of proving something. Rather, its purpose is to present all sides with scrupulous fairness. In the long run, no one in a technical profession will profit by letting his reports be or even appear to be prejudiced. Hard though it may be, you should plan an investigation in such a manner that you will not fail to discover evidence that might run counter to the conclusions you expect and hope to reach, and should present your findings in such a manner as to show that you have been impartial.

Objectivity

The term *objectivity* is sometimes used with practically the same meaning as *freedom from bias*. We will use it here, however, to refer to the quality that is the opposite of *subjectivity*. In urging that reports be objective, we are urging that they be based on concrete facts.

The need for objectivity becomes a matter of special concern whenever a report touches upon human actions or attitudes. For example, reasoning subjectively about what workers would do under certain circumstances might result in a radically different conclusion than would be reached by observing their actual conduct under such circumstances.

Some matters, of course, are basically subjective. The relative beauty of two makes of automobiles cannot be determined by measurement, nor can the question of whether a new process produces better-tasting instant coffee. But even when we deal with questions of taste, objectivity need not be surrendered. It can be attained by getting a substantial number of subjective opinions. Assuming a fair investigation has been made, though we might not be able to say objectively that Brand "A" tastes better than Brand "B," we might be able to make the truly objective statement that 70 per cent of the people who tasted both preferred the taste of "A" to the taste of "B."

Restraint

A report should be restrained both in substance and in style. Valuable though enthusiasm may be on some occasions, there is no surer way to lose a reader's confidence than to give him the impression that your enthusiasm has overbalanced your judgment.

Restraint in substance is more than a mere concession to reader psychology. We realize this when we think of the extravagant hopes aroused by the development of drugs that seemed promising but were later found to have undesirable side effects, or the development of insecticides that unexpectedly created problems related to public health.

Restraint in style should lead you to avoid such terms as *astonishing, startling, flagrant,* or *disastrous.* Rather than writing *a tremendous increase* it is advisable to write *a substantial increase,* but even better to say *a 50 per cent increase* and let the reader choose his own adjective. Or again, it is better to tell your reader that a flood drove five hundred people from their homes than to refer to it as *calamitous, appalling,* or *catastrophic.*

Restraint is especially important in stating conclusions. This does not mean that you should insert such meaningless phrases as "It is believed that . . ." or "It may be concluded that. . . ." But you should not go beyond the evidence in making claims or predictions, and should recognize the possibility that later developments can always lead to results that no one could have anticipated.

Appropriate Degree of Impersonality and Formality

A personal tone in writing, as contrasted with an impersonal tone, is the quality that results when a writer constantly refers to people, especially to himself. "I could hear the hum from a distance of 20 feet," for example, is personal. "The hum was audible from a distance of 20 feet" is impersonal.

In some of the simpler situations, especially in a letter or memorandum, a personal tone is natural and desirable. Much of the time, however, impersonality is better. If you write, "I weighed the sample at half-hour intervals," it is apparently your intention to tell us about your own actions. But if you write, "The samples were weighed at half-hour intervals," you are centering our attention on what was done to the samples. Of course if it is really significant that you were the one who performed some action, a personal approach would probably be suitable. Most of the time, however, an impersonal version is more likely to emphasize the facts that are really important, because we are usually writing about *things* rather than about ourselves.

As for formality versus informality, certainly there is no reason to be formal if you are reporting on a matter of temporary concern and addressing a reader with whom your personal relationship is informal. But if a report is likely to go beyond the immediate reader or if it is likely to become a matter for future reference, informality is usually inappropriate. It is usually better to call a microphone a *microphone,* not a *mike.* A laboratory is a *laboratory,* not a *lab.* Television is *television,* not *TV.* "He lost his temper" is better than "He blew his top." Even contractions are sometimes avoided, being considered colloquial. Following are some other examples showing the difference between formal and informal style.

Informal	*Formal*
bank on good results	feel confident of good results
a pretty good chance	a reasonable chance
come in handy	be useful
put up with	tolerate
flu	influenza
dope	narcotics
O.K.	satisfactory
has a different angle	has a different point of view (or opinion)
is going to	will

Obviously, some of the formal equivalents listed are not the only possibilities, for some of the informal specimens are variable or general in meaning.

In avoiding language that is too informal, do not go to the extreme of using language that sounds stiff and pompous. Suppose we wished to replace *you,* used informally for *one,* in the sentence, "You cannot make the trip in less than four hours." It is not necessary to write *"One* cannot make the trip in less than four hours." If *one* seems to be stiff, we can write, "The trip takes at least four hours," or "It is impossible to make the trip in less than four hours." In brief, there is no reason for formality to be painfully conspicuous. The only necessity is to write with enough dignity to suit the occasion. If you hold a professional position, you need to learn how to avoid excessive informality without letting your style become stiff and awkward.

Consideration of Emotional Factors

Reports, like other kinds of technical writing, should appeal to the mind rather than to the emotions. When it is our responsibility merely to present objective facts without making any attempt to say what should be done about them, this principle can be applied without modification. There are times, however, when the emotions cannot be disregarded. Though this point receives little attention in many discussions of technical writing, it is often emphasized within the broad field of industrial communication.

To be sure, an appeal to the emotions cannot be relied upon to do the constructive job of selling our ideas; but there are many occasions when *ignoring* people's emotions can destroy our chance of selling them. Why should this be true? The answer is that many actions recommended in reports affect not only things but also people—their egos, their pride, their status, their attachment to established ways. Suppose, for example, that an investigation shows a new method of doing something to be far more efficient than the method already in use. If the person who writes the report, in his eagerness to prove this, is too devastating in his attack on the old method, he may force people to defend it because the attack seems to reflect discredit upon them personally.

After all, those to whom we report are not always entirely independent in deciding what is to be done. They often need to secure the concurrence of other persons, whose objections could easily delay or seriously endanger the chance of favorable action. If we can present our findings in such a manner that we do not antagonize these other persons, we increase the chance that our recommendations will be followed.

The preceding warning is necessary because it is always a temptation to build the strongest possible case for what we believe in, and it is consequently a temptation to demonstrate that a contrary position is unthinkable. If we yield to this temptation, however, we may needlessly arouse resentment and opposition. And even if the opposition can be overcome, this antagonism may reduce the likelihood that our recommended measures will be successful.

This does not mean that when you write a report, you should be insincere in order to prevent people from disagreeing with you. However, you should give some thought to the question of who will be affected by your report. So far as possible, present your case without hurting these people, angering them, or humiliating them. Don't make anyone look bad when you can avoid doing so. Remember that even if your case is logical, people are less likely to see its logic if they feel hurt or resentful. In brief, don't increase the opposition to your ideas by ignoring the fact that people have feelings.

EXERCISES

Exercise 1

Rewrite each of the following sentences so that it shows the freedom from emotionalism, the objectivity, and the restraint that would be appropriate in a report. If necessary, you may make up the objective facts that desirable change in style would demand.

1. The appalling devastation caused by the explosion was frightful to contemplate.
2. The morale of the working force will be completely wrecked if this incredible miscarriage of justice is permitted.
3. The asinine preoccupation with minor technicalities is crippling our efforts to use our time in doing constructive work.
4. We have so much red tape, that we are operating a ribbon factory rather than a machine shop.
5. As a result of the new fire doors, ventilation is so bad that the fragrance of last year's cigarets still pollutes the atmosphere. If air-conditioning is not provided, workers may be overcome by smoke without there even being a fire.
6. Some of the staff let their work slide while they frittered away their time in prolonged coffee breaks.
7. The overweight trucks turned the highway into a pock-marked no-man's land.
8. The expected increase in production per man-hour will be sensational, and the flood of products will bury our competitors.
9. The clanking and clattering of the antiquated machinery is turning the office staff into a collection of nervous wrecks.
10. The stench of the fumes from the mill is nauseating throughout the entire valley.

Exercise 2

Rewrite each of the following specimens so that the language is standard English and the style is impersonal. (There is no intention to imply that every expression you eliminate would be wrong in circumstances where informality was suitable.)

1. The gadget that is supposed to control the water supply is always getting out of kilter.
2. When we gave him the lowdown he finally admitted that his assistant had tried to put something over on him.
3. I couldn't raise him on the squawk box because it had gone on the blink, so I had to give him a ring on the phone.
4. The brass didn't get the straight dope through regular channels, and when they got it elsewhere they raised the roof.
5. The newly designed loading mechanism looks hopeful, but we can't put it into production until we get the bugs out of it.
6. Since the supervisor was still pretty green, he blew his top when the manager began to ride him.
7. The crates had to be lugged over to the other end of the lab before they could be opened.

8. We could reduce the outlay for automobiles if we could convince the field men that they don't rate cars that are really loaded.
9. It ran pretty well at low speeds but conked out on us when we revved it up.
10. His attitude was okay at first, but he got sore when he wasn't promoted and has been awfully touchy for the last four months.

8

SPECIAL
TYPES
OF
REPORTS

There is no neat, generally accepted list of types by means of which all reports can be classified. To be sure, great corporations and government bureaus often develop types that suit their own needs and identify these types by whatever names they consider appropriate. This book, however, is addressed to readers who will produce reports for a wide range of employers and clients. Therefore, though the terminology and the list of types are as nearly standard as varied usage permits, there will be no attempt to establish a set of mutually exclusive classifications comparable to a botanist's classification of plants. Rather, the discussion will merely attempt:

1. To give you a better understanding of the wide ramifications of reports in form and purpose.

2. To make the names of commonest types familiar enough that if you are asked to write a report of a certain type and given no further guidance, you will know what is probably expected and will also realize how much latitude you enjoy.

3. To encourage resourcefulness and self-confidence, so that if you are asked to write a report but given no instructions about what kind, you will decide upon the type and form with assurance.

The types to be covered are reports made by filling in a blank form, letters, memoranda, periodic reports, progress reports, and laboratory reports. Formal and semiformal reports are only briefly identified, being covered in more detail in a later chapter. An important section at the end of this chapter comments on reports that cannot be considered as any distinct type.

REPORTS MADE BY FILLING IN A BLANK FORM

Many reports are made by merely filling in the spaces on a blank form on which headings are already provided. This can happen when, in a particular organization, some activity becomes so routine that the information about it will always occupy approximately the same amount of space and will always be covered by the same headings.

Frequently the information filled in consists merely of figures. In this case making the report is not a problem of writing at all. Yet sometimes the blanks must be filled in with ordinary prose. On these occasions the printed forms are used to make sure that the organization of the reports will always be the same, to prevent the writer from overlooking any essential routine point, and to discourage any tendency to make the report too long. Such reports are good in that those who read them always know exactly where to find what they are looking for. Their main limitation is their lack of flexibility. Sometimes flexibility is increased, however, by a section for comments.

Writing a report on a blank calls for no skill except the ability to gather the necessary information and to write clearly, accurately, and concisely. The style should be reasonably formal in a report that will become part of some organization's permanent records, but may be informal in a report dealing with a matter of only temporary concern. A report made on a form appears on page 143.

REPORTS IN THE FORM OF LETTERS

When there is no need for a report to include tables, figures, or any kind of stiff and bulky material, the natural form to use is often a letter. Most of what you need to know about reports that are letters can be learned when letters are discussed later in the book, for the same good practices apply for any letter, regardless of its use. The form for a report is no different from the form of other letters except that the use of a subject line is more likely to be desirable. In language, the letter serving as a report may not call for quite so much concern about tone, negative material, and good will, for the reader is likely to be in your own organization. However, if a letter is used in making a report to someone on the outside—a client rather than an employer—tone and good will are as important as in any other letter.

A letter can be used to report on almost any type of subject. Letters that serve as reports often run longer than the average business letter. Long or short, a report in the form of a letter should be just as carefully organized as any other piece of writing of comparable length and complexity. Such devices as topic sentences for paragraphs should not be neglected. (Topic sentences are discussed in the Handbook under Paragraphs.) Indeed, in a letter report of two or three pages, it may be desirable to use internal headings, as in any other report. Their use is covered in Chapter 9.

Reports in the form of letters can vary widely in formality. When addressing a close associate, you might often be justified in making your style extremely informal. There are occasions, however, when your sense of fitness—your imagination in visualizing how the report will be used and whom it might eventually reach—should make it apparent that more dignity is indicated.

One final caution is needed regarding the use of the letter form for a report. If the subject is likely to be of permanent concern, the letter form is sometimes undesirable because it may cause the report to be filed along with ordinary correspondence rather than as part of the organization's permanent records. When this likelihood exists, it may be advisable to prepare a report in some other form and write a covering letter to accompany it.

REPORTS IN THE FORM OF MEMORANDA

In many ways a memorandum resembles a letter. Like the letter, it is one of the forms used most frequently. Like the letter, it is not usually used for a report that is long or one that calls for the use of other material than ordinary text. Like the letter, it may range from informal to formal in style. But unlike the letter the memorandum is strictly for use within the organization—for communication within a department or between departments. Consequently, a memorandum may be unceremonious in style and may sacrifice niceties for conciseness. This does not mean that bluntness and tactlessness are to be condoned. Tact and diplomacy help to get results in dealings within an organization just as they do in outside contacts.

Originally the term "memorandum" implied something of a temporary nature. This is no longer true; yet there are times when a memorandum is written to make immediately available some information that will later be included in a longer, more formal report. Some of the largest corporations in the nation make this use of the memorandum.

For use in writing memoranda, printed forms are usually available. If no form is provided, however, you should provide the necessary information at the top of the first page, using the following form.

To: Date:

From:

Subject:

THE PROGRESS REPORT

A progress report, as the name indicates, is a report on the progress on some project. It may assume any form from that of a simple letter or memorandum to a full-scale formal or even a printed report. Progress reports may be made either when some stage of the work has been completed or at regular intervals. In the latter case they may also be considered periodic reports, the next type to be considered.

The very nature of progress reports affects their organization. Such a report is likely first to indicate the current status of the project and to tell what has been done during the period concerned. Then it tells about the work under way and perhaps covers the plans and outlook for the future. Incorporated into these points would be information on unexpected developments if there have been any, and any other facts that the reader would wish to know.

In writing a progress report on an investigation it may be necessary to decide whether to include some or all of the information already obtained. If some aspects of the investigation have been concluded and if the information would be of interest, there is usually no reason to withhold it. If there is a chance, however, that partial information would lead to hasty and possibly erroneous conclusions, it may better be withheld until the findings are complete.

It has been mentioned that progress reports fall naturally into a past, present, future pattern, but this pattern need not be the main, over-all division of material. If a report deals with a complicated project it is often better to base the main divisions on the various aspects of the job and apply the past, present, future pattern to each aspect.

When several progress reports must be written on the same project, they should all be organized in the same manner so far as the subject matter permits.

THE PERIODIC REPORT

A periodic report, like a progress report, is distinctive because of its purpose. It is merely a report made as a matter of course at regular intervals, frequently but not solely for the purpose of keeping records. If it deals with a project that will eventually be completed, it is also a progress report, for the two types are not mutually exclusive. In its simplest form it may be merely a filled in blank form—as when a weekly report is made on accidents, production, or the percentage of production failing to pass inspection. It may also be a letter or a memorandum. From these simple forms it may range upward to the elaborate form used in the annual reports of the board of directors to the stockholders of a great corporation—an expensive, illustrated product, printed and distributed by the thousand.

In any given situation the periodic report tends to settle into a well-established form because the points it must cover are usually similar on successive occasions. Consequently, unless you are the first person to fill a position, you will often be able to pattern your periodic reports on those written in the past. Thus the problem of organization, even in a long periodic report, may not be difficult. It pays, however, to be always on the watch for special points that call for unusual treatment and to remember that even when a report follows an established pattern, the difference between good and bad writing affects its quality. And finally, you should not neglect to change the established pattern if you find that it can be improved and are in a position to make changes.

THE LABORATORY REPORT

One of the commonest purposes of reports likely to be written by those who read this discussion is to tell the results of work done in a laboratory. Sometimes this work consists of merely running tests, the results of which may be stated without reference to the reason that the report was requested. On other occasions the report must not only tell the results of laboratory work but must also apply them to some specific problem and even recommend action. In the latter case the laboratory-report form may be discarded in favor of some other form more suitable to the specific occasion.

Most of the time, however, a report on work done in a laboratory may be written under headings that have become fairly well standardized. Though there is some variation in different organizations, the following list covers most of the divisions that a laboratory report is likely to contain.

Title page, or merely a title
Object (often called Purpose)
Theory
Method (or Procedure)
Results
Discussion of Results (often called Comments)
Conclusions
Appendix
Original Data

It is not always necessary to include all these divisions. Much of the time there will be no need to explain the theory; and if the method or procedure has become standardized, the section dealing with it may also be dispensed with. The results, of course, would always be given, though they might be placed on data sheets at the end if they consist of figures. There may or may not be reason to discuss the results; but even when such discussion is needed, it may be placed in the section "Results" rather than in a separate section.

Sometimes a section on conclusions will be unnecessary because the results themselves may be the only conclusions arrived at. A section on conclusions is desirable, however, when consideration of the results has led to convictions that go beyond the results themselves. For example, the results of a test of samples of a type of steel might consist of no more than the facts about its tensile strength and other qualities, but consideration of those results might lead to a conviction as to whether the steel would be suitable for some prospective use.

An appendix need not be used unless it is advisable to add materials omitted from the main report because they are too detailed, too technical, or too bulky. As for "Original Data," much of the time the full data are included under "Results." If the full data seem needlessly detailed, however, the figures under "Results" may be reduced to mere averages and the full data may either be omitted or be placed at the end to permit verification. If placed at the end, they may be included as part or all of an appendix.

The arrangement, as well as the selection of points, in a laboratory report may be varied. The order listed above is logically sound, but sometimes changes may be desirable for the reader's convenience. Conclusions might be placed early in the report, perhaps following the statement of the purpose, for the conclusions are likely to be what the reader wants to know at once. In fact, some of those whom a laboratory report reaches may read the conclusions and nothing else.

To sum up: If given a specific form you should follow it as closely as possible, for the reader will grasp the contents better if they are placed in a form with which he is familiar. If no particular form has been requested, you may use the heads listed above to the extent that you need them. The result will be standard in form so far as any general standard exists.

FORMAL AND SEMIFORMAL REPORTS

For the sake of completeness two more types of reports, formal and semiformal, must be identified here, although they are more fully discussed in Chapter 11.

A formal report is a report that is dignified and impersonal in tone and that presents its material in a pattern resembling the pattern used in books. The extent of this resemblance and the techniques that the pattern calls for will be expanded upon later. It is unfortunate that the term *formal* is used to identify these reports, for its use seems to imply that all other reports are informal. Actually, many reports not classified as formal are free from any flavor of informality. *Nonformal* rather than *informal* is a better term to apply to other types.

The term *semiformal report* has not been used widely enough to have acquired a generally accepted meaning. In this book *semiformal report* means a report that has the tone and general qualities of a formal report but that is simpler in design because it dispenses with some of the parts. Recognition of these reports as a distinct type is useful, because there are numerous occasions when the full apparatus of a formal report is needlessly elaborate but the use of some of its parts and compliance with its general conventions will produce exactly what is needed.

REPORTS THAT FIT INTO NO CLASSIFICATION

There are many varieties of reports that fit into no special classification, especially in their form. They are not made on blanks; they are not letters, memoranda, or laboratory reports; and they do not contain all the parts usually found in formal reports. This often causes uneasiness in inexperienced writers, who often worry too much about form and too little about the reader's needs.

There is no reason, however, to be unduly concerned if you are asked to write a report and none of the recognized types seems to fit the occasion. You should be able to get satisfactory results by handling the job as follows.

First of all, consider the function that your report is supposed to perform. And since it cannot perform its function unless it secures the desired reaction from its readers, think also about who the readers will be—what their interests are and what they already know about the specific subject and the general area in which the subject lies.

Next, turn to the question of what material you will need to include if the report is to perform its function—what points must be covered and what information on each of these points the readers will want or need. As you decide what information to include, always ask yourself how long a report the readers will wish to read.

After you have gathered the necessary information, organize it by using the method recommended in Chapter 3. This method is flexible enough to let you form a plan which organizes your material logically and at the same time makes it easy for a reader to find answers to the questions that are likely to be uppermost in his mind.

Unless the report will be short, decide whether the inclusion of any of the special elements discussed in the next chapter would make it more effective, and use any of them that seems likely to fit the occasion. In particular, use plenty of headings. If you have made a good outline, it will provide headings that cover whatever information you wish to present.

As you start the actual writing, decide whether the occasion calls for a style that is formal or informal—personal or impersonal. Having made your decision, be consistent in using the style that you have chosen as appropriate.

Start your report in such a manner that the reader knows at once that it *is* a report, can tell its specific subject, and can see what function it is supposed to perform.

Mention, near the beginning, any earlier reports or other written material that you will need to refer to or that are specially connected with the report you are writing. This material is sometimes headed *References* and listed before the text of a report begins. (Such a list of references is not to be confused, however, with a list of references placed at the end of the report for the sake of documentation.)

Always be sure that the date of your report is indicated at a point where it will be easy to see.

If you are writing the report as an individual, always identify yourself as the writer. One way to do this is to use the form you would use if you were writing an article. For example:

A Report on the Breakage of Laboratory Equipment

by

Robert A. Watts, Head of the Testing Bureau

July 15, 196–

When such a method seems needlessly elaborate, the necessary information can be placed in the first paragraph. If your report consists of a single page, you can identify yourself by telling your position at the opening and signing it at the end. (The phrase *Respectfully Submitted* is often placed before the signature under these circumstances.) If the report is more than one page long, however, it is better to mention your position at the beginning and supply your name by signing it at the end. A personally written signature is often desirable, under any circumstances, to indicate that the writer accepts responsibility for the report.

If you are writing in behalf of a committee, it is customary not only to identify the committee at the beginning but also to list the members at the end. Sometimes, in fact, it is desirable to have the members personally sign the original, official copy. The names of members are ordinarily arranged alphabetically except that the name of the chairman comes last and his position as chairman is indicated.

The simplicity of the preceding suggestions demonstrates that writing a report that is not one of the special types is not particularly difficult. All you need to do is observe a few simple conventions as you give the reader the information that he needs in a clear and easily understandable manner. If you do this, the question of whether your report can be classified as to type is likely to be inconsequential.

SPECIMENS OF NONFORMAL REPORTS

The following reports are not offered as models. Moreover, though they include most of the types discussed, they are not intended to encourage you to draw sharp boundary lines between types. To draw such lines would be unrealistic.

The real purpose of including examples is in part to make the business of report writing more concrete. Further, it is probable that among the specimens you will find some devices that you can utilize in your own report writing, even though the reports in which they occur may not serve as patterns to follow in full. Perhaps the most important function of the examples, however, is to show how little regimentation exists in report writing. The more experience you have with reports, the more you will realize that good report writing is a matter of intelligent analysis of the reader's needs, effective organization, and clear, concise style rather than a matter of blind compliance with rigid specifications. Accordingly, you should feel encouraged to use your own judgment when you write reports.

As you study the examples, remember that no report writer ever achieves perfection. Consequently, be on the alert for alternative methods of presentation by which effectiveness might have been increased.

(Illustrative Specimens Follow)

SPECIMEN NO. 1 *

Report on a Blank Form

The following page serves a dual function. As the printing at the top shows, it serves as the title page of a longer report; but it is also designed as a self-sufficient report to be distributed more widely than the other pages.

A surprising amount of information is carried in the eleven blocks of material inside the border. The brief abstract and the conclusions provide the absolute essentials of the full report. Examination of several reports of this type showed that the abstract sometimes merely lists the points covered and sometimes summarizes the contents of the full report.

Use of a report form like this—for it can be considered as an independent report made by filling in a form—undoubtedly makes it easy for anyone concerned to discover what is going on and to obtain more information on matters that interest him. Retrieval of information, a matter that demands constant thought in a large corporation, is facilitated by the card shape and ease of filing that results when the bordered portion is cut out and folded.

---

* Courtesy of The General Electric Company.

GENERAL ⊛ ELECTRIC

TECHNICAL INFORMATION SERIES
Title Page

AUTHOR *Ra P* RA Pettersen	SUBJECT CLASSIFICATION Bearings, Journal	NO. DATE 1-15-60

TITLE Evaluation of journal bearing by metallurgical and dimensional analysis.

ABSTRACT

Manufacturing quality of traction motor axle bearing was evaluated by dimensional measurement, metallurgical examination, and physical test.

G.E. CLASS I	REPRODUCIBLE COPY FILED AT	NO. PAGES
GOV. CLASS. None		

CONCLUSIONS

The manufacturing quality of the bearing, both dimensionally and metallurgically, is good and bearings of this type should perform satisfactority in GE motors.
The bearing contains a lead base babbitt as compared to our preference for tin base babbitt.
The bearing bronze used for backing in the sample evaluated differs from our standard and should not be used as a bearing material in non-babbitted bearings without field testing.

By cutting out this rectangle and folding on the center line, the above information can be fitted into a standard card file.

For list of contents—drawings, photos, etc. and for distribution see next page (FN-610-2).

INFORMATION PREPARED FOR_____ Motor Engineering Unit - Locomotive & Car Equipment Dept.

TESTS MADE BY_____ RA Pettersen, CR Rainesalo

COUNTERSIGNED_____ CF Simon *arl Simon* DIV._____ Equipment

DIVISIONS._____ Motor Mechanical Design Engineering

FN-610-1 (1-49)

SPECIMEN NO. 2 *

Report in Letter Form

In using the form of a letter for the following report the writer was apparently following an established custom, for examination of numerous reports from his office to the Los Angeles County Board of Supervisors showed that a great many were letters which closely resembled this one.

There were two common features in all of these letter reports. First, the subject of the report was always shown by a subject line, which actually functioned as a title. Second, the letter always ended with a brief, explicit statement of recommendations, identified by the heading shown on page 3. Also, internal headings were used whenever the report was long enough that they would be helpful.

It was obvious that the writer always based his report on earlier and more detailed reports that had been prepared for his own information. Occasionally he attached one of these reports so that more information would be available if called for, but the report proper—that is, the letter —always covered the essentials well enough to be self-sufficient.

Where the number of reports is great enough to justify such a degree of standardization, it seems probable that the form would be extremely efficient in satisfying the reader's needs.

---

* Courtesy of Los Angeles County Board of Supervisors.

February 10, 196_

HONORABLE BOARD OF SUPERVISORS
County of Los Angeles
501 Hall of Records
Los Angeles, California

Gentlemen:

REPORT ON WIDTH OF FIREBREAKS

On December 22, 196_, your Board instructed the Forester and Fire Warden
and the Chief Administrative Officer to prepare a joint report on the
"over-all program of width of firebreaks." At the time of your Board's
discussion, mention was made of previous orders concerning the width of
firebreaks and the anticipated increase in number of firebreaks to be
built in the near future with use of prisoner labor. A review of Board
files discloses that no prior action has been taken by your Board to
establish a minimum width for firebreaks.

The Forester and Fire Warden is of the opinion that a minimum width for
firebreaks should not be established by legislative action. As this
report will show, the widths of firebreaks are determined by several
factors and at the same time are limited by the possibility of erosion
and the willingness of private property owners to make their land available for this purpose.

Master Plan of Firebreaks, Fire Roads, and Cisterns

The Department now maintains 200 miles of firebreaks, 416 miles of fire
roads, eighty-eight 10,000-gallon water cisterns and over 135 water
tanks in accordance with a master plan which had its origin some 30
years ago. Revised annually, the present five-year program calls for
additional construction of 209 miles of firebreaks, 227 miles of fire
roads, and 60 water cisterns as well as numerous water tanks. The attached map pinpoints the location of existing and proposed facilities,
including:

> Fire roads for penetration of undeveloped areas with fire trucks
> and equipment. These are single lane, unpaved roads with fre-
> quent points for passing or turning of equipment.

> Cisterns to insure the availability of water at strategic loca-
> tions.

> Water tanks (wood and metal) where easements on private property
> are not obtainable for the construction of permanent concrete
> cisterns.

145

Firebreaks of varying widths serving two purposes:

--As a safe place from which men and equipment may work.

--As a break in fuel (ground cover) which may, under favorable weather conditions, retard the fire until suppressive action can be taken.

Firebreak Construction

Each firebreak is designed to meet the problems of a particular location. They are usually constructed on ridges where air currents created by the heat of a fire will dissipate the fire upward and lessen its chance of jumping the cleared area. Generally, the width of a firebreak varies from 30 to 100 feet or more, although negotiations are proceeding for construction of a 300-foot wide experimental firebreak in the Glendora area.

The Forester and Fire Warden, having witnessed fire jumping as far as three-quarters of a mile in strong winds, is of the opinion that it is impossible to build firebreaks of sufficient width to insure fire containment. Since wide firebreaks may create an erosion problem, land owners are often reluctant to enter into agreements to permit construction on their property. This is a matter of major consequence, since over 78% of the total miles of firebreaks included in the Master Plan requires the use of private property.

Development of Slow Burning Vegetation for Use on Firebreaks

The use of fire-resistant ground cover would deter erosion, permitting construction of wider firebreaks. The Director of the Arboreta is now experimenting with slow-burning vegetation which may in time be appropriate for use on firebreaks. The results of these experiments, however, will not be known for four or five years since plants must be tested over a long period of growth to determine their potential characteristics. When and if the development of a slow-burning or fire-resistent ground cover is successful, it may be possible to establish a fixed minimum width for firebreaks with some degree of practicality.

The Forester and Fire Warden is of the opinion that the firebreaks program for the foothill areas is developing satisfactorily, particularly with the recent action of your Board making prisoner labor available for such projects. The establishment now of a minimum width for firebreaks would not be in the best interest of this program because of the need to compromise width and the erosion hazard. The only foreseeable solution to this problem is the successful propagation of a slow-burning ground cover which would lessen the problem of erosion and greatly increase the effectiveness of firebreaks.

146

<u>IT IS THEREFORE OUR JOINT RECOMMENDATION</u>:

> That your Board take no action to establish a minimum
> width firebreak, and that the Forester and Fire Warden
> continue to be responsible for determining the width
> of firebreaks

Very truly yours,

/s/ K. E. KLINGER

K. E. KLINGER
Forester and Fire Warden

/s/ L. S. HOLLINGER

L. S. HOLLINGER
Chief Administrative Officer

KEK:LSH:ym
cc: Each Supervisor

SPECIMEN NO. 3 *

Progress Report in Letter Form

The following specimen illustrates the use of a letter as a report. Its form, as we would expect, is like that of any other letter. (Form of letters is discussed in Chapter 13.)

If we were classifying this report on the basis of purpose, we would call it a progress report. In this connection, though it does not formally separate the information into a past, present, future pattern, it lets the reader see what work has been done, what work is under way, and what will be done as time goes on. It was obviously written so soon after work was begun that long-range predictions were not possible.

---

* Courtesy of Washington State University Institute of Technology.

November 20, 196_

Senator Nat Washington, Chairman
Legislative Joint Fact-Finding Committee on
  Highways, Streets and Bridges
Ephrata, Washington

Dear Senator Washington:

   At your request, there follows a brief progress report on the priority programing and administration study being directed by the Automotive Safety Foundation for the Legislative Joint Fact-Finding Committee on Highways, Streets and
Bridges.

   Activity was started September ?5, 196_, with subsequent organization of staff
and offices in House Committee Room 8, in the Legislative Building at Olympia. Reports and data are being accumulated, reviewed and analyzed, and a basic approach
to the study process has been developed as a framework for further research and
analysis.

   City and county advisory committees have been requested, and a meeting was
held with the duly appointed county committee on November 17. We are pleased with
the enthusiasm, the general agreement with the basic approach and the acceptance
of certain committee responsibilities that were outlined. Messrs. Neil McKay and
Brian Lewis have been employed by the Foundation, on a part-time basis, to work
especially on county and city problems, respectively.

   The State Highway Department has made available certain staff people, two on
nearly a full-time basis and others as needed, to assist in all phases of the
study, and has begun work on a basic study of programing factors for state highway improvements. In addition, data are nearly completed for study of new revenue
projections to 1975, including those for individual counties.

   Conferences have been held with Messrs. Riedesel and Johnson of Washington
State University for the purposes of coordination of activities to avoid duplication, and of acquainting ourselves with methods, procedures, and data of the 196_
study of needs. Similarly, meetings were held with Messrs. Hennes and Ekse, of the
University of Washington, and Biesen and Jennings of the Association of Washington
Cities. These meetings resulted in full agreement for coordination and use of all
available information.

   The Foundation greatly appreciates the interest and cooperation extended to
us by all, and especially by Mr. William Bugge and staff of the State Highway Department. We anticipate the privilege of presenting a more formal and complete
progress report to the Joint Committee as soon as significant information is
developed.

                                        Yours very truly,

                                        /s/ JAMES O. GRANUM

JOG/mr   James O. Granum, P. E.
cc: Mrs. Elmo Fadling   Deputy Chief Engineer
    Mr. William Bugge   Highways Division

SPECIMEN NO. 4

Report in Memorandum Form

(PROGRESS REPORT)

The following report was made in the form of a memorandum, but in purpose it is a Progress Report. Note that it tells what progress has already been made on an investigation, and what work is under way. In doing so, it makes the current status of the project clear. It also tells what work will be undertaken next.

Though it includes some of the facts already revealed by the investigation, it makes no attempt to predict whether the ultimate recommendation will be favorable or unfavorable.

PALOMAR PRODUCE ASSOCIATION
(Inter-Office Memorandum)

To: Production Committee   Date: July 31, 196_

From: Fruit-Handling Committee

Subject: Handling Peaches and Pears in Bulk Bins

As you requested in a memorandum dated May 15, we have begun an
investigation of the desirability of handling cling peaches and pears
in bulk bins of half-ton capacity rather than continuing to use lug
boxes that hold 130 pounds.

Tests already conducted on the Parsons Ranch and Spring Valley
Farms have shown that when peaches are moved without first being cooled,
the bruise rate is higher in the bulk bins than in the lug boxes.

We are now conducting similar tests at the Dennis-Ryan Orchards in
order to see whether the results are the same when the fruit is cooled
and top-iced before transportation. We are also assembling information
that will enable us to calculate how large a capital expenditure will
be necessary to convert to bins if the final results of the bruise tests
show that the bin-handling method does not bruise the fruit too severely.

Arrangements have been completed to make similar tests on pears.
We shall begin these tests in Mesa Orchards as soon as the pears are
ready to pick.

We expect to have all the data necessary for our purposes by
September 15 and shall probably be able to submit our report and recommendation by the middle of October.

SPECIMEN NO. 5 *

Periodic Report in Semiformal Form

The following report covers laboratory activities of The Asphalt Institute for three months. The Institute is an organization that exists for the purpose of discovering new or better ways of using asphaltic materials, and of disseminating information about their use.

The first page is unusually compact, performing three functions: it contains all the information normally included on a title page; it presents a statement about objectives of the Institute—a statement that was apparently important enough to receive constant emphasis; and it provides a compact table of contents. The table of contents increases the chance that the report will arouse interest and is a real convenience to potential readers even though only four pages follow. The need for it is greater because the contents concern three separate subjects rather than three parts of a single subject.

The second page contains in full what was said about one aspect of work done in the first main division of the report. The material at the top consists of the headings that the table of contents leads us to expect, a line that relates the first main heading to the specific long-range objective concerned, and a line telling what earlier reports have dealt with the same project.

The text that follows tells about work done, work under way, and future intentions. Then it goes on to refresh the reader's mind about materials, to comment on an improvement in apparatus, and to tell where additional information may be obtained.

The remainder of the report deals in the same compact and efficient manner with the other subjects listed in the table of contents.

---

* Courtesy of The Asphalt Institute.

THE ASPHALT INSTITUTE
LABORATORY ACTIVITY REPORT NO. 60-1
Period: December 1, 1959 - February 29, 1960

by
John M. Griffith
Engineer of Research

The currently authorized research program for the Institute
Laboratories has the following long-range objectives:

1. To develop an acceptable, improved method of asphalt mix
   design for paving.

2. To develop procedures for improvement of base materials
   with asphalt.

3. To develop an improved method of asphalt pavement
   thickness design.

4. To develop improved design, inspection and construction
   practices for all the major uses of asphalt in paving
   and hydraulics.

CONTENTS

Distribution: Directors, Management Committee Members, E & D Committee
Members, Institute Offices and Groups 9D, 10H and LR.

No. 1A Sp

153

I. Paving Mix Design Program

(A phase of work toward long-range objective No. 1)

A. Mechanical Gyratory Compactor Studies

BACKGROUND AND SUMMARY OF PREVIOUS WORK: See Laboratory Activity Reports No. 58-4, 59-1, 2, 3 and 4.

Mechanical gyratory compactor studies are being made using aggregates and asphalt from test road pavements. The purpose of these studies is to develop procedures using the gyratory compactor for compacting test specimens, selecting an optimum asphalt content, and for evaluating plastic behavior of test specimens that may be related to stability or load bearing capacity.

Mix specimens having the same gradation as test road pavements were prepared through a range of asphalt contents. Several compactive efforts were used. Different compactive efforts were obtained by varying either ram pressures or number of revolutions. Families of density versus asphalt content curves were obtained. These densities ranged from below to above those of the test road pavement, both as constructed and after traffic compaction.

Test specimens prepared in this manner are subjected to additional gyratory compaction at temperatures corresponding to maximum field pavement temperatures. Both Marshall and Hveem tests are used on the specimens after the various levels of compaction. Recorded angles of gyration are also studied as an indication of the plastic behavior of test specimens. Recorded angles of gyration will be compared and, if possible, correlated with conventional stability test values. Data from previous studies indicate that a relationship exists between the recorded angle of gyration and Marshall stability and flow test values.

Aggregates and asphalts for the first series of tests were those used for AASHO Road Test surface course pavements. Aggregates and asphalts used for other test road pavements, such as the Virginia and Delaware, will be included in the study at a later date.

A modification to improve the operational characteristics of the gyratory compactor has been made in the design of the upper roller air-oil cell. This modification eliminates the completely filled oil cell system (fixed angle or fixed upper roller) used for initial compaction of specimens, and results in an interchangeable part with the present air-oil cell. The original air-oil cell will be kept for use in the air filled (variable angle) type of compaction, as this type is operational.

The modification does not affect any compactor measurements or sample characteristics. Its use was necessary due to difficulty in removing air from the oil filled system and preventing leaks in the system.

A paper entitled "Effects of Consistency of Asphalt Cements and Types of Mineral Filler on Compaction of Asphalt Concrete," based on mechanical gyratory compactor studies, was presented at the 1960 annual meeting of the Association of Asphalt Paving Technologists. A limited supply of preprint copies of this paper are available on request.

B. Sheet Asphalt Mixes Containing Activated Alumina and Calcium Oxide Fillers

BACKGROUND AND SUMMARY OF PREVIOUS WORK: See Laboratory Activity Reports
No. 59-1 and 2.

Marshall tests were made for sheet asphalt mixes containing calcium oxide and
alumina fillers. These tests are a continuation of a portion of the studies of
mineral fillers. All of the fillers included in the study are combined in a constant
volume concentration with the same fine sand aggregate.

These tests include studies of the effects of premixing filler and asphalt before
mixing with the fine sand aggregate. The effects of 18-hour water immersion at 140°F
of specimens before testing are also measured. Mixes were also prepared and tested
by standard Marshall procedures.

Sheet asphalt mixes containing calcium oxide, when immersed in water at 140°F
for 18 hours, increased in volume and disintegrated. This swelling and disintegration
occurred for both normally-mixed samples and for those prepared by premixing asphalt
and filler prior to mixing with aggregate.

Sheet asphalt mixes prepared with alumina filler were found susceptible to water,
particularly at lower asphalt content ranges. The test results for the alumina filler
mixes indicated that premixing filler and asphalt before mixing with aggregate
increased water susceptibility. Premixed samples when tested after 18-hour immersion at
140°F had lower stability values than did normally prepared samples.

Additional variables in the preparation and testing of alumina filler mixes have
been investigated. It was found that the time of storage at 275°F of premixed asphalt
and alumina filler had no effect on Marshall test properties. It was also found that
sample storage time at room temperature had no effect on Marshall test properties for
premixed samples. Storage times up to 4 days were investigated at both temperatures.

C. Adsorption of Asphalt by Mineral Fillers

Previous report (see Laboratory Activity Report No. 59-4) indicated that the
physical properties, such as viscosity or softening point of mineral powder and asphalt
mixtures, depend to a great extent on the type of mineral filler.

Adsorption has been considered the major factor contributing to these effects.
Therefore, adsorption of asphalt or asphalt constituents by the surfaces of different
mineral powders was measured. Two techniques were used, spectrophotometric and
gravimetric. The spectrophotometric method involves the measurement of light
transmittancy of a centrifuged and filtered asphalt solution in benzene (non-polar
liquid) after it was shaken with the varying amounts of different mineral powders.
The gravimetric method is made by weighing the unadsorbed asphalt after a measured
amount of the supernatant solution is dried to a constant weight. Since the higher
molecular weight constituents (asphaltenes or resins) contribute most to the dark
color of solution, it was believed that the comparison of results by these two methods
would indicate relative affinities of different fillers to the different asphalt
components and the asphalt itself. Since the liquid-solid adsorption is influenced
by a variety of factors, all tests were attempted under the same conditions.

3

Results thus obtained indicate great differences in adsorptive capacities of different fillers. For example, the adsorption by Fuller's earth is approximately one hundred times greater than that of linestone dust.

On the basis of these results, mineral fillers may be grouped arbitrarily as adsorptive (Fuller's earth, kaolin clay, asbestos, diatomaceous earth, activated alumina) and non-adsorptive (fly-ash, ground quartz, hydrated lime, limestone dust) materials, although the adsorptive capacities of individual powders within these groups vary appreciably. It is also evident that the investigated fillers adsorb higher molecular weight asphalt fractions (colored constituents) more pronouncedly than the lower molecular weight components.

An attempt was made to determine if the adsorption processes that occur in asphalt cements are similar to the adsorption from the benzene solutions. Viscosities of the Fuller's earth-asphalt mixture were determined using the sliding plate microviscometer, after the hot mixture was subjected to a strong centrifugal force. Despite the fact that the upper layers of the mixture, after centrifuging, still contained approximately three percent of filler, the viscosities at 77°F of these layers were approximately thirty percent lower than those of asphalt cement without the filler subjected to the same testing conditions.

It is believed that these lower viscosities were caused by the removal of higher molecular weight components of asphalt which were adsorbed by the mineral surfaces and transported to the bottom on the container during the centrifuging process.

A limited number of adsorption tests from asphalt-benzene solutions using several natural soils were also made. Differences in results indicate that these may possibly be utilized for determining the relative affinities of a given soil to the asphalt in asphalt cutbacks.

Tests are now being made to determine the sorption of glycerol by the different fillers. These tests, beside providing the measurements of surface areas of mineral powders, will enable comparisons of the sorption characteristics of isotropic glycerol and a non-isotropic material, asphalt.

II. Stabilization of Base Materials With Asphalt

(A phase of work toward long-range objective No. 7)

A. Effect of Degree of Mixing on Properties of Soil-Asphalt-Lime Mixtures

BACKGROUND AND SUMMARY OF PREVIOUS WORK: See Laboratory Activity Report No. 59-4.

Marshall specimens of asphalt cutback stabilized, lime-treated Maryland soil, at different water contents, were prepared using two previously described mixing procedures. Stabilities, densities and water absorption values during four days of complete immersion in water were determined for these differently-mixed samples.

The trends obtained in the test results indicate that the soil-asphalt-lime mixtures behave similarly to the comparable mixtures without lime. Uniform mixing causes lower densities, higher optimum water contents and also higher water absorption values. Regardless of these factors, the stabilities of the uniformly mixed, immersed samples tend to be higher than the stabilities of regularly mixed, compacted mixtures, both with and without lime.

B. Compaction of Cohesive Soil-Asphalt Mixtures by the Mechanical Gyratory Compactor.

An effort was made to determine the feasibility of compaction of fine grained soil-asphalt mixtures with the mechanical gyratory compactor. Since this instrument provides ready and accurate control of compaction effort, it was believed that it could be used to study the effects of the degree of compaction on the properties of soil-asphalt mixtures.

After several tests, indications are that the MGC can be used for such purposes. Well developed, water content-density curves obtained in this testing indicate that the scatter in results is less than that with other compaction methods. The only difficulty met was a considerable loss of mixture through the gap between the piston and the wall of the sample mold, when compacting mixtures with higher water contents. It is believed that this problem could be remedied by the use of a piston of closer tolerance.

III. Separation of Asphalt and Mineral Aggregates in Paving Mixtures Using an SMM Extraction Centrifuge

Separations of asphalt paving mixture components were made using a centrifugal separator manufactured by "SMM" (Spindles, Motors and Machines, Ltd., Switzerland). The purpose of these tests was to evaluate the efficiency of this instrument and compare it with the other separation or extraction methods presently used.

Previously analyzed asphalt concrete mixtures were used for these trial tests. In addition, mixtures of three filler materials (limestone dust, ground sand and short fibered asbestos) and asphalt cement were prepared at known filler concentration and separated in the "SMM" centrifugal separator.

Test procedures recommended by the manufacturer were used. Results indicate that this method offers fast and accurate determination of asphalt in the paving mixture. Even the mixtures of mineral powders and asphalt were separated effectively and rapidly.

However, it does appear that this method is not suitable for obtaining sufficient amounts of recovered asphalt (approximately 100 grams) required for subsequent specification tests. Not more than 500 to 600 grams of paving mixture can be conveniently handled in a single separation by this instrument. This means that at least three separations are required to obtain the above indicated amount of recovered asphalt in normal mixes. This results in a large amount of asphalt solution (3 to 4 liters) which is cumbersome and time consuming to handle in the distillation process.

SPECIMEN NO. 6 *

A Report That Is Not Classified as a Special Type

The following report, like the preceding one, was made to The Asphalt Institute. Similar reports were made on various other airports where it had become necessary to develop methods of keeping pavements clean.

This report cannot be classified as to form, bearing out the statement that although this book must recognize the existence of reports of various types, there is no reason to expect that every report can be classified.

The purpose of the individual report, obviously, is merely to swell the total amount of information available on a problem rather than to point the road to specific action; but this information plus the information in other reports could well lead to recommendations for dealing with the problem wherever and whenever it might arise.

---

* Courtesy of The Asphalt Institute.

INSPECTION OF ASPHALT RAMP AREAS

at the

SAN FRANCISCO INTERNATIONAL AIRPORT

        The purpose of this report is to tell what was learned when ramp
areas at the San Francisco Airport were inspected to see whether their
asphalt surfaces were damaged by detergents used for cleaning.

        Airline representatives who were interviewed stated that they have
experienced no trouble or damage to the asphalt surfaces as a result of
the detergents they used to clean ramps. Visual inspection bore out their
statements; the pavements appear to be structurally sound.

        The difficulties being encountered at the San Francisco Interna-
tional Airport are similar to the problems being experienced at other airports. Oil is spilled or drips from parked aircraft and is gradually
spread over a rather wide area by service vehicles which run through it.
Maintenance crews sprinkle a powder on the surface to blot up the oil,
and later remove the powdered material with the oil. Once a week the ramp
area is scrubbed with a detergent solution and the entire area is hosed
down, washing the detergent and oil down the drain.

        The only problem is apparently one of house-keeping. Using vir-
tually the same type of aircraft that sometimes cause trouble, some airlines have little difficulty in keeping the area clean, because a crew of
men cleans the ramp area very shortly after a spillage of oil occurs.
Other airlines, for various reasons, are not so prompt, and the spilled
oil and blotter material accumulate, causing the unsatisfactory conditions.

        One airline shop has fabricated a trailer on which is placed a
rather large tank with a spray-bar. At the back of the trailer is a
straight bristle broom which can be raised or lowered. The tank is provided with a valve through which approximately 150 to 180 pounds of air
pressure is applied prior to use. The detergent used consists of one
third Turco No. 2844 and two thirds deodorized spray-base solvent made by
Shell Oil Company. This deodorized spray-base solvent is a highly re-
fined kerosene with aromatics removed, and is the lowest in solvent power
of naphthas and solvents produced by Shell Oil Company.

        The normal procedure is to try to blot up the worst of the oil
spillage as it occurs and remove the blotter material, and then scrub the
area with the detergent solution once a week. During the scrubbing operations, it is attempted to hose the area clean of the solution within
thirty minutes of the time it is applied. This procedure, apparently,
has been satisfactory and is considered superior to procedures described
in a previous report.

        In comparison with the problems at Midway Airport in Chicago,
the problems at San Francisco are minor. If an analysis of the pavement

159

at San Francisco Airport were made, it would show that the pavement is structurally sound throughout and that no deleterious effects are being experienced from the detergent solution being used for cleaning.

- oOo -

SPECIMENS NO. 7 AND 8

7. Report in the Form of a Memorandum
8. Report in Laboratory-Report Form

The following material consists of two reports based on the same investigation, plus the covering memorandum that accompanied one of them. Presenting all three items makes it possible not only to show two reports, but also to provide a picture, in a relatively simple situation, of the manner in which a report may be put to use after it is written.

Chronologically, what happened was as follows. Merle Porter was asked to investigate the question of whether a Lippke Portable Moisture Meter would give satisfactory results in a paper mill. He submitted a report to Jack Macaulay, who sent copies of the report to several people, along with a covering memorandum that he wrote himself. One of these people, K. Barnhart, then wrote a report of his own so as to bring the matter to a head and to secure action. His report was made to R. Musgrove, but copies went to several others. He attached the Macaulay memorandum and the Lippke report so that all the details would be available to anyone who wanted them.

The material following is arranged as it was arranged by K. Barnhart, the last of the three writers whose work is included. It consists of:

A report in the form of a memorandum by K. Barnhart

A covering memorandum by Jack Macaulay, written to accompany

The original report, by Merle Porter

Thus as you can see, what a reader encounters first is what was written last—an entirely suitable arrangement because the latest word on the subject is what the reader is likely to want to read first.

COMMENTS ON THE BARNHART REPORT

The first paragraph identifies the material attached, tells its purpose, and refers to one of the results.

The second paragraph quickly orients the reader to the entire situation, probably because some of the readers were not so close to the case as Mr. Barnhart or Mr. Macaulay. It then provides an extremely condensed account of what happened while the investigation was under way. It does not attempt to present any of the data obtained during the tests.

The third paragraph is a definite attempt to bring about action, the action being that of making a decision. The writer makes his own recommendations, though he somewhat qualifies them by saying that he is expressing his "personal feeling" and by urging only that certain actions be "considered," not performed. It is not being implied here that he should have gone further, for definite decisions are often based in part on factors that lie outside the scope of a single report. He supports one of his suggestions by telling his reasons for making it.

All in all, the report probably serves its purpose. It indicates the need for action and provides enough information to permit each reader to limit his reading in the longer report to the parts in which he is especially interested.

TO: R. Musgrove   June 12, 196_

FROM: K. Barnhart

SUBJECT: LIPPKE PORTABLE MOISTURE METER REPORT

Attached are a report from Merle Porter and a cover memo from Jack Macaulay.
A lot of tests have been made with the Lippke portable meter and the results have been used to improve the paper machine operation. This report
is submitted to sum up the information for the use of everyone interested
in this project.

As a quick review of the Lippke project, we had a trial period using the
mounted traversing unit on the end of number one paper machine. This was
felt to be successful and has been discussed in meetings and covered in
other reports. It was then agreed to rent the portable unit to make some
studies of various positions on each machine. It was further agreed to
keep the mounted unit for purpose of calibrations and comparison and to
rent when both units were operative. After the solder melted out of the
head of the portable unit, we experienced no end of trouble in getting a
new head and in using it after we got it. The other problem we had with the
portable was that when moving it around, we pulled wires loose and caused
electrical troubles. We had earlier agreed that as soon as sufficient work
was done with the portable unit, we would then release the present equipment but make a decision as to any permanent installations.

As soon as everyone has reviewed this report, a decision should be made as
to whether any further work should be done with the portable equipment.
This will determine whether we keep or release our present equipment. We
should also decide what we want to do as far as permanent equipment is concerned. Previously and again in this report the technical department recommends consideration of three units--one before the size press, one before the wet stacks and one before the coating. These, of course, could
be added one at a time. There is some question as to whether we should
use traversing or fixed units. Cost, of course, is involved. My personal
feeling is that we should consider one traversing unit in order to check
the profile of our sheet. I would also like to suggest that we look into
the combination unit which would include basis weight. This would also
provide automatic compensation for moisture. As you know, on the present
unit, we have to set the basis weight manually in order to make the moisture indication accurate.

                                   /s/ K. BARNHART
                                       K. Barnhart

KB:cb
cc: A. Whitehead, M. Porter, J. Macaulay, V. Brown, V. Peterson

COMMENTS ON THE MACAULAY MEMORANDUM

The covering memorandum on page 165 identifies the accompanying material and moves it along through regular channels. Also, it gives its writer, who was the first person to receive the Porter report, a chance to express his own reaction to it as he brings it to the attention of those concerned.

TO: K. Barnhart   DATE: June 6, 196_

FROM: J. Macauley

Attached is a report from Merle Porter covering work using a Lippke
Portable Moisture Meter. The meter was used to check moisture at different points on the paper machines.

From the compiled data, I believe that if we had moisture measuring
equipment installed before the size press, before the wet stacks and
before the coating, this would be of great value to us in controlling
uniformity of our paper.

                              /s/   JOHN MACAULAY
                                    John Macaulay

JM/Dm
cc: A. Whitehead, V. Brown, V. Peterson

COMMENTS ON THE PORTER REPORT

The Porter report consisted of five pages of writing, one table, and twenty-six full-page graphs. Six of the graphs were placed in the body of the report but the table and the other twenty followed it. The graphs and the table are omitted, being unnecessary for the purposes of this book. It is worth noting, however, that the graphs placed in the body of the report were brought to the reader's attention by mention of their numbers at an appropriate point. The table and the other graphs comprise two appendixes, both of which were mentioned in the section headed *Results,* where their contents became relevant.

Though the work was done in the plant rather than in a laboratory, the form is essentially that of a laboratory report. As you can see, the writer used five headings: *History of the Project, Equipment, Procedure, Results,* and *Discussion and Recommendations.* As you read the report you might be interested in closely comparing the exact nature of the material in each section with the heading under which it appears. The function of each section seems to have been clear in the writer's mind, but apparently he sometimes found it hard to perform that function without using facts that were also covered by other headings. For example, there was no way to tell the history of the project without including a good deal of information about the equipment, yet there was a definite need for a section in which facts about the equipment were the main subject rather than an incidental element.

Actually, though their distinct nature is not easy to discover, the work covered by the report had two purposes. The first was to obtain information on which to base a decision about whether equipment to measure moisture would be desirable and whether one particular kind of equipment would be suitable. The second was to obtain information about the characteristics, at certain stages, of the product being manufactured and to use that information in improving the product.

Under the heading *History of the Project* the report narrated incidents in a chronological order. If the difficulties encountered had not been so numerous, the writer probably would not have found it necessary to offer such a narrative.

Under *Equipment* we are offered more detailed information about the portable meter that the report concerns. Attention is centered on the particular features responsible for the difficulties mentioned, and on the problems created by these defects. The readers undoubtedly knew enough about moisture meters that general information was not needed.

A Report on

LIPPKE PORTABLE MOISTURE METER TESTS

Prepared by Merle Porter

History of the Project:

The Lippke Portable Moisture Meter was first turned over to the Technical Department on February 2, 196_. Testing was started and proceeded until February 12, when part of the sensing head melted due to high sheet temperatures. A new high-temperature type of head was sent by Lippke, and on March 12 the instrument with the head was tested. During the next 13 days, the instrument was used for testing but was never found satisfactory. A meeting was held with Al Crandall on March 23 to discuss the instrument's faulty performance. It was decided to contact Fisher Porter, who handle the instrument in this country, and inform them of the situation. As a result of this, a factory representative of Lippke arrived April 11. He found that the new high temperature head was not compatible with the rest of the meter so he made the necessary changes to the head to make it work right. The instrument was turned back to the Technical Department on April 16 for calibration and testing.

The instrument calibration with the new high-temperature head was calibrated by stretching samples of paper of basis weights from 80 to 210# over the head. The paper samples were left in the test station to insure that they were all the same in moisture content, then tested with the Hart Moisture Tester in the test station. They all tested the same moisture. The basis weight compensation adjustment on the portable moisture tester was then adjusted so that the meter would indicate the proper percentage of moisture. Figure 1 shows the resulting calibration curve. When samples of basis weights higher than 160# were tried, it was found that they could not be stretched flat over the head, so the results above 160# are not too good. This pointed up one fault of the new style head: the paper must lie absolutely flat on it or it will not read properly.

The instrument with the old head that melted was calibrated just as the new one was, but it checked out perfectly and no calibration curve was needed. Also, the head was not as critical of the sheet lying flat on it.

Equipment:

The Lippke Portable Moisture Meter came to the mill equipped with a head identical to the one used on the traversing meter located at the dry end of number 1 paper machine. This head consisted of a quartz plate with five concentric rings cut into the plate and filled with lead. It was this head on which the heat of the paper melted the lead. The new high-temperature head which replaced the melted one consists of six parallel strips of metal turned up in front and back like a ski. The paper must be contacting the entire head in order to give an accurate reading while with the other style, with the quartz plate, only a small area of the surface of the head needs to lie exactly flat on the sheet.

After the new high-temperature head was installed, the instrument failed on so many occasions it would be impossible to mention them

The information under *Procedure* is limited to a description of the unusual procedures made necessary by the shortcomings of the equipment. A section on procedures would probably not have been included if only normal procedures had been called for in performing the tests.

Under the heading *Results* the writer first gives us information that the tests have revealed about the product. He offers us facts about the *range* of moisture and refers us to the appendixes for details about the individual tests. His reference to the apendixes appears in the second of the three paragraphs, accompanied by comments on two facts that the reader can observe on the graphs. The first of these facts merely lets the reader see that the limitations of the machine make the validity of the results doubtful. The other would be important enough to warrant a separate paragraph, for it concerns an improvement in the product made possible because of the information obtained in the early tests.

all. Tubes burned out, wires broke or shorted out, the instrument got out of calibration, the head would get loose. In general, its performance was very unsatisfactory. It finally settled down to more dependable operation but there were other problems. Being metal, the head expanded when it was hot as it is when on the sheet. This caused the metal strips to change their position in relation to each other and therefore changed the reading the meter gave. This expansion due to heating causes a shift of better than 1 per cent moisture. Calibrating it cold with strips of paper was therefore not too accurate. When a moisture profile or test was to be run, it was necessary to hold the head on the sheet for an extended period of time to heat it up before starting or taking a reading. It is extremely hard to keep the head flat on the sheet, especially when holding it overhead.

Procedure:

Due to the fact that the moisture reading would vary with head temperature, the calibration curve made with the head cold was not of too much value. In order to insure accurate readings, the portable meter was checked against the traversing meter on machine number 1 and the basis weight compensation was set so that the portable meter reading agreed with the traversing meter reading. Then tests were run further up the machine at the wet stacks, and so forth. With no meter to check against on number 2, very few tests were taken except on the lower basis weights.

In order to run a profile before the size press, a man had to remain inside the machine on the catwalk beside the last dryer for a period of 10 minutes. This procedure is dangerous. If a man would pass out due to the high heat he would fall to the basement.

In order to get moisture levels before and after the wet stack and coaters, the head had to be held above the man's shoulders and held on the sheet until it heated up. This was very difficult.

Results:

Figures 2 - 6 show the range of the percentage of moisture with basis weight for number 1 machine. It is seen from these graphs that the percentage of moisture is lower for the higher basis weights. The same pattern seems to hold for all the points tested. The ranges for the different points are as follows:

Before size press	2 - 5%	H_2O
After size press	8 - 11%	H_2O
Before wet stack	2 - 5%	H_2O
After wet stack	7 - 10%	H_2O
Before coaters	5 - 8%	H_2O

Appendix A contains test results obtained in February using the cold head that melted. Appendix B contains results obtained in April using the new high-temperature head. It is interesting to note the absence of variations in the moisture profiles taken before the size press in tests taken with the new head. There seems to be some doubt as to

-2-

Discussion and Recommendations. Not much of the material under *Discussion and Recommendations* consists of Discussion. In fact, only the first three sentences could be so classified. The content of the section consists mainly of two recommendations. The first of these is the negative recommendation that "no further profile or moisture level studies be made." The writer makes this recommendation partly because of the difficulty of making the tests, partly because the tests are a precaution rendered unnecessary by what has already been learned, and partly because of improvements made on the basis of tests already conducted. The second is the positive recommendation that a permanent moisture meter, in contrast with the portable meter reported on, be installed at a certain location. Actually, the phraseology presents the two recommendations as mere conclusions; but by implication, at least, recommendations have been made as the heading led us to expect.

FINAL COMMENT

The general tone of all three communications is somewhat informal. Each is apparently written for readers with whom the writer is regularly in contact. Also, the readers apparently know enough about the circumstances and about the process of paper-making that they can make distinctions and understand references that may puzzle a person outside the industry. The last of the three to be written, which is of course the first that you encountered, is notably more condensed than the first. If another piece was written on the subject, as is likely, and if it were available, we would probably find that since it would go farther up the line it would be less relaxed in manner.

whether the new head is as sensitive to moisture changes as the old one. There also was a shift in moisture levels, particularly before the size press, between the two testing periods. When the first tests were taken in February the percentage of moisture before the size press on number 2 was almost zero. When this situation was pointed out, the moisture level was raised and has been held higher ever since, as shown by the tests taken in April and May. The situation was much the same on number 1 machine.

Included at the end of Appendix B are moisture profiles after the wet stock on number 1 taken before and after the replacement of the King Roll on April 20.

Discussion and Recommendations:

The portable unit has rendered very poor service since the new head was installed. This is in no way a reflection on the traversing meter on the dry end on number 1 machine as the portable has a different head. It is moved around and the transmitter is taken into the paper machine, and it uses an electronic tube amplifier where the traversing type uses a magnetic amplifier. It is felt that further profile or moisture level studies would be of no value due to the many problems mentioned previously in this report. If all the profiles taken are correct, they show a fairly level moisture across the sheet at the size press and there couldn't be much improvement made.

A definite improvement has been made since the start of testing in February on the moisture level before the size press. The first tests taken showed a very low percentage of moisture at this point and the operating people in the mill corrected this situation as a result of these tests.

A permanent moisture tester located before the size press would prove to be of value to correct machine operation. A type which averages the sheet moisture across the sheet would probably be adequate rather than a traversing type.

/s/ MERLE PORTER
Merle Porter

-3-

171

SPECIMEN NO. 9 *

A Report That Is Not Classified as a Special Type

The following report was made by an engineer on the staff of a leading manufacturer of installations for the recovery of dust from flue gases. It was submitted to his own company and concerns the performance of one of the company's installations. It consisted of a conventional title page, three pages of text, two figures, and 17 pages of forms telling the results of tests. The forms are omitted.

---

* Courtesy of Western Precipitation Division, Joy Manufacturing Company.

ENGINEER'S REPORT

ON

W. P. RECOVERY PLANT

CONSOLIDATED WATER, POWER, AND PAPER COMPANY

WISCONSIN RAPIDS, WISCONSIN

Western Precipitation Corporation

Chicago Heights, Illinois

May, 196_

173

The first two headings in the report, *Summary* and *Description of Installation*, are standard in reports written by engineers of the company on comparable occasions. Careful study of the report shows the summary to be an accurate condensation of the material that follows. The general pattern is logical and results in good continuity, which makes the material under the next four headings easy to follow. It might be even easier if the longest paragraph under *Description of Installation* were broken up. Also, it might be helpful if there were a reference to the figure on page 5, a flow chart—though perhaps the presence and location of such a figure might be expected as a matter of course by anyone in the company.

Under *Description of Installation* in this and other reports written for the same company two kinds of information are blended: what the installation consists of and how it functions. Probably because the report is written for readers who already have easy access to details about what the installation consists of, most of the information concerns the way it functions.

The material under *Summary of Tests* is a statement of what occurred as the tests were conducted rather than a summary of the results. The results had already been partly covered in the general summary at the beginning, and they were fully summarized in two of the seventeen pages of forms. (The other fifteen gave the results of individual tests, consisting of gas volume data and of figures and calculations showing gas concentration.)

All in all, since the readers addressed would be familiar with the pattern, the background, and the type of information to be expected, they would probably find the report easy to follow.

Engineer's Report

on

Western Precipitation Recovery Plant
Consolidated Water, Power, and Paper Co.
Wisconsin Rapids, Wisconsin

SUMMARY

On May 12 to May 28, gas volume and filtration tests were conducted at
the W.P. Recovery Plant at Consolidated Water, Power, and Paper Company,
Wisconsin Rapids, Wisconsin, to obtain data for the design of a Precipitator
to replace the existing Multiclone.

Gas and dust conditions varied considerably due to many variations in
plant operating conditions. Since the process is new, there are changes
and refinements still being made in the process. In general, gas volumes ranged between 13,000 and 15,000 CFM and grain loadings ranged between 1.08 grains/cu. ft. and 1.89 grains/cu. ft.

DESCRIPTION OF INSTALLATION

Spent cooking liquors from the chemical preparation of paper pulp are
processed by W.P. Recovery Plant to recover the cooking liquors.

The spent liquors are mixed with sodium sulphide, then oxidized (The
Bradley Reaction) to make black liquor. The black liquor is then concentrated in a three stage evaporation to approximately 65 per cent
solids. The concentrated black liquor is then burned in a 20-ton Kraft
type recovery furnace made by Babcock and Wilcox. Sulfur dioxide gas,
sodium sulphate dust, and carbon dust are driven off. These dust-laden
gases pass through three air heaters. The air from Air Heater No. 1
is wasted up the stack. Its sole purpose is cooling the furnace exhaust gases. Air from Air Heaters No. 2 and No. 3 provides combustion
air for the furnace. A shot cleaning apparatus is used to prevent excessive dust-caking on the walls of the air heater tubes. Every 12
minutes shot (small metal pellets) are forced by compressed air to a
shot-disengaging tank mounted above the air heaters. Here the shot
is separated from the air and allowed to free-fall through the air
heaters. The air is returned to the top of Air Heater No. 3. Following the air heaters is a 9VG12 16-4 Multiclone. Due to excessive plugging in the Multiclone, the Multiclone vanes and Spiravanes originally
installed have been removed, leaving on the collecting and outlet
tubes. An I. D. fan following the Multiclone pulls the gases into a
downcomer to the base of a scrubber tower.

-1-

175

PLANT OPERATING CONDITIONS

Because of the nature of the plant (i.e. a pilot plant for a new process) it is very difficult to maintain normal operating conditions. The plant experiences frequent shutdowns, some of a short duration, others up to several days duration. Furthermore, there are many variables in the plant process itself which affect the firing rate in the recovery furnace. Up to now, the plant has attained a maximum firing rate of approximately eight to nine gallons per minute. The process is designed to recover a mixture of both the semichemical and acid sulphite spent liquors. It is intended, however, to operate this plant on only semichemical spent liquor, except for experimental processing of mixed liquors (semi-chemical and acid sulphite) to obtain design data for an enlarged plant. Eventually, if the larger plant is built, it will operate on mixed liquor.

TYPE OF DUST

According to plant personnel, the dust is composed primarily of sodium sulphate fume and carbon. Two types of "black liquor" are burned in the recovery furnace--one derived from semi-chemical spent liquor, the other derived from mixed liquor (semi-chemical and acid sulphite spent liquors). It was reported that the semi-chemical liquor has more inorganic constituents while the acid-sulphite has more organic constituents. This may affect the dust coming from the recovery furnace, giving a higher grain loading from the semi-chemical spent liquor and a lower grain loading but higher carbon content from the mixed liquor.

A separation of carbon and sodium sulphate particles was noticed. In the filtration thimbles there were concentric rings of black and white layers. In the barrel used for obtaining a resistivity sample, the sodium sulphate stuck to the filter bag, while the carbon dropped out in the bottom of the barrel.

Apparently the two types of dust come in waves. There are two theories why this may occur. The black liquor is sprayed into the recovery furnace, where it is burned. However, all of the liquor does not burn. Gradually, a bed of the unburned liquor builds up in the bottom of the furnace and burns off. The build-up and burn-off then repeats itself. Another theory is that the sodium sulphate cakes on the tubes of the air heater. Every 12 minutes the shot cleaning may then release a wave of the sodium sulphate.

Another consideration is that the sodium sulphate is an extremely sticky dust. When the Multiclone was installed, it could not be operated more than eight hours without plugging. The dust formed a build-up on probe pipe and other equipment placed in the flue. This build-up offered a high resistance to being dislodged by rapping the pipe.

-2-

RESISTIVITY SAMPLE

Two samples of dust for resistivity analysis were obtained, one with the plant operating on mixed liquor, the other with it operating on semi-chemical liquor. In each case, the dust removed from the bottom of the collection barrel was packaged separately from the dust removed from the bag.

SUMMARY OF TESTS

Pitot traverse Nos. 1, 2, and 3 were taken as preliminary readings while the method and rate of firing was being changed to establish maximum gas flows.

Filtration test No. 4, although it was completed, should be considered unreliable, for plugging of the nozzle and thimble prevented meter rates from being maintained. Test No. 5 was incomplete. Operating conditions changed and the nozzle plugged; and therefore, though the results obtained were reasonable, their validity was doubtful. These two tests were included in the report as preliminary and should only be considered as such.

Filtration tests 6, 7, 8, and 9, however, are completed tests and are considered representative of conditions.

ACKNOWLEDGMENTS

The writers wish to express their appreciation for the cooperation and assistance of Dr. Lemon, Project Engineer; Mr. Dave Johnson, Plant Foreman; Mr. William Kendrick, Superintendent of the Pulping Mill; and Mr. R. Q. Blanton, Chemical Process Division, Superior Precipitation Corporation, during these tests.

-3-

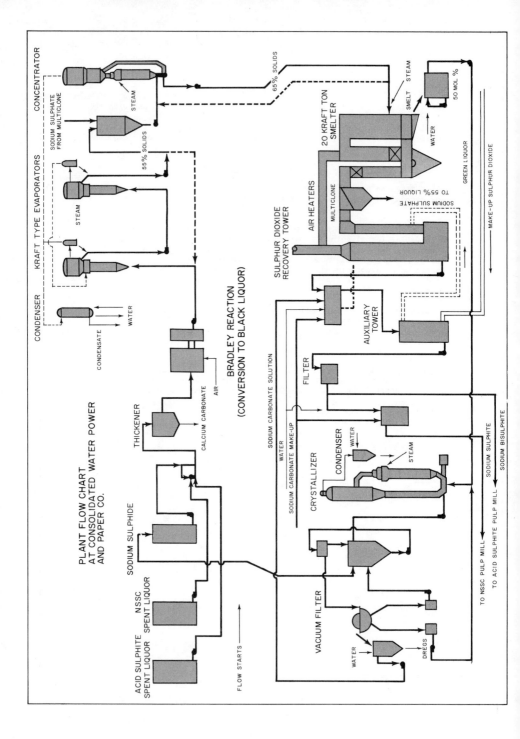

PLANT FLOW CHART
AT CONSOLIDATED WATER POWER
AND PAPER CO.

BRADLEY REACTION
(CONVERSION TO BLACK LIQUOR)

CONCENTRATOR

KRAFT TYPE EVAPORATORS

CONDENSER

CONDENSATE

WATER

STEAM

SODIUM SULPHATE FROM MULTICLONE

55% SOLIDS

65% SOLIDS

STEAM

STEAM

SMELT

20 KRAFT TON SMELTER

AIR HEATERS

MULTICLONE

SODIUM SULPHATE TO 55% LIQUOR

WATER

GREEN LIQUOR

50 MOL %

MAKE-UP SULPHUR DIOXIDE

SULPHUR DIOXIDE RECOVERY TOWER

AUXILARY TOWER

FILTER

SODIUM CARBONATE SOLUTION

SODIUM CARBONATE MAKE-UP

WATER

CRYSTALLIZER

CONDENSER

WATER

STEAM

THICKENER

CALCIUM CARBONATE

AIR

SODIUM SULPHIDE

NSSC SPENT LIQUOR

ACID SULPHITE SPENT LIQUOR

FLOW STARTS

VACUUM FILTER

WATER

DREGS

TO NSSC PULP MILL

TO ACID SULPHITE PULP MILL

SODIUM SULPHITE

SODIUM BISULPHITE

178

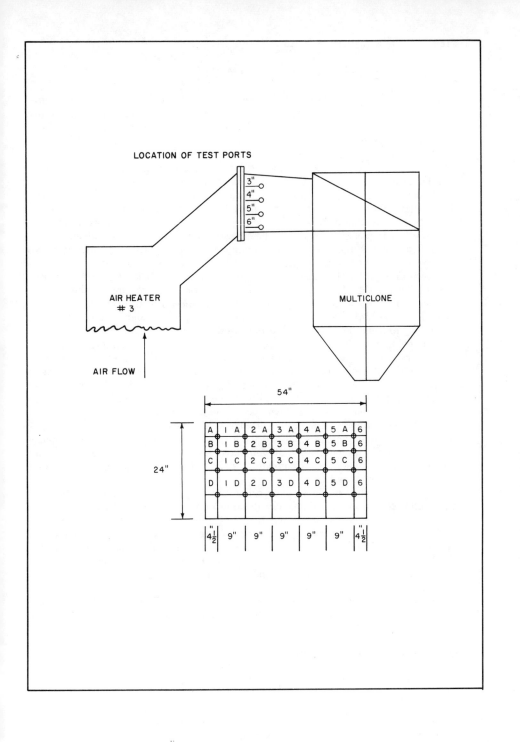

LOCATION OF TEST PORTS

3"
4"
5"
6"

AIR HEATER
3

MULTICLONE

AIR FLOW

54"

A	I A	2 A	3 A	4 A	5 A	6
B	I B	2 B	3 B	4 B	5 B	6
C	I C	2 C	3 C	4 C	5 C	6
D	I D	2 D	3 D	4 D	5 D	6

24"

4½" 9" 9" 9" 9" 9" 4½"

ASSIGNMENTS

A Note on Selecting Report Subjects: There is so much variation in the conditions in different schools, and in the courses, training, and opportunities to gather information, that it will probably be necessary to take many liberties with the suggested subjects listed. Each subject is likely to need adaptation and sharper definition.

In adapting a subject you may need to broaden or narrow its scope. You may be forced to assume that you are writing in a different season of the year, or that some recent project in your school or community has not yet been undertaken. Or if a subject proves too large to cover in full, you may need to assume that you are conducting only a preliminary survey intended to show whether a subject should be investigated further or abandoned.

In defining a subject you will probably be assuming that you are writing the report for an actual employer or client. Thus you will need to decide whom your report is being written for and why he needs it—that is, to set up a hypothetical set of circumstances. In actual practice, of course, the information you would include would depend on the needs of the occasion. In the classroom, the hypothetical occasion must be shaped to enable you to utilize whatever information it is possible to obtain.

Many of the subjects suggested could plausibly be used for more than one type of report. There is therefore no reason that in writing any assignment you should not feel free to use a subject from the list suggested for some other assignment, broadening it or narrowing it as the occasion demands.

You may prefer to write about subjects not included in the lists provided. To develop a subject of your own, you should start out by canvassing your own resources. Review, mentally, all that you have learned on any job you have held; all that you know about any technical line of activity some friend or relative might pursue; all that you have learned in any practical courses you have taken. Then try to create a hypothetical situation in which you can utilize that knowledge.

Regardless of the source of your subject, you should guard against making your reports too general, especially if some of your material must be drawn from printed references. In actual practice, a report may use general information but usually applies it to a specific case. For example, general information about killing weeds by use of chemicals is so easily obtainable in print that no one would ever be asked to write a report to present it. But the weed conditions on a specific tract of land could not be found in print, so it is quite plausible that one might be asked to write a report on the conditions on that tract and on the measures necessary to control the weeds there. Or again, anyone could find general information about fluorescent lighting systems, but it is quite possible that a report might be requested on the advisability of using fluorescent lighting in some specific building which was to be modernized or remodeled. In this report, the general, printed information would be applied to the specific facts about the building.

All this should be taken into consideration as you choose your subjects, for the wisdom of your choice will strongly affect the merit of any report you write—an unfortunate condition that will not exist when you are on the job, but cannot be avoided in the classroom. It is possible, of course, to write a poor report on a good subject; but it is impossible to write a good report on a poor subject, for a poorly chosen, unrealistic subject simply does not give you an opportunity to exercise many of the skills that make a report good.

Assignment 1

Write a report in the form of a letter using a subject from the list below or, with the instructor's permission, a subject of your own choice. Subjects 1 and 2 in Assignment 2 might also be suitable if properly adapted. The specimen letters on pages 274 and 275 should be sufficient guidance as to letter form.

Since this report is a letter, you would need to assume not only that circumstances make it natural for you to report to the reader, but also, if you and the reader are supposedly employed by the same organization, that circumstances make it natural to write a letter rather than a memorandum. For example, you might assume that you are writing the report while on a trip to a different town; or you might, in using some of the subjects, assume that you are reporting to an out-of-town property owner.

It is suggested that this report be 300 to 600 words long.

1. Report on the condition of some apartment house, fraternity house, or trailer court that you have inspected by request. (The report on a fraternity house could be made, supposedly, to an alumni group.)
2. The company that made or sold some piece of equipment has received a complaint about its performance. You are asked, while on a trip to the town where the complaint originated, to find out what is wrong and submit a report. Maybe the goods were faulty, but possibly they were installed wrongly or have not been properly maintained.
3. You are visiting a school or research institute where research is under way on a project that may be interesting to your employer because it applies to his own company's activities. This research could concern some industrial process. You are to report on its prospects, applicability, stage of development—anything that might interest the company you work for.
4. Efforts are being made to locate some establishment such as an automobile wrecking yard, a supermarket, a playground, or a garage near a residential area. An out-of-town property owner is worried about its effect on his property—for example, an apartment house. You are asked to look into the case and report to him, so that he can decide whether he should try to prevent the intended action. Your report should not be just a general discussion of whether an establishment of the type concerned is a bad neighbor for an apartment house. Rather, it should give him such information as how close it will actually be, how much it will be visible, how traffic will reach it—specific facts that will help him to judge the seriousness of the particular case.
5. The laundry facilities at a trailer court need replacement. (You might assume that there has been a fire, if you like, or that the court has changed hands and needs substantial improvement.) Write a report suggesting the number and models of machines to install.

Assignment 2

Write a report in the form of a memorandum using a subject from the list below or, with your instructor's permission, a subject of your own choice. Since your report should be made to a reader whom you might logically report to, you will need to assume that you and the reader are connected with the same organization.

It is suggested that this report be from 300 to 600 words long.

1. Pick one or more buildings on your campus that need extensive reno-

  vation or upkeep, and tell the general amount and type of work needed, and the best order for doing the work.

2. Because of a building program, new classrooms are to become available on your campus in the near future. Report on the possibility of converting two or three existing classrooms into offices. (You may make a simple diagram to accompany the memorandum if you so desire or the instructor requests it.)

3. Write a report on the problems of handling traffic at some type of public event in your school or its area, suggesting improvements in the existing arrangements, or report on the general traffic or parking conditions in some region to which you have easy access, and suggest improvements if you think they are necessary.

4. Your school has decided to teach certain classes by television. Select a room or rooms to use for this purpose. Suggest how many receivers to install and recommend, if you are able, the kind of receivers that should be used. (As in Assignment 2, a diagram could be used to supplement the report.)

5. Report on the condition of equipment, the need for new equipment, or the need for additional space in any shop, laboratory, farm, or other establishment with which you are familiar.

Assignment 3

Write a progress report of a length specified by your instructor. It may be in any form you desire unless you receive instructions to the contrary.

Any project that calls for a final report, unless it is small enough to be completed in a very short time, may also call for progress reports. Consequently, the subject on which your progress report is based may be any of the subjects provided for other report assignments. Another possibility is that if you have been assigned a long report in a Technical Writing class or a project that will last for several weeks in some other class, you might write a report telling your instructor about your progress.

Assignment 4

Assume that you are an officer or committee chairman of some organization, and that it is your responsibility to write quarterly, semi-annual, or annual reports. Write a report of this nature.

The organization may be connected with your school—a social, professional, or honorary club or fraternity, for example—or a ski club, flying club, religious group, political group, or any other group that is active on the campus. As an alternative you could write a report of similar nature for a school enterprise such as a newspaper, magazine, or yearbook, or for some nonschool organization.

Assignment 5

If your course of study has included a laboratory course to supply you with subject matter, write a laboratory report on some test or experiment you have performed. The subject should call for enough writing to make the report a writing assignment. It may include tables, figures, or filled-in blanks, but should not be limited to such material.

9

SPECIAL
ELEMENTS
IN
REPORTS

To produce some kinds of writing a writer may need only the ability to select his material, organize it, and express himself effectively. To produce good reports, however, these general skills are not enough. A report writer must also be able to plan the layout of a report —that is, to decide which of certain special elements will be useful in each report and to handle them so that they form an effective framework for his material.

To be sure, some reports are so short and simple that no special elements are needed; and laboratory reports are so standardized that their layout is often in accordance with the pattern already described. Nevertheless, certain special elements are needed so frequently that they call for considerable attention. They are most conspicuous in formal reports, but most writers are not called upon to write full-scale formal reports until long after they have had occasion to use these elements in reports that are less elaborate. Therefore, we will discuss them in connection with reports in general, and supplement the discussion as necessary in the chapter on formal reports.

The elements in question are the covering memorandum, the title page, the table of contents, the headings, the summary, the introduction, the conclusions and recommendations, and the appendix. They have been listed in the order in which they are likely to reach the reader's attention, but they should be used only to the extent that they are needed. The body of the report is not listed because it is not a special element and performs a general rather than a special function; but it would normally comprise a substantial portion of the report and might either precede or follow the conclusions and recommendations.

THE COVERING MEMORANDUM

When a report that is not extremely short and simple is submitted, it is often accompanied by a covering memorandum (or a covering letter if it is sent through the mails). Such a memorandum is especially useful when a report will be of lasting rather than only immediate interest or when it will go beyond the person who first receives it.

A covering memorandum gives the writer an opportunity to make any extra remarks he feels the occasion calls for. These remarks may add up to no more than an identification of the report, a reference to the subject that the report deals with, and a statement of the reason this subject is reported on. Remarks of this limited nature grow out of the same impulse that probably causes you, in a personal contact, to say, "Here is that book (or list, or drawing, or estimate) that you asked for." In making such remarks in a covering memorandum, however, you usually do more than just gratify your natural impulse to say something. You also make it easier for the person who first receives your report to grasp or recall certain facts that concern it.

Sometimes a covering memorandum does a good deal more than this. Since the first recipient of your report is likely to be the person to whom you are immediately responsible, you may wish to tell him things that perhaps should go no further. For example, you may want to explain why you have emphasized some points and played down others. You may want to refer to obstacles you encountered or events that occurred while you were preparing the report. You may want to mention additional information that can be provided if it is needed. In general, you may want to give him facts that it would not be desirable or appropriate to place in the report itself; and the covering memorandum gives you an opportunity to do so.

A typical covering memorandum follows.

To: City Engineer
From: Ralph Hunt, Staff Engineer
Subject: Progress on Well Number 6   Date: March 28, 196_

As you requested in a memorandum dated March 7, I have inquired into the progress being made by the Inland Drilling Company on the well it is digging under contract with the city. Attached is a report of my findings.

My report is based partly on what I observed during two visits to the well site and partly on conversations with John Atkins, proprietor of the drilling company, and with the foreman in charge of the actual work. It was not easy to get definite information from either. Mr. Atkins assured me that he expects to complete the well by July 1, the date called for in the contract; but he was reluctant to answer questions on the average daily rate of drilling in recent weeks. The foreman, Walter Kelly, impressed me as being worried about the chances of the bit again getting stuck in the well. He is apparently finding the job unexpectedly difficult.

I feel that you should know about these casual impressions even though they do not consist of the kind of factual data it would be desirable to include in a report that must be released to the public. In my opinion we should constantly check on this job. If you wish to have me do so, let me know and I will step up the frequency of my visits.

I hope that for the present the report I am submitting includes the facts that you need to know in answering questions from the council and the press.

THE TITLE PAGE

The title page normally indicates (1) the subject of the report, (2) the person or body to whom the report is made, (3) the person or body making the report, and (4) the date of the report. Also, in large organizations, it may bear the number assigned to the report and information on the project that the report concerns.

The title itself is more than just a label. Though it should not be so long as to be cumbersome, it should give the clearest possible information about the exact subject covered. *Selection of a Fin-Tip Antenna for a KC-135 Airplane*, for example, would be a better title than just *Selection of a Fin-Tip Antenna*.

If a report is a matter of mere routine—for example the periodic report of normal operations of a division of some company—there would be no need for the title page to indicate to whom or by whom the report is made. Identifying it as a monthly or quarterly report makes these facts clear to anyone likely to be concerned.

The material on the title page should be pleasingly arranged, with the

A Report on

UNITIZING INCOMING RAW MATERIALS

to

THE MATERIAL-HANDLING DEPARTMENT

by

Robert L. Peterson
Industrial Engineer

May 17, 196_

Figure 13.   Well Designed Title Page for a Report.

optical emphasis on the upper half of the page. Figure 13 is a typical title page for a report in which there was no need to use a specific company form.

THE TABLE OF CONTENTS

The table of contents of a report is basically the same as that of a book in that it lists all the headings used and indicates the page on which each heading appears. Since indentation makes the rank of each heading apparent, the table of contents functions as an outline of the report as well as showing where various points are taken up. Occasionally each point is preceded by a number or a letter as it would be in an outline, but most of the time these symbols are discarded or are limited to the Roman numerals identifying main divisions.

Like the table of contents of a book, the table of contents of a report has headings that indicate the presence of appendixes, calculations, detailed data, or any other type of material that follows the report proper. These headings are likely to include the titles of individual tables and figures when such nonverbal devices are all placed after the body of the report. When the tables and figures are scattered through the body, however, their titles appear in a separate list.

Our discussion here has been brief, for two reasons. First, most of the work for a table of contents—deciding on the substance and phraseology of the headings—is done when the outline is made. Second, some of the questions that occur in connection with a table of contents are covered later, in the discussion of formal reports, because that is where they are most likely to arise.

It is important to realize, however, that a table of contents is a valuable part of any report that is more than a few pages long. It lets the reader see at a glance what ground is covered, shows him how the material is organized, and makes it easy for him to turn quickly to whatever he is looking for.

Following is a typical table of contents for a report.

CONTENTS

USE OF HEADINGS

The Value of Headings

One of the useful skills you can acquire as a report writer is skill in the use of internal headings. Such headings, regardless of whether you provide a table of contents, make it easier for your reader to grasp the nature of your material, the general plan governing its organization, and the relationship among its various parts. They help him to find what he is looking for when he wants to find out about some one portion of your subject. They can catch his attention and arouse his interest when he first glances over your work, and thus tempt him into the heart of the report before he has even taken time to read the preliminary sections. They reduce his reluctance to start reading by making the pages of text appear less formidable. And finally, the very fact that you are using them can improve your writing by reducing the temptation to wander away from the point you are supposed to be discussing.

To provide all these benefits, however, headings must be used systematically and must cover everything in the report—a vastly different matter than casually inserting them as they are inserted in newspaper articles or most articles in magazines. The headings used are drawn, of course, from the outline on which the report is based, and their value depends on its soundness. Headings cannot bring order out of confusion; they can only show that order exists.

Form for Headings of Different Ranks

Since the headings are intended to show how your material is organized, the form of each heading should indicate its rank. Headings of the same rank should be identical in form. Headings of different rank should differ in form. Headings of higher rank should look more important than those of lower rank. And finally, a form used for topic headings should

4

Safety problems of system-wide importance are referred to the Technical Safety Committee.

SAFETY PROGRAM

Safety Standards and Instructions

Safety standards and codes are developed by the Technical Safety Committee, which works both independently and in co-operation with state and national authorities. Design standards and specifications for equipment must also be passed upon by this committee from the standpoint of preventing accidents and fire.

Safety instructions are issued by the committee in a Safety Manual. Their observance by all employees and supervisors is mandatory. It is the responsibility of the supervisors to make sure that their employees are thoroughly familiar with the manual and abide by its regulations.

Prevention of Accidents

Safety Inspections. Regular inspection of physical facilities, working conditions, and employees' work habits is a responsibility of all supervisors. The safety staff also makes occasional inspections and recommends improvements to the supervisors.

Protective Equipment for Personnel. Protective equipment for personnel, such as hard hats, safety glasses, and goggles, is furnished by the company. Employees are required to use such equipment as directed by the Safety Manual. It is the responsibility of the supervisors to make sure that they do so. The use of special safety equipment for the use of employees exposed to unusual hazards is encouraged.

Training in the Prevention of Accidents. Training in the prevention of accidents is a continuous program of the safety staff, assisted by the supervisors. The main cause of most accidents is shown by experience to be human failure rather than mechanical failure. Every effort is therefore made to develop safety consciousness in all employees. Safety education is an important part of all supervisory training and employee development. Orientation of new employees in safety attitudes and knowledge is an important part of this program.

Fire Prevention and Control

Fire prevention and control, and regular inspection and maintenance of fire-fighting equipment are functions of all levels of supervision. The safety staff advises supervisors and recommends to them such actions as may be necessary to prevent fires or to minimize fire damage. The safety staff also assists supervisors in training selected employees in fire-fighting techniques.

Figure 14. Specimen Page from a Report, Showing Headings of Three Ranks.

not be used for any other purpose, such as the title of a list or a set of rules.

No single set of forms has become standard, but the following treatment is widely used and would be hard to improve upon.

A *heading of highest rank* (used before special parts such as introduction, conclusions, etc., and for the main divisions of the body) is centered, underlined, and capitalized throughout. It is placed three or four spaces below whatever precedes and a double space above whatever follows. It is not followed by any punctuation.

A *heading of second rank* begins at the left margin. It is underlined and capital letters are used only to begin important words ("upper and lower case capitalization"). It is placed a double or triple space below whatever precedes and a double space above whatever follows. It is not followed by any punctuation.

A *heading of third rank* is identical in form to a heading of the second rank, except that it does not appear on a line by itself and it is followed by a period. It is indented because it comes at the beginning of a paragraph.

Underlines are strongly recommended for typewritten work because they make the headings stand out more distinctly.

One feature that commends this system is that it does not include a centered upper and lower case heading. Consequently, that form can be used for the titles of lists and rules without being confused with topic headings. Figure 14 illustrates the form described.

Phraseology of Headings

With rare exceptions, headings that are used systematically to show the organization of a report or any other kind of writing are worded as topics. That is, each heading is a noun (or nouns) plus any modifiers needed. It is sometimes assumed that any phraseology that is not a sentence is a topic, but this is not the case.

Though it is doubtful that most writers analyze the grammatical structure of their headings, the fact remains that their headings almost never turn out to be prepositional phrases, adjectives, infinitive phrases, or sentences. Occasionally, in a brief piece of semipopular work, headings are phrased as questions or declarative sentences; but for the most part, discriminating writers use bona fide topics because they instinctively feel that other forms do not sound right. And most readers feel a sense of strangeness when they encounter headings that are not topics, even though they may not analyze the reason for their feelings.

The following examples should further clarify the difference between topics and nontopics.

Defects of Sorting Equipment (a topic)
   Mechanical (an adjective and hence not a topic. *Mechanical defects* would be better phraseology and also convey more meaning.)
   Electrical (comparable to "Mechanical")

Performance unsatisfactory (unsuitable. It is an elliptical sentence, the verb being omitted.)
   Vibrates excessively (unsuitable. It is an elliptical sentence, the subject being omitted.)
   Gets clogged frequently (comparable to "Vibrates excessively")

Unsatisfactory performance (suitable)
   Excessive vibration (suitable)
   Frequency of clogging (suitable)

Reasons for postponing decision (suitable phraseology)
   To conduct cold-weather tests (unsuitable. It is an infinitive phrase.)
   Need for cold-weather tests (suitable revision of the preceding heading)

In Colfax County (unsuitable. It is a prepositional phrase.)
Infestation in Colfax County (suitable phraseology, also conveying more meaning)

If you doubt your own ability to phrase your headings suitably by applying grammatical principles, you can probably get good results by asking yourself as you look at each heading, "Does this sound like a name? Would it seem natural to say, 'The title of this section of my report is . . . ?' " If the answer is no, a change in phraseology is probably indicated.

Another point to remember about the phraseology of headings is that each heading should be as explicit as possible. When a subpoint appears in the text of a report, its main point may be on an earlier page. Consequently, a heading should be as nearly self-sufficient as you can make it without letting its length become cumbersome. For example, a reader seeing *Power Lines* in an outline as a point under *Removal of Obstacles* would know at once exactly what material it covered. But if he encountered *Power Lines* as a heading on page 12 of a report when *Removal of Obstacles* was on page 6, he would have only a vague idea of what to expect. On the other hand, if he encountered the heading *Removal of Power Lines,* he would instantly know the exact nature of the material it covered. What might appear to be needless repetition in an outline can be highly desirable when the points of that outline appear in the report itself.

A report writer should never forget that, except when they are extremely short, reports are not always read from beginning to end as one reads a story or an editorial. On the contrary, they are repeatedly consulted by readers who at the moment want information only on one particular point. And the headings should be phrased so that these readers can find what they are looking for with a minimum of effort.

General Suggestions

The question of how many headings to use cannot be answered by rigid rules; but if you observe the frequency of headings in this book and in other material where headings are used systematically, you will be able to form a good idea of what is normal. Your aim should be to place headings close enough together to keep the reader constantly aware of what is being discussed, but not so close together as to reduce continuity.

You will also notice that the presence of headings somewhat reduces the need for transitional sentences and paragraphs. And finally, you will notice that the text does not depend on the headings for completeness. That is, words such as *this*, and *these* are not used in a manner that forces the reader to turn back to the heading in order to discover their meaning.

All in all, headings have an effect that is hard to overestimate. They encourage a reader to start reading a report by opening up its contents, they help him constantly as he is reading, and they subject the writer to a discipline that improves the orderliness of his writing.

SUMMARIES AND ABSTRACTS

The problem of discussing summaries and abstracts is complicated by the lack of anything approaching a general agreement about terminology. In a set of instructions for use within a single organization, the problem can be solved by the use of arbitrary definitions; but in a book for general use, this simple solution is unsuitable. The basic definitions that would probably gain widest acceptance are as follows.

An abstract is a brief section—rarely more than six or eight lines long—the purpose of which is to tell the reader what points are covered in some piece of writing without attempting to tell him what is said about them. It may be written for a report or various other kinds of writing. If it is written as a section of a report, it is one of the first parts that a reader encounters. It is an independent element rather than an integral part of the body. Such abstracts sometimes appear by themselves in publications devoted entirely to abstracts of material in some particular field.

A summary—at least the summary of a report—is a section that presents in a highly condensed form the most important information that the report contains. It is brief, but not so brief as the type of abstract described above. It is placed, as an abstract would be, extremely early in the report (one rarely finds both an abstract and a summary in the same report); and like an abstract, it is an independent element rather than part of the body. Its functions will be described in more detail later.

Unfortunately, the situation is not so simple as it would be if the distinction established above were universally accepted. If one examines a substantial number of reports from different sources, he quickly discovers two additional facts:

1. The term *abstract* is often used before a section that would be a summary according to the preceding definitions.

2. The term *summary* is used widely and legitimately in reference to a section at the *end* of some piece of writing—a section that is an integral part of the piece and is used to summarize what has already been said. (In a working-level report, however, a summary of this kind is not often used, and even when used it is likely to appear without a heading rather than to be headed *Summary*.)

The problem of terminology is further complicated by the fact that in an effort to facilitate discussion, at least three other terms have been coined for use in books of general circulation. The term *descriptive abstract* is sometimes used to identify what was called merely an abstract in our original definitions. The term *informative abstract* is used in reference to what our definitions called a summary. (In fact one sometimes finds that the definition of *informative abstract* is sometimes followed by the statement that such an abstract is sometimes called a summary.) The term *introductory summary* is sometimes used in reference to what we called merely a summary, and sometimes in reference to a "summary" at the beginning that emphasizes such matters as an explanation of the problem or a review of the background. These three terms serve their purpose in the books that use them, but they rarely appear in actual reports—nor do the writers who use them tell us that we will find them as headings.

The discussion of terminology might be further expanded to cover the occasional use of at least two other terms—*foreword* and *digest*—but we are concerned with other matters of more importance than mere terminology. The first major purpose of the present discussion is to emphasize the importance of the section at the beginning of a report that presents its most important contents in a condensed form—which for the sake of simplicity we shall henceforth call a summary. The second is to tell what a writer can do to make such a section, whatever it is called, serve its purpose effectively. It is unnecessary to deal with descriptive abstracts in the same manner, not because they are unimportant but because they are relatively easy to write.

If a report contains a summary, no other section with the possible exception of conclusions and recommendations is more important. This is the case because readers farther up the line than the writer's immediate superior may read the summary and little else. Also, readers who read the entire report on a single occasion may later refer to the summary repeatedly to refresh their minds. Still others will use the summary to decide whether to read the full report. In many great corporations, summaries of reports are widely distributed so that those whom they interest may request copies of the full version if they so desire. Also, by looking at summaries that are kept in carefully indexed files, people can tell what information is available from other departments than their own and avoid needless duplication of effort. In brief, when you prepare a summary of your report you may expect that it will be read more frequently, read by more people, and read by more important people than will the full report.

The condensation that is characteristic of a summary is achieved by leaving out preliminaries, details, illustrative examples—everything except the main facts and ideas. The relationship of the summary to the full report is roughly similar to the relationship of a topic sentence to a fully developed paragraph. (There is a difference, however. The topic sentence is an integral part of the paragraph, whereas the report is independent of its summary.)

To write a good summary you should not approach the job too casually. If you try to read a few lines and then condense them, read a few more and condense them, and continue this process to the end of the report, the result will be ineffective. Instead, you should go over the entire report—or an entire section if the report is extremely long—and make notes of the matters you consider essential for inclusion. Next, write the rough draft of your summary by using these notes and by referring to the full version whenever necessary. Then polish what you have written until it reads as smoothly as it can be made to read without the waste of space on introductory and transitional material.

Make a special effort to avoid wordiness. (A summary should rarely exceed 10 per cent of the length of the full version; and it is unfortunate to waste words when you are constantly being forced to cut out facts and ideas you would like to include.) If you can preserve grace and variety of style in a summary, well and good; but if you must sacrifice those qualities for the sake of brevity, there is no reason for undue concern. In a summary, conciseness outweighs all other qualities of style except precision, clarity, and readability.

In writing a summary you will need to take special pains in order to make your work accurate. Figures must be double-checked to avoid error. Facts and ideas must not be distorted by the cutting out of words. Care is needed in the selection of material for inclusion, for if its contents are unrepresentative, a summary can be misleading even though it contains no statement that was not in the original. In matters such as emphasis—in the implications as to what was important and what was less important, a summary should give the same impression that the reader would receive if he read the full report.

Still another consideration in writing a summary is the question of whether the reader or readers will be the same people who read the full report. When a report contains a good deal of technical material, it is very likely that some of those who read the summary will not have the technical background of the writer or the original receiver. Consequently, a summary will often be more useful if technical information and technical vocabulary are held to a minimum. You might do well to keep in mind three types of reader: the original reader, who wants a thorough picture but will not check everything (he reads the introduction, body, conclusions, and recommendations); the person whom the original reader depends upon to check everything for him (he studies the appendix, with all its data, calculations, tables, and figures to make sure that there are no errors or discrepancies); and the executive further up the line, who may not be a specialist in the area that the report concerns, but who wants to know what is going on and who may say "Yes" or "No" to the entire project (he reads the summary and whatever is offered in the way of conclusions and recommendations).

To indicate how a summary compares with a full treatment of the same material, the following summary is presented. It covers all that was said in Chapter 7 about what reports are, their importance, and the difference between professional and school reports.

> Though reports vary widely in form, length, and other respects, they are a distinct species of writing because they possess one characteristic in common: the responsibility of the writer of the report to the reader.
>
> Reports are extremely important in government and industry because they are a major source of information for those who need it. Their importance to those who receive them makes skill in producing them important to the writers.
>
> The merit of a report written on the job depends on the extent to which it meets the needs of the reader. This test of merit does not exist in the classroom. When a student graduates and takes a job, it is important that he realize this difference and form the habit of constantly asking himself, "Does the reader need this?" as he decides what information to include in a report and what to omit.

THE INTRODUCTION

Naturally, a report that is extremely short and simple needs little or nothing by way of an introduction. All that is necessary is to say what is required for the sake of self-sufficiency and to start smoothly enough that your reader feels at ease as he gets into the subject.

When a report is longer, it may be necessary to choose between an ordinary introduction and what we will call a formal introduction. The ordinary introduction in a report is no different from the introduction in any other kind of writing. It may consist of general comment on the subject as a whole. It may give background information on whatever the report concerns. It may explain the general plan that the report is to follow. It may serve, without being so labeled, as a summary of the contents. It may attempt to arouse interest. (The presence or absence of a table of contents and a summary will of course affect the need for some of these types of material.) In general, the normal introduction may say anything that needs to be said about the subject of the report before the first main division of the material is taken up.

Example of a Normal Introduction

When concrete pipe is buried in the earth, its movement as it expands and contracts is restrained by the seizing power of the soil. Consequently the spacing of expansion joints is not so simple as it would be if the pipe were on the surface. If the tendency of the pipe to expand and contract cannot overcome the restraint, longitudinal stress develops. This stress, coupled with the circumferential stress that results from hydrostatic pressure, may cause the pipe to fail.

To cope with this problem a study has been made to develop an equation that can be used to determine how far apart expansion joints should be placed in any given installation. The following report first presents the major equation and the reasoning by which it was developed. Then it presents a subsidiary equation to be used in determining soil resistance—a value included in the major equation that depends on the specific conditions in any one installation. And finally, it applies the two formulas to a specific set of circumstances to show how they would work out.

There is no reason to doubt that if he uses reasonable values, a design engineer can use the equations with the assurance that the resultant spacing of expansion joints will be satisfactory.

In contrast, a formal introduction to a report is much like the introduction to a thesis or dissertation. That is, it deals not so much with the subject of the report as with the report itself. This type of introduction is likely to be used in a long formal or semiformal report that is written for some nonroutine purpose—often for the purpose of presenting the results of a special investigation. It will be discussed in more detail in Chapter 11, which deals with the formal report. Suffice it to say, at present, that in nonformal reports a formal introduction may be used to tell the reader whatever he needs to know about the reason the report is written, the function it is intended to perform, the scope of the problem it concerns, and the name of the person or organization that authorized it. A specimen of a formal introduction is included in Chapter 11.

Such an introduction may be followed by an ordinary introduction if one is needed; but in this case the ordinary introduction is placed under a heading such as "Background Information," "General Comment," "History of . . . ," or any other appropriate phrase.

CONCLUSIONS AND RECOMMENDATIONS

Though some reports, because of their purpose and content, do not need to include conclusions or recommendations, such material is almost always called for in a report that presents the results of an investigation. When it is included, it should usually be drawn together in one place and headed in a manner that identifies its special nature. In this connection, the term *conclusion* or *conclusions* means "convictions arrived at on the basis of evidence" rather than merely "the section that consists of an ending."

Though conclusions and recommendations sometimes merge naturally into a single section, their nature should not be confused. *Conclusions* is a term used to identify mere convictions. *Recommendations* refers to actions that are called for on the basis of such convictions. We might reach certain convictions without being in a position to recommend action because the wisdom of possible actions may depend on matters beyond the scope of our particular report. It might be possible, for example, to conclude that a certain site would be physically suitable for a factory, without being in a position to recommend that a factory be built there.

Logically, conclusions and recommendations should follow the body of the report because they depend on its contents. Often, however, they are placed before the body on the grounds that the reader wants to read them immediately. Most large organizations will have a standard practice regarding placement; but a writer who is not bound by a prescribed format may place them in either location with the assurance such placement is not unusual.

In a section labeled *Conclusions,* regardless of where it is placed, every statement should grow out of facts given elsewhere. A reader has a right to assume that you are not stating conclusions except on the basis of evidence. Overstatement should be carefully avoided. When some of the evidence seems opposed to the conclusions, that fact should be conceded; and in explaining away such evidence, the report should be scrupulously fair. If the evidence points toward some conclusion but does not definitely establish it, you should frankly say that the evidence is not conclusive. There is nothing wrong with offering an opinion if it is openly identified as such.

This advice to use judicious restraint should not be construed, however, as encouragement to hedge in your statements by means of evasion. In a conclusion, as elsewhere, such statements as "It is believed that . . ." are obviously meaningless unless we know who does the believing.

When conclusions are placed at the end of a report, the facts and reasoning that they are based upon may be pointed out briefly; but when they appear before the body, this support is not usually offered. Wherever they are placed, conclusions should be numbered if there are more than one; however, you should not assume that the use of numbers is a substitute for careful grouping of material into unified elements and careful arrangement in a logical sequence. Use of numbers does not achieve organization, but merely reveals it.

Sometimes the nature of a report makes it natural to offer a conclusion at the end of each major division. But even when this is done, it is advisable to draw all the conclusions together in a single section unless the report is short and simple. It would be inconvenient for a reader who wished to study the conclusions and nothing else to be forced to hunt for them on several pages.

When recommendations are called for and do not merge naturally with conclusions, they should be keyed to the conclusions (that is, given similar numbers), when such treatment is possible. Like the conclusions, they grow out of the facts and reasoning offered in the body of the report. (Sometimes the recommendations grow out of the conclusions as the conclusions grow out of the body.) The occasional tendency to treat *Recommendations* as a section consisting of a few helpful suggestions on incidental questions is unsound in any report based on an investigation; rather than being incidental, the recommendations are the focal point of everything else in the report—the reasons for its existence.

One final point should be heeded. Like so many other tasks in report writing, writing conclusions and recommendations is a matter of judgment, not merely compliance with rigid rules. In the preceding discussion, we have attempted to demonstrate that these materials should be presented in a manner that helps the reader to find what he is looking for as easily as possible. The organization and the choice of headings should be whatever is necessary to accomplish that result.

Following are the conclusions and recommendations arrived at in a report by the Technical Extension Service of a state university to a legislative fact-finding committee.

Conclusions and Recommendations

Conclusions
1. The evidence secured during our own tests indicates that damage to county-type roads would be more than doubled if the maximum weight allowed to bear on a single axle of a truck were increased from the present 18,000-pound limit to 24,000 pounds, as requested.
2. There is no legal way in which the request could be granted except by amending the present state statutes.
3. Compliance with the request would result in the state's being ineligible to receive some of the federal aid it receives at present.

Recommendations

1. It is recommended that the Beet Growers Association be notified that it is not possible to grant their request under the existing conditions.

2. It is recommended that when analysis of the data now being studied by the American Association of Highway Officials has been completed, the present decision be reviewed; and that if these data show that an increased axle load would not cause unsatifactory road life, an effort shall be made to secure whatever legislative action, both state and federal, is necessary if load limits are to be increased.

3. It is recommended that the educational campaign among agricultural produce truckers be intensified in order that these truckers may not be justified in pleading ignorance of the regulations and in order that the need for such regulations shall be widely understood.

THE APPENDIX

An appendix is often desirable in a report, as in a book, because it permits the writer to make material available without placing it in the main text. In a report, a typical example of this material would be the full results of a series of tests. The average of these results might be significant, but the results of the individual tests would often serve no function except to make it possible to confirm the average and perhaps to see the extremes. Other material sometimes relegated to the appendix includes tables, figures, calculations, lists (for example, lists of equipment), specifications, and even supplemental reports.

Various reasons can make it desirable to put something in an appendix. The appended material might be technical information that most readers would not use, though they might want to have it available for examination by specialists. It might consist of detailed or supplementary information that would be consulted on special occasions but otherwise would only be in the way. It might be material to be studied separately rather than during normal reading. It might be material such as photographs, that would make the report physically hard to handle if scattered through the body.

Obviously, anything placed in an appendix is not so closely integrated with the rest of the report as it would be if placed in the body. Sometimes, indeed, it does not need to be closely integrated. But when material in the appendix is closely related to something in the main report, it should be referred to at the appropriate point in the text.

Ordinarily the appendix is preceded by a title page bearing the single word *Appendix;* but if the appendix is brief and if the first item is not of full-page size, the title *Appendix* may be placed at the top of the first page rather than on a page by itself.

When the material appended is of more than one kind and when its amount is great enough to justify the extra complication, two or more appendixes can be used. In this case, each is identified by a letter, and its title indicates the nature of its contents. (For example, *Appendix A —Tables, Appendix B—Photographs.*)

In brief, use of an appendix is often a handy method of presenting material that should be available in support of the main report without causing the main report to become needlessly cluttered and complicated.

FINAL COMMENT ON SPECIAL ELEMENTS

Before the subject of special elements is dismissed, two more points should be brought out. The first is that in the report-writing world, uniformity is sadly lacking in the labels attached to these elements and in the details of their use. For example, what is called an *abstract* in one company may be a *summary* in a second and a *synopsis* in a third. The term *references* usually means a list of books and articles, but in some companies it means conversations, letters, and memoranda that are related to the subject of the report and are listed at the beginning. In short, though most of what has been said in the preceding discussion will apply in any position you may hold, it would be impossible for any book to give instructions that are entirely suitable for every occasion, because terminology and details of procedure vary.

Second, we should not lose sight of the fact that special elements of reports are merely tools. We should know how to use them, but we should decide in each case which ones are needed, and not use all of them just because they are available. In other words, planning the layout of a report is not just a matter of following hard and fast rules. On the contrary, it is a process of designing a product that will do its job effectively —and its job is simply to make sure that the reader can grasp the contents of the report as accurately and as easily as possible. Each of the elements is merely a means to that end.

EXERCISES

Following are excerpts from outlines made with the expectation of using the points of the outline as headings within the completed report. Revise the phraseology, when necessary, so that each point is worded as a topic and so that the principles of parallel form and self-sufficiency are applied.

1	2
Steps in the new welding process	Results of underloading
Vee out the area	Higher line losses
Use of a sealing electrode	Higher voltage drop
Completion of the weld	Motors lose torque

3

Methods of measurement
  Exhaust olefins
  Eye irritation

5

Corrective measures
  Use of synchronous motors
  Install synchronous condensers
  Avoidance of overloading

7

Characteristics of the new mixture
  Homogeneous
  Void-free
  Heat resistant

9

Reasons for rejection
  It is noisy
  Poor appearance
  Inefficient
  Too heavy

4

Possible applications
  In feed mills
  In detergent plants
  In kaolin clay plants

6

Reasons unit A is better than unit B
  Lower starting torque
  Maintenance is easier
  Requires smaller base
  Ease of inspection

8

Discussion of rods
  Rod consumption
  Rod size distribution
  Method of calculating rod sizes
  Broken rods spoil efficiency

10

Duties of Fire Inspector
  To check wiring and motors
  Fire extinguishers
  To inspect for fire doors
  To have flammable waste removed

10

PROCEDURE
IN
WRITING
A
REPORT

The procedure described in this chapter is suitable when the complexity of a situation or the probable length of a report creates uncertainty about how to tackle the problem. It is offered not as a formula to be followed rigidly, but merely as a systematic approach that may be modified as circumstances require. It would call for the following steps:

1. Analyze and plan the job as a whole, so that you have in mind a picture of the kind of report you must produce and what you must do to produce it.

2. Form a general, tentative plan for presenting your material. This can include a preliminary decision about the entire layout of the report (what elements to include) and a highly tentative plan or outline for the substance.

3. Gather the facts that you need and interpret their significance.

4. Revise your tentative plan so that your outline reflects your final ideas about organization.

5. Decide so far as possible what use you will make of tables and figures if it seems likely that they will be helpful.

6. Write the first draft of the body of your report, and of your conclusions and recommendations.

7. Make your final decision about what elements (introduction, summary, etc.) you will use as a framework for the body, conclusions, and recommendations, and write those that you have not yet written.

8. Revise and polish all parts as necessary.

9. Care for such final details as providing the title page and table of contents. Go over everything carefully to be sure that it contains no errors, and then go ahead with the mechanical business of copying and fastening it together.

The occasions when you will follow this procedure exactly will be few and far between. When a report is long and complicated, preparing it is a matter of pushing forward on more than one front as conditions permit. It may be necessary, for example, to gather and analyze facts on one point before deciding whether another should be included at all. Again, you may produce a rough draft of one section, complete with tables and figures, before the investigation for another section has gone beyond its opening stages. Nevertheless, the procedure suggested is sound whether applied to an entire report or to a single section of a longer report. It at least provides a systematic sequence of action so that you do not need to start work with no plan at all and improvise as you go.

One more point should be mentioned in connection with the procedure as a whole. The order in which a writer produces the various parts of a report is not the order in which a reader encounters them. Such parts as the title page, the summary, the introduction, and the conclusions and recommendations are brought into existence as the work nears completion; but most of these parts are placed early in the report. A person who expects to produce a report of any length and complexity should grasp this essential point at the outset.

ANALYZING THE JOB

Analyzing the job really consists of analyzing two problems—the problem that the report itself is intended to solve, and the problem of what you must do to produce a report that will serve its purpose.

To analyze the first of these problems you will need to center your attention on the subject and purpose of the report. It is often the function of a report to answer some large, comprehensive question. As you think about the question that the report as a whole concerns, you will usually find that the answer depends on the answer to various other questions —many of which themselves depend on the answers to even smaller questions. For example, to answer the question of whether to produce some product by a new method it would first be necessary to answer questions about the quality of product that would result, the equipment needed, the space needed, the skills needed by the operators, the cost, and countless others. When such a list of questions to be answered has been drawn up, the scope of the original problem becomes clearly understandable.

But the second problem still remains: what you must do or have others do in order to produce your report. That is, you will need to figure out what methods of investigation will be necessary. You will need to decide when and by whom each portion of the total investigation will be performed. You will need to decide what kind of report (how detailed and what elements it should consist of) is necessary in presenting the information after you have gathered it. In brief, you will need to form a clear mental picture of the finished product, to anticipate the jobs that the production of such a product involves, and to lay plans that will result in orderly progress.

Admittedly, the two aspects of analyzing the job are not sharply distinct. The second is to some extent based on the first, for it is obviously impossible to decide where and how to get information without first deciding what information must be obtained. But in spite of this overlapping, the analysis of a report-writing job usually goes better if you think of it actually as the analysis of two separate problems.

MAKING A TENTATIVE PLAN OR OUTLINE

It is almost impossible to analyze the subject of a report without forming a general idea about your outline, at least in its larger aspects. As you think of various questions, you will consider their relationships toward each other, and these relationships will point the way toward main points and subpoints of an outline. And as you think of all your questions in relation to the function of your report, a general plan for presenting your material will begin to take shape. It is a mistake, however, to think of these early ideas on organization as final. Only after you have gathered enough information to be dealing with answers instead of just with questions can you be sure that any plan you form will be satisfactory. Then, some matters that looked important will dwindle into insignificance; points that seemed likely to be minor will assume importance; facts will emerge that you had not realized would call for consideration. All in all, though forming a tentative idea about organization is natural and useful, the principle urged in Chapter 3 is still sound. Only when you have gathered information and interpreted its significance can you decide definitely about the best way to organize it.

GATHERING INFORMATION

In a book dealing mainly with the process of writing, a discussion of gathering information for reports must be extremely general. The fact is that gathering information is not really a writing problem. Still, a few general comments about the sources of information apply widely enough to justify their inclusion. These comments will apply first to the reports you will write on the job and then to reports you may produce in a course such as the one based on this book.

Reports Written on the Job

When you are actually on the job, regardless of your field, your first step in gathering information will probably be to check the files of your own company in order to locate reports or other records that might answer some of your questions. Many companies have extensive indexes of reports and abstracts of their contents. Where no formal system for retrieval of information has been developed, personal inquiries as well as checking the files will often open leads that will enable you to avoid duplicating the work that others have done.

Published material may be the next source to try. A systematic survey of published literature is often the starting point when an extensive investigation of a scientific question is to be undertaken.

Another common method of obtaining information is by correspondence. Sometimes this involves the use of questionnaires, but a mere letter of inquiry is more frequently appropriate. Such letters are discussed in the section on letter writing. To a person on the job, the occasions when a letter is the best means of obtaining information are so obvious that there is no need to discuss the subject in detail.

In place of writing letters you may sometimes find it better to get information by personal interviews. Such interviews are of course more expensive than letters and are sometimes slower, but the flexibility of a personal conversation can bring out facts that would not come to light in an exchange of letters.

When the information needed for a report cannot be gathered from other people, personal observation and inspection is a possible method. A typical use of personal observation would be a visit to a factory to watch some process in operation, a field trip to observe the performance of a piece of farm machinery, or a trip to a mine to investigate its condition. Personal inspection might be the method used in an attempt to determine why accidents were frequent on a construction project, or what conditions were causing an epidemic.

Scientific tests and experimentation are of course the main source of information for many reports. Sometimes as a report writer you may do such work yourself and sometimes you may have it done for you by others whose special services are available. The contributions of scientific research to modern industry and government—contributions that are made available by means of reports—are so vast that it would be impossible to do more here than recognize their importance. However, we should not overlook the fact that reports based on scientific research are not always related to practical problems of the kind we have been discussing. Many a scientific investigation is made for no further purpose than to increase the fund of human knowledge, and many a report is written just because new knowledge exists and should be reported. The purpose and probable use of this book justify a focus of attention on practical rather than purely scientific problems; but many of the techniques recommended can be applied in reporting on scientific research that is not intended to solve a specific and immediate practical problem.

One final and general means of gathering information must be mentioned because, though it overlaps the others, it will often be the main method you will use on the job. It consists of merely doing the work that your profession calls for—sometimes with the help of others whose services are available. For many who use this book, such work will mainly consist of the scientific tests and experiments referred to above; but these and the other possible activities are so numerous and varied that no list could cover more than a small proportion of them. Actually, the work done in gathering information for a report can include any of the technical work done in our complicated industrial civilization.

It should also be noted that the information in a report does not necessarily come from a single source, and conversely, not all the sources are likely to be used on a single occasion. The fact is that though the information needed for a report may sometimes be far from easy to obtain, it will not necessarily be hard to decide what sources are promising and what method to use. The nature of the problem is likely to make the type of source and the method fairly obvious.

Reports in a Writing Course

Most of the sources of information described above may be utilized for a course in technical writing. But the problem of gathering information is complicated by the fact that resources available to a person holding a position in government and industry are often unavailable to a college student. On the job, the person who is asked to report on a problem has access to relevant files, opportunity to make necessary visits and inspections, and the time, facilities, assistance, and financial support that he needs in seeking a solution. In the classroom, finding a real or at least a realistic subject based on specific facts may in itself be a major difficulty —especially since the problem should not only be realistic but must also be practicable for a student to handle. Consequently, instead of starting with a problem and then figuring out the sources of information and method of investigation, a student must often discover a subject he can obtain information about and then try to set up a problem that this information will be useful in solving.

Information available in books and magazines may unavoidably be a larger element in a report for a writing course than is usually the case in a report written on the job. To prevent a situation in which mere reference papers masquerade as reports it is well to remember that a school itself may provide suitable subjects. These would include such matters as parking, lighting, utilization of land, arrangement of laboratory equipment, condition of buildings, sanitation, equipment in kitchens, and many other questions that constantly arise in the physical operation of even a moderate-sized institution.

Also, a job past or present might provide information or access to information that can form the basis of a suitable problem and its solution. In any event, unless a subject is assigned or suggested by an instructor, it may call for considerable ingenuity for a student to figure out where information can be obtained and to develop a subject that permits him to use the facts available.

INTERPRETING THE FACTS GATHERED

A report writer's job is not limited to gathering facts and stating them. He must often interpret them for the reader's benefit. The nature of this interpretation is comparable to what happens when a patient goes to a doctor. The patient describes his symptoms, the doctor administers tests, makes examinations, and discovers facts about metabolism, blood pressure, and other physical conditions. Then the doctor must interpret these facts about the patient's condition in order to diagnose the ailment.

Other examples would be as follows:

FACT: When a slide prepared by a medical technician is exposed to a certain stain, the smear upon it retains the color of the stain.

INTERPRETATION: A colony of bacteria has developed.

FACT: When the concentration of elk in a national forest is greatest the browse gets scantier each year.

INTERPRETATION: The herd is too large for the food supply.

FACT: The water above an industrial plant contains more oxygen than the water below, and the industrial wastes contain organic matter.

INTERPRETATION: The oxygen is being used up in the decomposition of the organic matter.

FACT: A Geiger counter ticks faster than usual.

INTERPRETATION: There has been an increase in radioactivity.

To be sure, the statements labeled *interpretation* in the preceding examples are themselves intended to be statements of fact, but the facts
stated are a different kind. They are discovered not by observation alone
but by observation plus reasoning, and they reveal the significance of
the observed facts on which they are based.

Another kind of interpretation is the interpretation of the meaning of
written material, as, for example, when the meaning of a statute is interpreted by a court decision. This kind is not so common in report writing
as the kind previously described, but it is sometimes called for. For example, when there is doubt whether certain work is covered by a contract, interpretation of the meaning of the phraseology of the contract
would be necessary, and the results of this interpretation might affect the
recommendations of a technical report. To be sure, everything should
originally be written in a manner that reduces the possibility of a dispute
about interpretation. Nevertheless, in your technical writing, you will
sometimes have to demonstrate the fact that a general or abstract statement covers a specific, concrete situation. And in doing so you will be
interpreting the meaning of the statement.

The process of interpretation may call for any of the generally recognized processes of reasoning, such as generalizing on the basis of individual cases, applying a general rule to a specific case, ascertaining the
cause of incidents or conditions, deciding what results will follow if certain actions are performed, or ascertaining the specific applications of a
rule or regulation that is phrased in general terms.

Likewise, the errors in interpretation resemble the errors in reasoning
in general. They include generalization on the basis of insufficient or
unrepresentative evidence, failure to consider alternative possibilities
(that is, the possible existence of undiscovered facts or other possible
interpretations of facts discovered), or the failure to realize that an entire
line of facts and reasoning may be based—in fact is likely to be based—on
assumptions that might themselves be subject to question. Much of what
was said in Chapter 7 under the heading of *Thoroughness* deals with
these errors.

Whether to explain in detail the reasoning by which you reach your
interpretation of the facts is a matter of judgment. Certainly it is not
desirable to prolong a report by explaining the self-evident. There are
times, however, when a reader will probably be unable to see why you
interpret the facts as you do unless you tell him. And there are also times
when it is desirable to tell him even if he might be able eventually to
think his own way through, for with your assistance, he will be able to
see the connection faster than he could figure it out for himself. Also, he
is more likely to accept your interpretation if you show him how you
reached it.

One more point needs to be cleared up: the distinction between interpreting the facts in your report and the process of forming your conclusions. Actually, there is no *essential* difference between the two. When you interpret a fact or a group of facts, you are drawing a conclusion, and when you settle upon the conclusion or conclusions for the report as a whole, those conclusions amount to an over-all interpretation of all the facts. Nevertheless, at a practical, working level, a distinction is justified unless the report is short and uncomplicated. The difference lies in the scope. In stating the conclusions of a report you will be telling the convictions arrived at in connection with the major question or questions the report is supposed to answer. But in interpreting your facts you will be trying to find and reveal the significance of individual facts or small groups of facts. When you eventually draw your main conclusions, you base them on the interpretations that have occurred throughout the report.

MAKING THE DETAILED OUTLINE

As mentioned earlier, you are almost certain to form a general, tentative plan for a report before you gather all the information it will contain. But when you have gathered the information and analyzed it to ascertain its significance, you will usually need to revise the plan so that it will be a good organization for the facts as they actually turned out, and to develop it into a detailed outline. In most respects, making an outline for a report is not essentially different from making an outline for any other purpose. True, you may sometimes be required to place your material under a standard list of major headings; but even then it will still be necessary to plan the presentation of the material within each main division; and there will be innumerable occasions when you will be free to plan the entire treatment. Therefore, you should not overlook the techniques of outlining presented in Chapter 3.

In that chapter it was pointed out that making an outline is primarily a matter of organizing your material. As you organize the material of a report, one consideration needs special emphasis. A report, more than most kinds of writing, is written in order that it may perform a specific function when it reaches the attention of specific readers who read it for specific reasons. Consequently, it is especially important, in planning it, to refrain from concentrating on the subject matter only. It is usually possible to organize the same subject matter in more than one way, and the best of these possible organizations is the one that makes it easiest for the reader to find the answers to the particular questions he is likely to have in mind.

Consider, for example, a study made by a highway research laboratory to determine whether subgrade soil might be improved by mixing certain materials into it. Tests were made to determine, in regard to each admixture, its effect on the strength of the soil, the ease of compaction, the resistance to penetration of moisture, and the tendency of the soil to swell when moisture penetrated. Two of the possible organizations that would accommodate the facts are as follows:

(1) An organization in which main points were based on the admixtures and the subpoints were based on their effects. This organization would make it easy for a reader to learn all the results that would follow when a given substance was added; but in order to discover what substance to use if a certain result were desired he would have to look in as many places as there were substances.

(2) An organization with main points based on effects. This would make it easier to see what material might be used if a certain result were desired, but information about all that would happen if a certain substance were used would be scattered in several places.

Both of these treatments are logical, but on a given occasion one or the other might be decidedly superior.

PLANNING THE USE OF TABLES AND FIGURES

If a report calls for the use of tables and figures, you must decide whether to scatter them through the text, place them all at the end, or divide them between the two locations. It is usually best to make this decision before you do much writing. In fact it is better if you not only decide where figures and tables will be placed, but also decide what specific figures and tables you will use. If you cannot make this latter decision for the report as a whole, you can at least make it in connection with each section before you begin writing it. The reason for settling this question early is that your text itself will be affected by your decisions in regard to these nonverbal forms.

The technical aspects of using tables and figures in a report is no different from that of using them in other technical writing. Therefore the discussion in Chapter 6 makes a detailed explanation at this point unnecessary.

WRITING THE FIRST DRAFT

If the preliminary work has been done properly, the actual writing of a report is much the same process as writing anything else and should not be abnormally difficult. A few special suggestions, however, might be of value.

The first of these concerns the question of getting started. How to get under way may be a puzzle, of course, in any kind of writing. In writing a report, the preliminaries that must often be cared for present an additional complication. Consequently, if you find it hard to get a report started, the sensible thing to do is to postpone writing the opening and go to work on the earliest section that you feel ready to handle. If this is not feasible, start at the beginning in the simplest manner possible. Don't worry about smoothness. Just write the bare facts that are necessary if the report is to be self-sufficient, and then plunge into the first main section of the body. Later, you can revise your opening or write a new one; but it may surprise you by turning out to be better than you had expected.

In writing a report on an extensive project, you will probably not even consider writing the opening first. Rather, you will write up each section as soon as the information it will include becomes available. Your work will go faster and its quality will be better if you write while your information and ideas are fresh in your mind. Under these circumstances the preliminary portions of your report may be among the last to be written.

In any event, when you start writing, push ahead without worrying about details. If your flow of words is slowed down by an effort to improve your style, the flow of ideas may also slow down and it will be harder to preserve continuity. If something worries you as you put it down, make a note in the margin and settle the question later.

As you write or revise you should be especially alert for spots where ordinary text is ineffective. When you have a list to present, for example, you may be able to help your reader by presenting it with each item on a separate line. A typical use of such a list (sometimes called an informal table) would be as follows:

Gradation of Samples

Percentage passing ¾-in. screen and retained on ½-in. screen	16.7
Percentage passing ½-in. screen and retained on ⅜-in. screen	16.6
Percentage passing ⅜-in. screen and retained on No. 4 screen	16.7
Percentage passing No. 4 screen	50.0
	100.0

The use of nontextual form may often be carried even further with good results. To show how this helps the reader, the same facts are presented below in two forms, the second of which makes them easier to grasp than the first.

(1)

The savings in labor cost that we can realize by manufacturing the newly designed bobbin rather than the present bobbin will be in the neighborhood of $158,000. This figure is calculated as follows: We hire three crews to manufacture bobbins, each crew consisting of 45 men. The size of each crew, if we make the change, will be cut to 35, a reduction of 10. Thus the labor force will be reduced by a total of 30. As we now operate, a laborer normally works 1,920 hours per year. If we made the change, the elimination of 30 laborers would mean a saving of 57,600 man-hours. Our present wage to members of these crews averages $2.75. Thus by cutting the crews as indicated we would reduce cost of labor by a total of $158,400.

(2)

The savings in labor cost that we can realize by manufacturing the newly designed bobbin rather than the present bobbin will be in the neighborhood of $158,000, as shown by the following calculations:

Number of crews		3
Size of each crew		
Present	45	
Proposed	35	
Reduction	10	
Total reduction of labor force		30
Hours worked per man per year		1,920
Man-hours saved per year		57,600
Average wage per hour	$2.75	
Savings in cost of labor		$158,400

REVISION

Unless you write with unusual skill, your work will probably call for considerable revision. If your schedule permits, you should not do your revising until you can look over your work with the feeling that you are a reader rather than a writer. It is possible, however, to let your work cool off too long. You should revise while your subject is still fresh enough in your mind that you will notice omissions and recognize errors.

The amount of time devoted to revision depends partly, of course, on what the project justifies, partly on the amount of time you have available, and partly on your degree of success in producing an acceptable version at the first attempt. If a report includes complicated ideas and deals with an important subject, there is no reason you should feel frustrated if it must be worked over three or four times. Most of us must face the fact that writing is not easy.

Since revision is tedious, one point needs to be emphasized. When you have revised a passage for what you think should be the final time, read it over once more from beginning to end to make sure that the changes you have made do not call for additional changes elsewhere. Many times an improvement at one point makes it necessary to change something that precedes or follows.

CARING FOR FINAL DETAILS

Caring for the final details of a report may include preparation of a title page, a summary, a table of contents, and a letter of transmittal or covering memorandum. Suggestions on the purpose and treatment of most of these elements have already been provided.

Also, one final task must always be performed: the close examination of the entire report for errors in manuscript, in form, or even in such simple matters as the order of pages. Everyone dislikes to make this final check, but it is so easy for errors to pass unnoticed that a final scrutiny is well worth the time it takes. Errors in figures are especially likely to slip in during the process of copying, and can easily escape detection. A typist can accidentally change *now* to *not*. *Dejected* can be miscopied as *ejected*, or *grout* can become *trout*. A writer who intends to change *not conspicuous* to *inconspicuous* may add the *in* and forget to remove the *not*. Such errors do not catch the eye, and close scrutiny is necessary if you are to succeed in actually writing what you intend to write.

In closing, it should be re-emphasized that the foregoing procedure for writing a report cannot and need not be followed exactly. Projects that call for reports develop in so many ways that it would be not only undesirable but probably impossible for you to follow a rigid set of instructions. But at least the steps suggested are definite and their sequence is logical. Though deviation may be necessary from time to time, you need not feel uncertain about how to tackle the job of writing a report if you will regard the recommended procedure as normal.

ASSIGNMENTS

Assignment 1

Analyze the problem one of the following subjects would present if it were to be reported on. That is, draw up a list of questions that would lead to a decision about what facts were needed. Break large questions down into smaller questions that would need to be answered first. Make your chosen subject more specific, if possible, by limiting it to some particular local situation that you know about or can learn about.

1. The method to use in controlling the growth of weeds on the right of way along a stretch of road or in some other specific area.
2. The question of whether fire protection is adequate in a dormitory or some other campus living space, and what if anything should be done to improve it.
3. The question of what treatment, for the sake of sanitation, would be desirable for the water in some college, city-owned, or private swimming pool.
4. The question of what snow-removal equipment should be provided for a new area of your campus or some other area you are familiar with, and the plans that should be made for its use.
5. The question of what location would be best for a new building that you think might be added to those already in use in your school.
6. The question of whether some manufacturer shall make a certain part for one of his products (for example, seat coverings for trucks or tractors) or hire it made.

Assignment 2

As directed by your instructor, write one or more reports of unspecified form resulting from an investigation of one of the following subjects, a subject listed in Assignment 1, or a subject of your own choice. Like all other subjects suggested, any of these subjects would have to be defined and adapted by setting up a hypothetical situation in which the report would be submitted to some person or organization that needs the information. The scope of your subject may also need to be broadened or narrowed so that you can use the information obtainable and have the size of the subject suitable to the assigned length of the report.

1. The route (general or specific as circumstances permit) to have through traffic follow in order to miss a business or residential area.
2. The use of auger conveyors to automate a feed lot (the feed lot to be a definite one where specific conditions exist). As an alternative, you could report on the possible automation in handling some other problem existing on a farm.
3. The establishment of one-way streets in some area to increase the amount of parking space available and improve the flow of traffic.
4. The lighting system for some building under construction or being modernized—probably a building in the school you attend. As an alternative, you could recommend good lighting for a baseball, softball, or football field, a pool, or an area in your campus or community.
5. An air-conditioning system for some building such as those mentioned in Number 4.
6. The arrangement of equipment in a laboratory in your school. This could be varied so as to apply to some industrial establishment such as a machine shop or food-processing plant if your interests and sources of information make such a subject practicable.
7. The selection of a heating system for use in a new building or to replace the system used in an existing building. This could be a report on changing from coal to oil, from oil to gas or electricity—from any type of heat source to some other that has emerged as a possible alternative.
8. An investigation of what is causing white paint to turn gray in an area where air is polluted by fumes from some industrial establishment. A solution to the problem could be included if your investigation reveals one.
9. The use of sprays to dwarf ordinary fruit trees as an alternative to the use of trees that are naturally dwarf size.
10. An auxiliary source of electric power to be used in your school, or in some such place as a hospital, when power is interrupted. In a school, for example, many a research problem might be ruined if electricity should be unavailable for long.
11. An investigation of whether your school should install an automatic sprinkler system, rather than using hoses on the lawns and spending large amounts for labor.
12. The heating and purification of water used in a pool such as the ones mentioned in Number 3 of Assignment 1.
13. The problem of paint peeling off some building or buildings and a recommendation of a remedy for the condition.
14. The condition of some farm. (This would presumably be made for some person or organization contemplating the purchase of the farm

—certainly for some reader other than a farmer who already owns and is farming the land.)

15. The choice of make and model of automobiles to be purchased for use of representatives of some large company. This could include a recommendation of a system for trading in such cars after a certain period of usage in terms of time or mileage. (The report might also take up the question of whether cars should be leased rather than purchased.)

16. The question of how to cope with large flocks of starlings that have caused waste of food and unsanitary conditions on a large feed lot, or how to solve any other problem caused by starlings.

11

FORMAL
AND
SEMIFORMAL
REPORTS

Though formal and semiformal reports have been mentioned briefly in earlier chapters, they give rise to so
many special questions that they call for separate treatment.

DESCRIPTION OF FORMAL AND SEMIFORMAL REPORTS

The term *formal report* is somewhat misleading. Actually, the formality of reports can vary widely; a report
can be quite formal in tone, and still not be classified as
a formal report under most systems of nomenclature.
Still, the term is widely used, and anyone concerned with
reports should know what people are most likely to have
in mind when they use it. The distinctive characteristics
that the term implies, as gathered from observation of
reports from many sources, are as follows:

1. A formal report has a title page.
2. It is usually accompanied by a letter of transmittal.
3. Unless it is unusually short it has a table of contents
that includes or is followed by a list of nonverbal materials if any are used.

4. It has a summary (sometimes called an abstract) near the beginning.

5. It contains the kind of introductory information found in what we have called a formal introduction (see page 225).

6. If it contains conclusions or recommendations, it identifies them by suitable headings.

7. It has internal topical headings, usually of more than one rank.

8. It is formal in tone and impersonal in style.

9. It includes tables and figures if they can increase its effectiveness. These may either be placed in the text that concerns them or gathered together at one place at the end.

10. It is documented by some conventional system if published information is used to any significant extent.

In this book, as mentioned earlier, the term *semiformal report* means a report that has the general qualities of a formal report but omits some of the elements. As you read the remainder of the chapter, remember that use of the elements of a formal report is not an all-or-nothing matter. On the contrary, if you are free to plan a report exactly as you think it will be best, you can profit by following the suggestions about each element that you decide to use, but can dispense with any element that you feel can be spared. Though the term *semiformal report* has not been widely used, reports of that kind have been widely written and you need have no misgivings that they will seem strange to those who read them.

Formal reports are considered a distinctive type on the basis of form and tone, but they may be used for varied purposes. A formal report may be a progress report, a periodic report, a report on the completion of a project, or a report on the results of a special investigation. Obviously, however, it is suitable only when a report must be long enough to justify the somewhat complicated mechanism involved and when the occasion calls for dignity in treatment. Rarely would a formal report be written for a single reader. On the contrary, it is justified only when the contents will be of interest—in fact of more than temporary interest—to a number of people.

The general nature of a formal report becomes clearer when we note that its pattern is much like the pattern followed in most books. Like a book, it may have a cover and always has a title page. Just as a book has a preface, a formal report has a letter of transmittal. Like a book, it has a table of contents that includes or is followed by a list of nonverbal materials. Like a book, it starts its sequence of Arabic numerals on the first page of text that follows the table of contents or the list of nonverbal materials. Like a book, it may have an appendix and a bibliography or list of references after the main text. It might be an overstatement to say that every element in a book has its exact counterpart in a formal report; but certainly a writer who is puzzled by some question of form can often solve his problem by recalling or observing what is done in the books in his own field.

The resemblance of reports to books is worth remembering because it would probably be impossible to set down a rigid set of rules about form which would enable us to label each possible way of doing things *right* or *wrong*. But by following the conventions used in books we can at least use forms that our readers are accustomed to. The sensible attitude on questions of form is to settle them not so much on the basis of right and wrong as on the basis of effective versus ineffective communication. And we communicate more effectively when we do not depart from what is customary unless we have good reason to do so.

ARRANGEMENTS OF THE PARTS

The most important variation in the arrangement of the parts of a formal report concerns the placement of the conclusions and recommendations. Sometimes these materials follow the body, and sometimes they precede it. The first of these alternatives is logical in that it presents evidence before conclusions; but some users prefer the second on the grounds that readers want to know the conclusions at once. This variation in the placement of materials is shown in the two following arrangements:

Title page	Title page
Letter of transmittal	Letter of transmittal
Table of Contents	Table of Contents
Summary (sometimes called Abstract)	Summary
Introduction	Conclusions
Body	Recommendations
Conclusions	Introduction
Recommendations	Body
Appendix	Appendix
Bibliography	Bibliography

When the conclusions and recommendations follow the body, the other parts are almost always arranged as shown above; but there is no set order of arranging the introduction, summary, and conclusions and recommendations when they precede the body. The writer may arrange them as he thinks best unless he works for an organization that has standardized upon a single system. Whatever it may be, the arrangement has some effect on the contents of the various sections. The reasoning behind the conclusions, for example, is more likely to be explained when they follow the body than when they precede it. And the summary will cover the introduction when it precedes that section but not when the reader encounters the introduction before the summary. A writer's good judgment should enable him to adapt his treatment to the order he is following.

COMPONENT PARTS—ADDITIONAL COMMENT

Since many of the parts that comprise a formal report appear in other reports also, they have already been discussed in a general manner. But there is more to say about the treatment of three of these parts—the letter of transmittal, the table of contents, and the introduction.

Letter of Transmittal

The letter of transmittal in a formal report is more closely integrated with the report than is true of the covering letter or memorandum sent with reports of other kinds. In fact it is bound into the report, usually following the title page. It may vary widely in length and contents. If the report is entirely routine, it may consist of only one or two sentences, as for example: "Following is the annual report of the Kinman Soil Conservation District for the year ending December 31, 1960." At the other extreme, it may replace the summary and present the essence of the report in condensed form. Most of the time, however, its length is within the normal range of business letters and it presents at least the minimum of facts necessary to orient the reader to the report that follows. For example, it may identify the project the report concerns and also, if necessary, the specific subject of the particular report. It may indicate the scope and limitations of the contents if the title leaves any doubt about them. It may tell where and how the information was obtained and how the report came to be written. And finally, by its signature it may identify the writer. Of course any of these facts that is obvious is omitted, and other facts can be included if they are needed.

Since the letter of transmittal is by its very form a personal communication from the writer to the immediate receiver, it provides the writer with an opportunity to acknowledge assistance, to express his hope that the information will be useful, to offer to be of future service—in fact to say anything that he considers appropriate to the occasion.

There is no reason, unless it replaces a summary, that the letter of transmittal must provide a preview of the contents of the report, but if the contents are likely to be pleasing, there is no reason that they should not be indicated.

Being an integral part of the report, the letter of transmittal should not be conspicuously informal in style, but its style need not be as formal as that of the report proper. For example, it is not necessarily limited to the third person.

In general, the letter of transmittal in a formal report permits the writer to address his original reader personally and submit his report gracefully, and it enables the reader to start reading with the assurance that he understands the occasion for the report.

Its form is basically the normal letter form, but in case of doubt "Dear Sir" rather than use of the receiver's name is desirable as a salutation. In governmental reports the salutation may even be the single word "Sir," which is the most formal of all salutations, and the complimentary close is usually "Respectfully yours."

Following is a typical letter of transmittal.

Mobray, Washington
May 17, 196_

Mr. K. L. Keller
Head of the Transmission Design Section
Northern Empire Utilities System
Random City, Washington

Dear Mr. Keller:

As you requested me to do in your letter of November 18, 196_, I have investigated one of the possible causes of unexplained outages that have occurred on the Northern Empire Utilities System.

My investigation concerned the possibility that the outages might have been caused by the melting of ice on the transmission line suspension insulators. To check on this possibility we negotiated a contract with the Central University Technical Institute, arranging to have them test the insulators under icing conditions in a low-temperature laboratory and compare their wet-flashover resistance with the standards established by the A.I.E.E. Since the resistivity of water varies considerably, samples with water of varying resistivity were used. The variation was produced by adding sodium chloride to the water used in these laboratory tests.

A second line of investigation was also followed. We arranged for the collection of rain water samples at 26 substations. The number of samples collected was 339. The resistivity of all these samples was tested in order that we might be able to judge the significance of the laboratory tests of the insulators in view of the actual qualities of the water comprising the precipitation in this area.

The data secured in all the tests mentioned above are presented and discussed in the following report. Our studies must be carried further before we can definitely conclude that the outages resulted from the conjectured cause; but the data obtained thus far make it apparent that further investigation is warranted. We are asking the A.I.E.E. Lightning and Insulator Subcommittee to review this report, and will submit a proposal for further investigation when we receive its comments.

Very truly yours,

John Doe
Principal Technical Assistant
Transmission Design Section

Table of Contents

What has been said earlier about the table of contents applies with special force to the formal report. That is, a table of contents is a list of the headings that appear on the pages of the report; headings except those of highest rank are indented to indicate their rank; they are phrased as topics, and are worded exactly as they are worded where they appear in the text; and as a result of all this they make it easy for the reader to see what ground the report covers, how it is organized, and where each point is taken up.

Since a formal report is longer and more complicated than other kinds, unusual care must be taken so that the table of contents will be easy for the readers to use and so that it will observe the conventions that they are accustomed to. The danger of going astray is greatest when tables and figures must be listed. In this connection, two conventions should be borne in mind:

1. The titles of tables and figures are not mixed in among the headings that indicate topics discussed.

2. The items in any single list are arranged in the order of their occurrence. That is, an item with a smaller page number never comes later than an item with a larger page number.

In order to comply with both of these conventions, it is necessary to use a different system when the tables and figures are placed at the end of the report than is used when some or all of them are placed in the text. When tables and figures follow the text, they may be listed as part of the regular table of contents. But when tables and figures are scattered through the text, it becomes necessary to list them under a new heading, equal in rank and hence similar in form to the heading *Table of Contents*. The heading of the list of nonverbal materials can be anything appropriate: *Figures,* or *Tables,* or *Tables and Figures,* or *Exhibits*—anything that lets the reader see what kind of material is being listed.

The treatment can of course vary in detail; but the results will be acceptable if each kind of material is listed separately, if the items in each list follow the order in which the material referred to appears, and if the lists of nonverbal material are not treated as part of the main table of contents unless the report proper is complete before the first such material appears.

The terminology used to identify various kinds of material is not rigid, but comment on some of the terms should be useful. *Exhibits* is the broadest term used. Being practically all-inclusive, it can be used to head a list of specimens from outside sources or as a general heading under which figures and tables are separately listed. Tables and figures are of course different from each other in nature and would not be mixed together in a single list. The term *figure* includes graphs, charts, photographs—any of the kinds mentioned in Chapter 6. All the figures are usually listed in a single numerical sequence, but if there is a reason for doing so, each kind can be listed separately and given its own set of numbers.

The term *appendix* can be used to refer to material that follows the body of the report. (Separate appendixes, for example "Appendix A—Tables" and "Appendix B—Figures," can be used when the material is varied enough and extensive enough to warrant such treatment.) If the term *appendix* is used in the table of contents, it should of course appear also at the point in the report where the appended material begins. If the material in the appendix is extensive, a page bearing the single word *appendix* is useful because it makes the beginning of the appendix easier to find.

In spite of the numerous points made in this discussion, the listing of nonverbal material is not primarily an exercise in obeying rules. Rather, the main consideration is to make it easy for a reader to see what material of this nature the report contains and to find what he is looking for. The best system to use on any occasion is the simplest system that will accomplish that result. In order to increase your resourcefulness in doing this task and at the same time become better aware of the conventions that prevail, you should constantly notice the methods used in the books that you encounter.

Chapter 9, on Special Elements in Reports, contains a specimen table of contents, but to illustrate how the listing of visual materials can vary, some additional specimens follow. Each consists of the last heading preceding the list of visual materials (in order to show what page it appeared on) plus the titles of tables and figures. Where a centered heading appears, it may be assumed that its form matches the earlier heading *Table of Contents*. The examples do not show every conceivable situation, but they are adequate to illustrate the principles upon which a treatment for almost any situation can be devised.

(3)

LIST OF ILLUSTRATIONS

(4)

TABLES AND FIGURES

Specimen 1 shows an acceptable method of listing visual material when it consists entirely of figures, all of which follow the written material and are placed under the heading *Appendix*. It would have been equally appropriate to have replaced the heading *Appendix* with *Figures* and to have dispensed with the separate page on which *Appendix* appeared.

Specimen 2 varies from specimen 1 in that two kinds of visual material were used, each being treated as a separate appendix. Also, the writer placed his headings *Appendix A* and *Appendix B* at the tops of the pages where the appended material began rather than on separate pages.

Specimen 3 illustrates the form used when figures (presumably the only kind of visual material used) are placed in the body of the report. Whether the list of illustrations appears on the same page as the regular table of contents or on a separate page depends on the space available.

Specimen 4 is like specimen 3 except that both tables and figures were used and were placed in the body of the report.

Introduction

The introduction of a formal report is not the usual type, in which the writer begins his discussion of the *subject* of the report. Rather it concerns the report itself. (The introduction to a thesis or dissertation is this same type.)

In order that the report may be self-sufficient, the introduction answers such questions as the following to the extent that the writer thinks they might come to the mind of the readers: What is the purpose or function of this report? What circumstances caused it to be written? Who asked, or ordered, or decided that it should be written? How much territory (assuming that the title does not precisely show the scope and limitations) does it cover? Where and how was the information obtained? Until the reader knows the answer to these questions, he is not ready to receive the facts and discussion that the report offers him.

There is no single form for the treatment of this introductory material. One system is to use the general heading *Introduction,* and then place the facts under specific subheadings such as *Purpose* (or *Objective*), *Scope* (or *Limitations*), *Source(s) of Information,* and *Authorization.* When it is not top-heavy, this system is good because it reduces the likelihood that any of the various kinds of information will accidentally be omitted. Another system is to use the heading *Introduction* without any subheadings. A third possibility is to dispense with the heading *Introduction* and make main headings of the above-mentioned subheadings. Yet regardless of the headings under which it is placed, the introductory information is the same. For convenience in our discussion, we will assume that a main heading *Introduction* is used, plus whatever subheadings are needed.

Under *Purpose* or *Objective* the introduction explains as fully as necessary the conditions or events that created a need for the report and tells the exact function that the report is expected to perform.

The material under *Scope* or *Limitations* settles any possible doubt about what the report covers and what it omits. When the title itself performs this function, a section on *Scope* is superfluous; but it is often impossible to indicate the exact limits in the title without making it cumbersome.

The discussion under *Source(s) of Information* tells where and how the facts were obtained. If their source is obvious, this section may be omitted. If some of the information comes from printed sources, they may be named in this section provided there are not more than three or four; but if numerous, they should be placed in a list of references at the end, and this list should be mentioned in the introduction.

The section headed *Authorization* is extremely brief, merely telling who authorized the report, when, and how (letter, memorandum, personal conversation, or whatever other means). In a large organization this section is often replaced by something such as a project number, which would let the reader know under what authority the work was done.

The introductory material under each of these headings should usually be held to one or two paragraphs. If a long discussion on any of these points is necessary, it can appear under an appropriate heading in the body of the report, and the coverage under *Introduction* can be reduced to a brief general statement and a reference to the full discussion that will come later.

All in all, the formal introduction merely orients the reader. Rather than discussing the subject of the report, it tells about the report itself. Consequently, there may sometimes be a need for what we referred to in Chapter 9 as an ordinary introduction, which actually opens the discussion of the subject. If so, this ordinary-introduction material can be placed in the body of the report under a heading such as *General Discussion of . . .* , or *Background Information,* or *The General Problem of . . .* , or *Historical Review of. . . .* But whenever there is a formal introduction, the ordinary introduction is identified by some other heading than *Introduction.*

Some question may arise over why it is necessary to include parts of the introductory material mentioned. Since a report is usually submitted to the person who authorized it, it would seem that he might already possess most of the introductory facts. This is true; but the passage of time may have caused many of the details to fade from his memory. Also, the report may reach readers who are not familiar with the problem, or it may be filed and used again after a long time has passed. Therefore the report should provide all the information any likely reader may need at any time, and thus be self-sufficient.

It is true, also, that some points in the introduction may have been touched upon in the letter of transmittal; but there, they will probably have been barely mentioned rather than treated in full. The slight repetition is justified because there will be times when the letter of transmittal will be read yet the report itself may be set aside until later.

Following is a formal introduction of the kind recommended:

INTRODUCTION

Purpose

In local areas, highway engineers have found it necessary to use deposits of basalt rock as a source of aggregate for the base course of highways. Some of these deposits yield an aggregate that is entirely satisfactory for such a purpose, but others yield an aggregate that deteriorates rapidly, causing failure of the highway base within a year or two.

To cope with this condition the Highway Materials Testing Laboratory has developed tests intended to indicate in advance whether basalt aggregate from any particular source will degrade rapidly. Also, it has carried on experiments to see whether treating aggregates with asphalt emulsion would slow down the deterioration of those known to be unsatisfactory in their natural condition. The purpose of this report is to present the results of these tests and experiments.

Sources of Information

Information on the sources of aggregates that have not held up as should be expected was obtained from the State Highway Department. The techniques of testing were based in part on work done in other states, as indicated by the citation of references. Most of the facts presented were obtained, however, by the direct testing and experimentation done in the laboratory.

Authorization

This report and the investigation on which it is based were authorized in a letter from Hugh D. Lockhart, Chairman of the State Highway Commission, dated April 3, 196_.

STYLE IN A FORMAL REPORT

In Chapter 7, the difference between formal and informal styles was discussed. Obviously, preparing a formal report is one of the occasions when the language should be formal and impersonal. The desired effect is secured, however, not so much by aiming at formality as by avoiding noticeable informality. Slang is obviously ruled out. Colloquialisms—including contractions—are avoided. Technical jargon, handy though it may be, should be used only as a last resort.

The formality and impersonality prevail to such an extent in a formal report that little if any use is made of first and second person. "I" and "you" are avoided, and "we" is used only when it means the organization in which both the reader and the writer are included. One reason for avoiding "I" and "you" is that they simply seem out of place in any piece of writing where the occasions for their use are few and far between. (Notice how seldom you see them in technical books and articles.) A second reason is that the meaning of these two words depends on who is writing and who is addressed. Consequently, when material by several writers is included in a single report, as often happens, the need of revision is reduced if each contributor avoids "I" and "you."

To be sure, formality and impersonality can be misused. Such a sentence as "It is believed that . . ." dodges the significant question of *who* believes, and overuse of *the writer* in place of *I* sounds stilted. But the real objection to these forms goes beyond the formality and impersonality. Basically, in the first instance the defect is vagueness and the desire of the writer to promote certain ideas yet leave himself an escape hatch if it turns out that he is mistaken. In the second, it is probably sheer awkwardness, for it is not usually difficult to construct a sentence in which neither *I* nor *the writer* appears. Formal style should not be condemned because it is bad when it is handled awkwardly, for if informal style is handled awkwardly it is equally bad.

In summary we need only say that the purpose of formal, impersonal style is merely to secure a reasonable degree of dignity when dignity is called for. Well handled, it is not stiff, pompous, indirect, or excessively ceremonious. It is a tool that a writer should learn to use, for informality is not always appropriate despite its many good qualities.

THE EFFICIENCY OF FORMAL REPORTS

A person who has never had a chance to see how reports are actually used may wonder why some of the features of a formal report are necessary. To understand their value we must remind ourselves that a report is not always written with the expectation that all of those who receive it will read it from beginning to end. On the contrary, there are many more occasions when a long report will be read in part than when it will be read in its entirety.

A formal report meets whatever demands are placed upon it. The reader who cannot remember or has never known the circumstances that caused it to be written can learn them as soon as he picks it up, and can decide how soon he must read it. When he reads it in full, he will find that it unfolds smoothly and that he can study the technical details, skim them, or ignore them as he desires. The executive farther up the line, who wants only a general picture, including the conclusions and recommendations, can get exactly what he wants without wasting time on details. The person who is interested in only part of the subject, or who wants to refresh his mind on some particular point, can easily find what he is looking for. The person who wants to study the full technical details thoroughly finds them easy to locate and identify.

All in all, experience will show that a well-designed formal report is an extremely effective instrument that performs not one but a variety of functions smoothly and efficiently.

(Illustrative Specimens Follow)

SPECIMEN FORMAL REPORT *

The following report is reproduced in full except that all figures but the first are omitted. The list of figures following the Table of Contents shows what the other figures were and where they were placed.

The report was produced, as the title page indicates, for a research institute. The version published here was printed by the offset process for outside distribution. For this reason it is not addressed to any specific person or organization and is not accompanied by the letter of transmittal.

---

* Courtesy of Washington State University Institute of Technology.

Washington State Institute of Technology

Bulletin 271

A PRESSURIZED-HEAD PERMEAMETER

FOR

FINE-GRAINED SOILS

by

Earl Sibley & John Miller

Highway Research Section

Published by the

Division of Industrial Research

1962

Washington State University   Pullman, Washington

TABLE OF CONTENTS

LIST OF FIGURES*

    *None of the figures except number 1 has been included in the follow-
ing pages.

Page 1: The abstract is extremely brief, but careful reading of the full report shows that it presents the major fact brought out by the investigation.

The introduction does not include some of the elements that would be present if the report had been written in industry rather than in a research institute. The source of information, for example, is so obvious that there is no need to mention it; and in a report intended for public release, it was not considered necessary to mention authorization or refer to a specific project by number. The purpose, however, is clearly indicated in the introduction and is extremely important to know in order to understand the point of what follows.

Page 2: As the introduction pointed out, the selection of a permeameter was one of the major purposes of the investigation. Under the main heading *Apparatus,* the report first tells what kind of a permeameter was chosen and why. Then, under a second subhead, it tells of certain special adaptations of the type of permeameter chosen and refers to the figures that illustrate this permeameter and the set-up of the entire apparatus. These figures made the physical arrangements much clearer than they could be made by words alone.

Pages 3, 4, 5, and 6: These pages bore full-page figures, one of which is included.

ABSTRACT

This research indicates a pressurized-head permeameter is effective for
measuring permeability of fine-grained soils. The data obtained by this
equipment matched closely that obtained by the standard falling-head
type. Principal advantage of the pressurized-head type is that it requires much less time for making a determination.

INTRODUCTION

Soil permeability is important in determining such factors as the seepage loss from canals, settlement of buildings, seepage through and
around earthen dams, drainage of subgrades and fills on highways, and
the rate at which a soil will gain strength.

Permeability determination for most soils is well established; however,
permeability for the fine-grained soils has not received much study.
It has been only recently that such soils were used extensively for
construction purposes. Such uses are becoming more and more common.

This study, then, was designed for two purposes: (1) to select a permeameter, and (2) to develop a technique and procedure for its use.
This was accomplished by testing characteristics and responses of five
fine-grained soils.

APPARATUS

Selection of Apparatus

After extensive experimentation, the type of apparatus chosen was
a pressurized-head permeameter. This device will accommodate either
disturbed or undisturbed specimens of different heights. The falling
head permeameter usually used for such work was inadequate because an
excessively long standpipe was necessary to produce measurable flows.

Pressurized-head permeameters are of two basic types. In the
first type, the compressed air is applied directly to the water in a
standpipe, giving it additional head. The flow is measured by observing the fall of the water in the standpipe. In the second type, the
compressed air is applied to the water through a closed system and the
flow is measured as a discharge from the base of the specimen. Both
methods have the disadvantage of applying compressed air directly on
the permeant fluid, thus saturating it with dissolved oxygen. With
the latter method, it is difficult to compare the rate of permeation
with the discharge. Such comparison is important for a state of equi-
librium is obtained only when these are equal. However, with additional
time, the same result can be achieved by measuring the discharge at various times and when it becomes constant, or nearly so, a state of equilib-
rium can be assumed.

Means must be available to control and measure the consolidation
of expansion of the specimen during testing. To accomplish this, some
means of loading the specimen coupled to a measuring device must be provided.

Test Apparatus

The permeability apparatus is shown in Figures 1, 2, 3, and 4.
The permeameter is quite similar to any standard closed system except
that the cell is adapted for loading the specimen (See Figure 3).
The top porous stone (F) is filtered into a movable loading block (J)
which is connected to a piston (D). This piston protrudes through the
top of the cell to provide a means for loading the block. The loads
are applied directly to the piston through a yoke assembly. This allows the consolidation or control of expansion of the specimen by varying the loading.

-2-

234

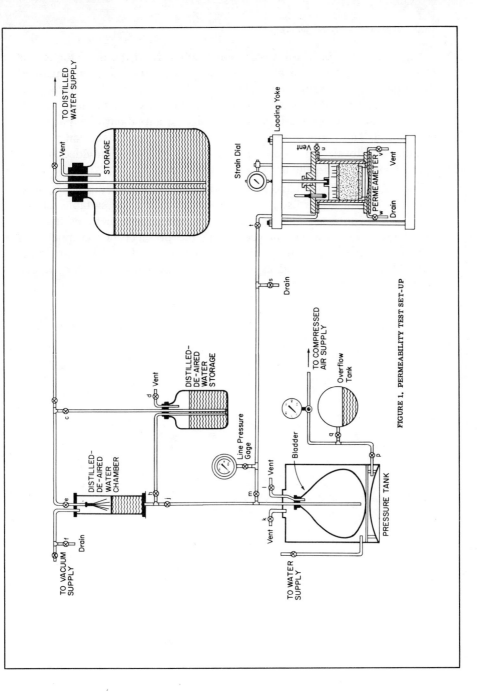

FIGURE 1, PERMEABILITY TEST SET-UP

235

Pages 7, 8, and 9: The investigation resulted from the need for means of determining the permeability of fine-grained soil. Having explained the apparatus, the writer next tells about the soils chosen for testing. As the introduction indicated, the purpose of the tests was to check a testing procedure rather than to obtain information about the particular soils tested. The material on page 7 is drawn from the table on page 8. Additional information on one quality of the soils was provided by the figure (omitted) on page 9.

Pages 10 and 11: On page 10 the writer explains the difficulty of making sure that the water used in testing permeability was suitable for the purpose. As you can see, it was only after trying four methods that the investigators found a way of preventing the presence of too much dissolved oxygen in the water, which would have made results unreliable. Page 11 (omitted) showed in graphic form the facts about the oxygen content of water under the four circumstances mentioned.

SOILS TESTED

For these tests, it was considered expedient to use only materials which could be re-sampled in any phase of the test program, should the need arise. These materials are by no means representative of "typical" soils but are merely materials that have been tested in the soils laboratory for one reason or another. However, they do represent five of the nine classifications usually included in triangular fines classifications. The characteristics of these materials are summarized in Table 1 and Figure 5.

The material used in test series A was a yellowish brown clay sand from east central Oregon. When compacted under standard AASHO conditions, the maximum dry density was 111 lbs per cubic foot at an optimum moisture of 19 per cent.

Nearly 40 per cent of the material passed the No. 200 sieve and the liquid limit was 36.0 per cent with a plasticity index of 12.3 per cent. Colors referred to are on the air-dried soil and are taken from the 1954 edition of the Munsell Soil Color Charts.

Series B material was a yellowish brown silty clay also from east central Oregon. One hundred per cent of this material passed the No. 200 sieve. The liquid limit was 41.3 per cent and the plasticity index was 17.6 per cent. Standard AASHO compaction resulted in a maximum dry density of 92 pounds per cubic foot at an optimum moisture of 28.0 per cent.

A brown to yellowish brown clay silt, known locally as Palouse loess, was used for series C. Its liquid limit was 30.4 per cent with a plasticity index of 11.2 per cent. Nearly 80 per cent of the material passed the No. 200 sieve. Maximum dry density, when compacted under standard AASHO conditions, was 108 pounds per cubic foot at an optimum moisture of 18.2 per cent.

The material used for series D was a brown gravelly sand from west central Idaho. Standard AASHO compaction resulted in a maximum dry density of 124.5 pounds per cubic foot at an optimum moisture content of 14.0 per cent. Only 9 per cent of the material passed the No. 200 sieve. The liquid limit was 30.0 per cent and the plasticity index was 5.7 per cent.

The material for series E came from the Olympic peninsula in western Washington. It was a light brownish grey sandy clay with a liquid limit of 27.2 per cent and a plasticity index of 15.1 per cent. Standard AASHO density was 110.5 pounds per cubic foot at an optimum moisture content of 10.5 per cent. Slightly over 60 per cent of the material passed the No. 200 sieve.

A slightly coarser gradation of the Palouse loess was used for Series F. It was a yellowish brown clay silt that had a liquid limit of 22.0 per cent and a plasticity index of 8.8 per cent. Nearly 70 per cent of the material passed the No. 200 sieve. Standard AASHO compaction resulted in a maximum dry density of 116 pounds per cubic foot and an optimum moisture content of 13.5 per cent.

-7-

TABLE 1. LIMITS, GRADATION AND CLASSIFICATION OF MATERIAL USED IN TEST SERIES

SERIES	Liquid Limit	Plasticity Index	Specific Gravity	% Passing				Classification	
				#4	#10	0.05mm	0.002mm	Wash. Dept. of Highways	Hwy. Res. Board
A	36.0	12.3	2.85	100	90	29	6	Clay Sand	A-6(1)
B	41.3	17.6	2.83	-	100	80	17	Silty Clay	A-7-6(11)
C	30.4	11.2	2.68	-	100	62	14	Clay Silt	A-6(9)
D	30.0	5.7	2.84	100	75	7	1	Gravelly Sand	A-2-4
E	27.2	15.1	2.75	-	100	53	17	Sandy Clay	A-6(9)
F	22.0	8.8	2.72	-	100	59	13	Clay Silt	A-4(7)

PERMEANT FLUID

To a greater or lesser degree, dissolved gases are inherent in all water. The water used in molding the specimens was distilled water which contained 5 to 6 ppm of dissolved oxygen. Mixing this water with soil undoubtedly increased the dissolved oxygen content. In addition the pore spaces of the specimens after molding contained various percentages of gas depending on the saturation.

For representative test data, the gas content of the pore fluid and the permeant should be equal to what will exist in nature. These conditions are nearly impossible to determine or maintain. The next best thing is to test the specimens at as high a saturation as possible and to use a permeant which is nearly free of dissolved gases.

The distilled water, as stored in the laboratory, usually contained 5 to 6 ppm of dissolved oxygen as determined by the Alsterberg Modification of the Winkler Method. Two cycles of de-airing, as explained in Appendix B, would reduce the dissolved oxygen content to 2 or 3 ppm.

In the preliminary stages of this investigation, compressed air was applied directly to the de-aired water. Figure 6 demonstrates by curve A how rapidly the water picked up oxygen while under pressure. For tests that were being performed under 60 psi for a week or more, the dissolved oxygen content would increase to approximately 22 ppm.

It was felt that a thin coating of hydraulic fluid on the surface of the de-aired water would reduce the oxygen intake. Tests run under these conditions are shown by curve B. This method did reduce the oxygen intake; however, the amount of dissolved oxygen increased to approximately 13 ppm within a week.

Another method was used. In this instance, the de-aired water was placed in a 16-inch diameter natural rubber bladder which was placed inside the pressure tank. The bladder had an average wall thickness of 0.055 inch. The compressed-air was applied to the outside of the bladder. Results from this method, as shown by curve C, were no more successful than the others. Sufficient air penetrated the rubber wall to increase the dissolved oxygen content to approximately 13 ppm after seven days.

The method used throughout the investigation, except preliminary stages, was placing tap water around the outside of the rubber bladder. Compressed air then was applied to the tap water. Results of the tests for dissolving oxygen in the de-aired water within the bladder are shown on curve D. After four days, the dissolved oxygen content began to decrease and after 10 days become almost imperceptible. Many tests substantiated this tendency. Curve D represents results of these tests.

The dissolved oxygen content under these conditions would be expected to increase slightly with time, or at best, remain unchanged. The only explanation could be that the bacterial growth inside the bladder utilized the remaining oxygen. This is substantiated by the downward trend in dissolved oxygen content after four days.

-10-

Pages 12 through 25: Note that at this point in the report, the writer has told us what we need to know about the apparatus and the two kinds of material involved—soil and water. He is now ready to tell us about the testing and its results.

Pages 12 through 25 discuss the performance and present the results of ten kinds of tests, each telling some effect of a certain specified condition. The results of each kind of test are shown in a figure, and the figures provide the basis for comments. The figures are omitted, but the comments are included.

RESULTS

Effect of Molding Water Content on Dry Density and Permeability

Figure 7 presents the dry density and permeability of five materials as a function of the molding water content. Complete density-permeability tests were made on series A, B, C, D, and F. Since series E material was not tested for permeability through a complete range of density, this data is not presented.

These data show the lowest permeability occurs at slightly greater than optimum moisture content. Density comparisons between materials are not a measure of permeability. Material B (silty clay) has the lowest density but does not have the greatest nor the lowest permeability. The lowest permeability is exhibited by material C (clay silt) which does not have the greatest nor lowest density. Materials F (clay silt) and D (gravelly sand) possess approximately the same lowest permeability; however, (the gravelly sand) D has a higher density.

Effect of Permeation on Dry Density

Figure 8 presents data on the effect of permeation on the dry density of the materials included in this investigation. Most of the tests produced a final density greater than that obtained when the specimens were molded. This represents a compression of these specimens because of the applied head or a loss in moisture content, or both. The loss of moisture usually occurred on specimens molded on the wet side of optimum. A few of the specimens showed a final density less than that obtained when they were molded. This resulted from the expansion of the specimens during permeation and/or a gain in moisture content.

Effect of Permeation on Moisture Content

Figure 9 presents data on the effect of permeation on the moisture content for five of the six materials used in this study. The curves appear to take the form of inverted density curves. Permeation causes the specimens to gain moisture when compacted on the dry side of optimum, and, in most instances, to lose moisture when compacted on the extremely wet side of optimum. Those specimens compacted at or near optimum lost moisture in some instances and gained it in others. However, if the curves drawn in Figure 9 can be considered typical of the general trend, the point at which moisture was neither lost nor gained during permeation occurred on the wet side of optimum for all materials except D (the gravelly sand). For this material the transitional point occurred at optimum.

-12-

Effect of Permeation on Saturation

Figure 10 presents data on the effect of permeation on saturation for five of the materials. The general pattern for materials A, B, and C is a gradual increase in final saturation as the molding saturation increases. The pattern for materials D and F is the same except there is an initial decrease in the final saturation with increasing molding saturation followed by an increase which is consistent with the other materials.

Two significant features are: (1) specimens experienced a loss in saturation with permeation, and (2) no specimen resulted in 100 per cent saturation even after permeation of 24 hours. Saturation was determined by measuring moisture content, void ratio, and specific gravity. Possibly this standard of measurement cannot be achieved. Another approach would be to permeate a specimen for a given length of time and call its resulting saturation 100 per cent and equate all test results on that material to that basis.

Effect of Permeation on Permeability

Figure 11 shows the effect of permeation on the permeability of all test specimens. The initial permeability was taken as the first value that was determined after a perceptible flow. In some instances, this flow occurred within a few hours and in others it occurred after a few days. The final permeability was that value which could be repeated within reasonable limits of accuracy of the equipment. The time for this, like the initial permeability, was quite variable. However, every specimen required at least a full day.

The general significance of these data is that permeation decreased permeability of nearly all the specimens. Most specimens showing an increase were molded on the wet side of optimum. Specimens in the higher permeability range, especially those molded on the dry side of optimum, vary more than those in the lower ranges.

Effect of Permeation on Permeability and Saturation

Figure 12 presents data on the effect of permeation on the permeability and saturation of material E (sandy clay). Seven specimens of material E were molded by standard proctor compaction at as equal moisture contents as possible. The initial saturation of each specimen is shown by the curve labeled "initial." Each specimen was permeated under a head of 25 psi for a definite length of time. The curve labeled "final" indicates the saturation after permeation. For this material which had an initial saturation of about 48 per cent, 24 hours of permeation resulted in 97 per cent saturation.

The permeability of the specimen that had a final saturation of 99 per cent is presented as a function of time. Complete permeability data on the other specimens was not determined because permeation times were cut short. Since all specimens were nearly identical, the upper curve indicates the permeability that could be expected at various intervals of permeation. It appears it requires at least a full day to conduct an acceptable test.

-16-

242

Effect of Molding Water Content on the Permeability--Time Relationships

A series of tests was performed on material B (silty clay) to determine what effect the molding water content has on the permeability-time relationship. These results are shown in Figure 13. The molding moisture contents are shown on each curve. The permeability of the specimens molded on the dry side of optimum generally took longer to stabilize than those molded on the wet side. All specimens became quite stable after two days of permeation. The first possible permeability determination for specimens compacted above optimum is representative of what would be obtained from a prolonged testing program but not so for those compacted on the dry side.

Effect of Applied Head on Permeability

Tests were performed on material B (silty clay) to determine the effect of the applied head on the permeability. These data are presented in Figure 14. For six tests the final permeability is plotted against the final void ratio for various applied heads. Each specimen first was tested under an applied head of 20 psi and, after the discharge became constant, the head was increased to 40 psi, then 60 psi, and finally in one instance to 80 psi. Under each application of pressure, the specimen would compress, thus creating a new void ratio. This compression appeared to occur only in the upper fraction of an inch of the specimen. When plotted as a new void ratio, the compressions were hardly perceptible.

Applied heads made little difference in the permeability. With two exceptions, the lowest head resulted in the lowest permeability. This may be because of the sequence of testing. The soil would become conditioned to each pressure before the next head was applied. The opposite effect would probably result had the pressures been applied in reverse.

Effect of Permeation on Head Loss and Permeability

Series E material was tested to determine the head loss through a specimen and the effect of permeation on head loss. These results are shown in Figures 15 and 16.

To measure the head loss, three hypodermic needles were inserted through the lucite chamber wall. As can be seen from the data in Figure 15 for chamber pressures below 40 psi the pressure drop is almost linear. Pressures above this indicate that there is channeling along the walls of the cylinders and the length of the needles. This channeling effect is evident in the first phase of the test results shown in Figure 14 where the pressure gage No. 3 is greater than in gage No. 2. As permeation continues, the sample becomes more saturated and swells forming a seal between the soil and the chamber, hence reducing the effect of channeling.

Effect of Specimen Size on Permeability

Figure 17 compares permeability values determined by the large permeameter with values determined by the small one. The curves show a close correlation except on the extreme wet side of optimum. This could be attributed to greater consolidation of the small diameter samples. Twelve samples of Series C soil were used.

-20-

243

Page 26: Under the heading *Summary of Results and Conclusions* the writers first restate the facts included in the abstract, and then make a comment on the apparatus that they had not made before, though they had provided a basis for it in the section headed *Apparatus*. They end by re-emphasizing the conclusions based on one kind of test, apparently considering it important enough to merit special treatment. They conclude the report proper with a brief acknowledgment of assistance received.

SUMMARY OF RESULTS AND CONCLUSIONS

The pressurized-head permeameter using distilled de-aired water is effective for measuring the permeability of fine-grained soils.

This apparatus has two distinct advantages over the conventional falling-head permeameter. Testing is faster (24 hours) and larger volume of flow is possible.

The apparatus is relatively inexpensive. It can be fabricated of standard materials in almost any machine shop. The test can be done by most soils testing technicians. The equipment is versatile enough to accommodate either disturbed or undisturbed specimens of different heights.

Values obtained for permeabilities varied little with differences in applied head (Figure 14). However, other results indicate that pressures above 60 psi should not be recommended. Even at this pressure, there was some undesirable consolidation of the speciments.

ACKNOWLEDGEMENT

Bill Lee and Clifford Appling did most routine testing and data reduction. Laura Simmons typed the manuscript and tables.

-26-

245

Pages 27 and 28: The writers apparently felt that the full details of the test procedure should be made available but that they would not interest a large enough proportion of the readers to justify including them in the body of the report. They therefore added them as an appendix. The procedure consisted of four main parts, though the steps are numbered 1 to 12. These parts are: preparation of the specimen (numbered 1 - 4), preparation of the apparatus (numbered 5 - 7), the actual testing (numbered 8 - 10), and the follow-up actions and observations (numbered 11 - 12).

Page 29: Early in the report the writers told of the problem created by the presence of dissolved oxygen in the water used to test permeability and of the problem of keeping this oxygen from increasing when pressure was applied. In Appendix B they tell what was done before the water was used in order to solve this problem.

GENERAL TEST PROCEDURE

The following method was used to determine the general permeability data. Exceptions, made to obtain specific information, are noted.

1. The material to be tested was air dried and mixed with sufficient water to bring it to a de-aired moisture content. Mixing was done with a bench-type rotary mixer. Mixing time was held constant for 15 minutes in an attempt to eliminate the effect of the degree of mixing on the properties of the material. The material then was sealed in a polyethylene bag and stored in a humidity cabinet to temper for approximately 24 hours.

2. The material was compacted in three lifts in a 5 1/2 inch diameter lucite chamber (K)[1]. The compactive effort was equivalent to standard AASHO. The material was separated into three pre-determined weights to keep each lift approximately the same height and to maintain the total height of the specimen approximately equal. Specimens varied in height from 3.2 inches to 3.4 inches.

   To prevent channeling along the walls of the chamber, a light coating of rubber cement was applied to the inside area of the chamber just preceding the compaction of each lift. This produced a good bond between the chamber and soil. It also allowed the head to be applied much faster. Channeling also can be prevented by gradually wetting the specimen and allowing it to swell and force itself out against the wall, thus creating a natural bond.

3. The surface of the specimen was then squared off with a rotary knife trimmer to remove impressions left by the last few blows of the hammer. Normally it was necessary to remove approximately 1/8 inch when the material was compacted on the dry side and up to 1/4 inch on the wet side of optimum.

4. The trimmings were removed and the specimen and mold were weighed. The specimen was then measured at three locations around the lucite chamber. The height was expressed as the average of the three measurements.

5. The porous stones (F), loading block (J), and pedestal (G) were assembled as shown in Figure 3.

6. The base (A) and cover plates were then secured to the top of the cylinder by three tension rods (I). Rubber gaskets were placed at both ends to prevent leakage and to distribute evenly the compression of the three major parts resulting from the tension rods.

7. The loading piston (D) was seated in the loading block and the yoke (see Figure 4) was centered over the piston. The Ames dial used to measure deflection (see Figure 4) was then clamped in place and an initial reading was taken to correspond with the initial height of the specimen. The loading yoke, without hangar and pan, put a seating load of 0.5 psi on the specimen. At this stage the permeameter with

the compacted specimen was ready for permeability testing. Figure 3 shows the permeameter arrangement during a typical test. The permeability test set up is shown schematically in Figure 1. With all valves closed, the test proceeded in the following manner.

8. Valves p, m, and n were opened. The compressed-air regulating valve r was opened so that approximately 5 psi pressure was obtained on the line pressure gage.

9. Vent valve u was opened. Valve t was opened to allow the water to flow into the permeameter. When the water reached the top of the permeameter, vent valve u was closed making certain no air was trapped in the top of the permeameter. Appropriate weights were placed on the loading yoke hangar to offset the pressure against the piston.

10. As the wetted front reached the bottom of the specimen, vent valve v and drain valve w were opened. Except in cases where initial permeability was important, the specimen was allowed to stand under these conditions for approximately 16 hours. At the end of this period vent valve v was closed and the line pressure was increased to the desired value. Additional weights were placed on the loading yoke hangar to balance this pressure against the piston. Drainage time, line pressure, strain, and temperature data were taken at appropriate intervals to define the permeability. These readings were continued until the permeability became constant or nearly so.

11. At the conclusion of the test, valve t was closed and vent u was gradually opened. The yoke was removed and the specimen was allowed to rebound from the effect of the applied head. Normally this occurred within 15 to 30 minutes after removal of the yoke. The amount of expansion was measured by replacing the yoke of the piston and reading the strain dial.

12. The permeameter was dismantled and the test specimen and chamber were re-weighed. The specimen was ejected from the chamber and used for a moisture content distribution.

As previously mentioned, exceptions to the above procedure are noted where these data are presented.

APPENDIX B

DE-AIRING THE PERMEANT FLUID

The permeant fluid used in this investigation was distilled, de-aired
water. In Figure 1 the de-aired apparatus is shown at upper left. Assuming all valves were closed and there was a supply of distilled water
in the storage carboy, the following procedure was followed in de-airing
the distilled water.

1. Valve g was opened and the distilled, de-aired water chamber was
   evacuated.

2. Valves b and e were opened and distilled water from storage was sprayed
   into the de-airing chamber. When the chamber became approximately two-
   thirds full, valves g, b, and e were closed and the negative pressure
   was released from the top of the chamber by opening valve f.

3. Valve h was opened and the de-aired water was stored in a carboy. The
   pressure on top of the stored water was regulated by vent valve d.

4. The water was de-aired a second time by closing valve h, evacuating
   the de-airing chamber, and opening valves c and e.

5. The twice de-aired water was then placed in the bladder, which was inside the pressure tank, by opening valves j, k, and l.

-29-

ASSIGNMENTS

Write a formal or semiformal report (length to be specified by the instructor) on one of the following subjects or on a subject of your own choice.

1. The possibility or feasibility of developing a skiing area in some location that has been suggested for that purpose. This could cover such questions as access, type and number of lifts, accommodations, runs needed, and work to be done to develop runs. It can be expanded or limited as circumstances permit. A possible variation would be a report on desirable improvements in an existing area.

2. The desirability of spraying or not spraying a forest area by use of airplanes to control an infestation of harmful insects.

3. The development of an ice-skating facility, either indoor or out of doors, for a school or community.

4. The choice of one type or make of prefabricated building for some specific use in your school or community.

5. The practicability or impracticability of producing a machine for the extrusion of prestressed concrete slabs for use on floors or roofs.

6. The measures that are necessary to protect a certain area from floods.

7. A program for controlling erosion on some specific farm or tract of farm land.

8. Measures necessary to protect a stretch of road or some other area from landslides, avalanches, or both.

9. Provisions that might be made for bringing about centralized control of the equipment on some large building (that is, having pumps, compressors, thermostats, fire security systems, etc. all regulated at a single point).

10. The desirability of changing the method of handling produce of a certain kind (peas, peaches, or something of the sort). This might involve the use of a different kind of equipment.

11. The causes of break-up in the surfacing of certain parking lots and recommendations for upkeep or reconstruction.

12

PROPOSALS

A major development in technical writing during recent years has been the intense concern with proposals—a concern that has caused the proposal to gain recognition as a distinct problem calling for special attention.

What is a proposal? It is just what the word implies: a communication proposing that something be done (often but not necessarily by the writer or the organization that he represents), addressed to the person or body whose favorable decision must be secured before the proposed action can be taken.

Proposals vary in length and complexity as widely as do reports, but those that have been receiving greatest attention are the ones that grow out of the following kind of situation:

A branch of the government decides that it needs certain goods or services. It may know definitely what it wants done, or it may know only that it wants certain results and may be unsure how they should be accomplished. It therefore explains its needs to selected corporations and invites them to submit their proposals for doing the job. After the proposals thus obtained have been carefully analyzed, and usually after further negotiation, the business is awarded to the corporation whose proposal is most satisfactory.

This explanation, oversimplified though it is, makes it easy to see why proposals are so immensely important. In many an industry the proposal is the major instrument for getting business, and poor preparation of proposals means serious trouble. Consequently, a major proposal prepared by a great corporation is a large, elaborate piece of work based on the findings of highly trained scientists and engineers. It is prepared at great expense by experts—including professional technical writers, editors, and artists as well as scientists, engineers, and executives. Also, its written material—backed up by every kind of visual aid—is often presented in person by a team of specialists.

It will probably be a long time before you will be involved, except perhaps in a very minor role, in the preparation of these long and elaborate *major proposals*. However, major proposals serve as a good starting point for our discussion, partly to reduce the danger that, as a newly hired employee, you will appear ill-informed about the way industry operates, and partly because the principles on which they are based can be applied to the simpler proposals that you may have to produce in any position of responsibility.

MAJOR PROPOSALS

As might be expected, many of the qualities and conventions related to proposals are not peculiar to that form. These include the principles of organization, the use of tables and illustrations, the use of effective style, and the use of headings, all of which have been covered as elements in reports or in technical writing in general. Also, what is said about many of the elements appearing in reports—the cover, title page, letter of transmittal, table of contents, and appendix—applies equally well to proposals. What remains to be said about major proposals as a distinctive kind of writing concerns the introduction and the body.

Introduction

The introduction of a proposal, like the introduction of a formal report, must cover certain routine matters. It immediately gives the reference number of the project (which is practically certain to have one) unless that number has already been shown above the point where the text begins. To get under way smoothly it usually identifies the material to follow as a proposal. And it tells as briefly as possible what is proposed: that is, what services are to be performed and for whom.

After these formalities, the introduction can begin to introduce the contents of the proposal. It may concentrate attention, for example, on the problem that the proposal concerns, showing that the problem was understood correctly and describing any new problems that arose as a solution was looked for. It may explain the general nature of the solution to be presented and tell its advantages as compared with other possible solutions. It may provide an over-all picture of the proposal by listing the major points to be covered in the body. It may focus the reader's attention on whatever is most vital in the discussion to follow. And finally, it may provide a necessary minimum of information on any question that might normally be answered in the body but does not, on this particular occasion, call for a full-scale answer.

Content of the Body

In describing the body of a proposal we shall assume, since we are mainly concerned with writing, that a potential customer or client has already decided to embark upon some project, and that the study preceding the actual writing of a proposal has been completed. Under these circumstances those who write the proposal would develop the body by considering the following questions, some of which grew out of questions already considered when the substance of the proposal was decided upon:

1. What do we propose to do?
2. How do we propose to do it?
3. What evidence must we present to show that the program we propose will really get the job done?
4. What evidence must we present to show that our way is better than any other way of obtaining the desired results?
5. How can we demonstrate our ability to do what we propose to do?

The fact that these questions suggest the nature of the material in a proposal does not mean that they always dominate its treatment. There are occasions, for example, when the result to be accomplished has already been specified by the potential customer in such detail that there is nothing more to be said about *what* shall be done, but only *how* we would accomplish the result demanded. And even when a customer has only presented a problem, and the proposal must itself answer the question of what shall be done, a writer is merely giving details about *what would actually be done* when he explains *how* that result would be accomplished. Thus, the material on *what* and the material on *how* may be either kept separate or combined in a single section.

Likewise, though it is sometimes desirable to use a special section to present evidence that the things we propose to do would really accomplish the result demanded, there will also be occasions when this evidence may better accompany the material dealing with *what* and *how*, or else be combined with the evidence showing that the approach suggested is better than other approaches to the problem. In brief, though the first four of the questions may always demand individual consideration, the material necessary to answer them should be handled in whatever manner best fits the occasion.

As for the final question, "How can we demonstrate that we are capable of doing what we propose to do?" there is at least a presumption that we probably can do it or we would not have been asked to submit a proposal. Nevertheless, our proposal will be weak indeed unless it explains our qualifications in an effort to show that they compare favorably with the qualifications of competitors.

A statement of qualifications will usually need to cover personnel, facilities, and experience. Information on personnel may go so far as to include the names and records of people who might be assigned to a project, emphasizing any name that is entitled to special respect. Information on facilities may go so far as to include an extensive list of facilities available, and would certainly draw attention to those of unusual importance. Information on experience would obviously be entitled to thorough coverage, for past performance may be the best possible evidence of what can be expected in the future. It is not necessary, of course, that the body be the only part of the proposal to offer facts about qualifications. Some of this material, especially lists, may well be placed in an appendix. But if this is done, the body should include at least a strong general statement on each point and should refer to the information in the appendix in order to ensure its receiving attention.

Organization

The questions we have been considering were arranged in an order that would appear to be logical under any circumstances, but other possibilities should be considered. As our chapter on organization pointed out, the function of a piece of writing is never merely to get statements down on paper. Always, the function is to be conceived in terms of effect upon the reader. In planning a proposal, then, it is necessary to consider not only impersonal logic but also such questions as the following: What will those who receive the proposal want to hear about first? What do they think is important? What are they most worried about? What obstacles do they expect to be most formidable? How can we give special prominence to the areas where we show up most favorably? How can we avoid emphasizing areas where we compare least favorably with the competition?

Nothing we can learn about the attitudes of those whom we address —from their request for a proposal, from our own former dealings with them, from others in our organization who have dealt with them—should be overlooked when a proposal is planned. In brief, the writer must decide what points are most likely to be crucial, and then develop a plan that is reader-oriented but is not lacking in either logic or continuity.

For still another reason we should not assume that the questions used as a starting point will always dominate the organization of a proposal. These questions may have served their purpose in our discussion, but they oversimplified the situation. When the job to be done is complicated, the best over-all basis of organization is likely to be a division of the job into its major component parts. This would mean that the questions would be used not as the basis of an over-all approach but as the basis for the internal organization of major divisions or subdivisions.

Final Comment on Major Proposals

The preceding discussion sounds as if the creation of even a major proposal were a relatively simple matter, but this is true only because it has been impossible to treat the subject in general terms without oversimplifying it. As we mentioned earlier, a major proposal is a long, expensive, elaborate product, based on contributions by numerous teams of specialists. Merely preparing the document itself is a job that calls for some of the best talent within any organization.

Then too, the situations leading to the submission of proposals vary. An idea that we ourselves have originally conceived may have been discussed at length with the potential customer before the steps leading to a full-scale proposal. And when submitted, the written proposal that concerns a large project, even when it is supported by exhibits and reinforced by oral presentation, may be only one stage in the involved process by which a project is finally embarked upon. Variations from the original requirements may be suggested by the proposer and accepted or rejected by the potential customer. Only after extensive negotiations is a contract likely to be agreed upon.

But despite the unavoidable oversimplification, the preceding discussion can serve two purposes. It gives at least a rudimentary picture of an immensely important form of industrial communication, and it contains ideas that also apply to the writing of the less ambitious proposals that are next to be considered.

MINOR PROPOSALS

Unfortunately, so little has been written about proposals in books intended for general circulation that there is no generally accepted terminology to identify proposals of different kinds. *Minor* is a relative term. Our so-called *minor* proposals are minor only in that they are not produced by a great corporation and submitted to a potential customer, usually the government, in an effort to secure a multimillion-dollar contract. Actually, they range from short and simple letters and memoranda to documents as long and complicated as most formal reports.

Certainly these proposals are not of minor importance in their service to industry. They serve an important function in securing the decisions and action that are essential to industrial operations. They are important, also, to those who write them, for they are one of the means by which anyone holding a significant professional position gets a chance to push his work ahead and thus to advance in his career.

Proposals and Reports

The terms *proposal* and *report* are not mutually exclusive. Many proposals are reports and vice versa. For example, when a writer submits his work to readers who have requested that he investigate some problem to decide what should be done about it, his report may amount to a proposal—or we might well say "his proposal is a report." Yet there are certainly proposals that are *not* reports; and since any proposal is essentially an effort to sell the idea that certain action should be taken, it would be undesirable and inaccurate to dismiss proposals as a subject that could be covered adequately in a discussion of reports.

Circumstances That Lead to Proposals

The circumstances that lead to proposals are far more varied than one would expect. Proposals may be made either to those within our organization or to outsiders. They may concern action to be taken either by the proposer, by those addressed, or by some third party. The ramifications become clearer when you imagine yourself holding a position of moderate responsibility in the production department of a small factory. In such a position:

1. You might propose to your superior that you be permitted to try a new method of packaging a product in order to reduce shipping costs.

2. You might propose to those in charge of the physical plant that a new system of lighting be installed in certain places where lighting is not up to modern standards.

3. You might propose that those who procure certain supplies both for you and for others get them from a different source in order that quality and service may be improved.

4. You might propose to the manager that he order a change in maintenance procedures so that the work you supervise will not be interrupted so seriously.

5. You might propose that your own section of the plant, rather than a rival section, be given the chance to make some new product.

These cases all concern the internal affairs of the company, but proposals are not limited to internal operations. A corporation might propose to a city government that zoning or traffic regulations be changed. The city government might in turn propose to the corporation that it landscape the surroundings of its plant as part of a city-improvement program, or adopt smoke-abatement measures. In brief, the role of proposals is so extensive that when action occurs in industry, government, or education, it is very likely to have been preceded by a proposal.

Suggestions for Making a Proposal Effective

Our understanding of proposals would be incomplete if we were unaware of the possibilities that have been mentioned above, but it is neither necessary nor desirable to discuss each of these possibilities separately. Whatever the situation may be, it can be handled by good, logical presentation of facts, reinforced by skillful persuasion. The first necessity is to realize that decision-making (and action on your proposals amounts to that) often involves far more than the obvious considerations that bear upon the case, without reference to surrounding circumstances. A person who makes a proposal should so far as possible put himself in the reader's place. He should think of the people his reader will have to deal with before the proposal can receive final approval. He should face the question of whether the proposal is in line with established policy—or justifies being made an exception if such is not the case. He should consider the possibility that in securing favorable action on the proposal the reader, who may not be a law unto himself, might be forced to obligate himself to others to too great a degree or perhaps endanger other proposals. In general, he should realize that innumerable considerations influence the decisions of men in executive positions, and should do everything possible to present his proposal so that its prospects will not be damaged by extraneous considerations.

The idea that you should put yourself in your reader's place is in one respect misleading. It implies that the reader is either a person possessed of your own individual outlook or else is an impersonal being who is merely the occupant of a certain position. Neither of these implications is likely to be entirely true. The reader's slant—his standard of values, his susceptibility to various appeals—may resemble your own or may be sharply different. And certainly he is not just a robot filling a position. He is a human being whose tastes, previous experience, sense of values, and personal situation will always affect his reactions and actions.

Thus, you should not just imagine *yourself* in the position of those receiving your proposal; rather, you should try to visualize what will happen when your proposal reaches the attention of the specific readers who will actually receive it.

This does not imply that catering to the whims or peculiarities of your reader is as important as the development of a sound case. But there are times when three or four different appeals might all be sound, and when it is really important to accent the particular appeal that you believe to be in line with your reader's sense of values. The considerations that might do most to secure favorable action from your reader are not always those that mean the most to you.

Also, the need of good timing should not be overlooked. Many a proposal has a better chance of getting the necessary attention if it is made at a time when the pressure of other matters is not at a peak.

Many proposals can be made more effective by application of the traditional sales letter formula: interest, desire, conviction, and action. But just as the use of this formula in a sales letter does not mean there must be distinct sections based upon it, its use in a proposal does not mean that the sections must be separate. Rather, it means that we should make sure that none of the elements is overlooked if it is called for on the specific occasion. If a sales letter approach—modified to suit the occasion —is used, a proposal can be developed as described in the following sections.

The Opening

The opening of a minor proposal is not basically different from the opening of a major proposal. Rather than being dramatic, it is merely a simple, direct identification of the nature and purpose of the communication being submitted.

Interest and Desire

In a proposal where it is necessary to arouse interest and desire it is usually best to try to arouse both of them at the same time. That is, secure interest by making the reader immediately aware that the proposal is related to something he desires. The phrase *create desire* was intentionally avoided because we do not attempt to create desire. Rather, we look for an approach that associates our proposal with a desire the reader already feels: desire to save time or money, desire for expansion, desire for freedom from burdensome details, desire that work be done more smoothly and efficiently.

The effort to arouse interest and desire really amounts to answering the question, "*Why* should the proposed action be taken?" And though you should usually tell the general nature of your proposal right at the beginning, you will probably be wasting your efforts if you give full details about what you think should be done before you tell the desirable results that may be hoped for.

Conviction

In a proposal, as in a sales letter, the business of instilling conviction actually amounts to showing that the action you advocate will gratify the desire with which you have associated it. In a proposal, however, the portion designed to instill conviction must usually be the part where the proposal is presented in full detail. You trust that as the reader gets a complete picture of what is to be done, he will see for himself that the action proposed will give the benefits aimed at. Of course if it is not obvious that the benefits will follow, it is naturally necessary to present enough evidence and explanation to settle any doubt. Sometimes the details of what is proposed and the proof that the results would be as desired blend together naturally, but there are many occasions when the proof should be delayed until the things to be done have been stated, in order that the latter can be made clearer and shorter.

Amount of Detail. As in many other kinds of communication, it is constantly necessary to consider carefully the question of how much detail to include in a proposal. No formula will provide an answer to this question. The decision must be based on the tastes of the reader so far as you know them, and the extent to which you feel he is willing to leave details to your judgment. Excessive detail leads to boredom and impatience; skimpy detail can create a doubt about whether you have really thought the problem through.

Unless a proposal will be short even with the details included, it is probably better to include too little detail than too much. After all, acceptance or rejection of a proposal does not necessarily hinge upon a single communication, and you can offer to provide whatever additional details are wanted. Of course, the main proposal can be followed by an appendix providing more details, or it can be accompanied by a supplement. (In this case, the supplement should be mentioned in the main proposal so that the reader will know that it is available.) Still another possibility would be to include details in the main proposal, but use headings in such a systematic manner that the reader may read or skip various blocks of material as he sees fit.

Answering Objections. The process of convincing includes more than just demonstrating that the proposal would accomplish the result desired. You will also usually need to answer at least some of these questions: Is this proposal really practical? Would the benefits justify the effort and expense involved? Are there other and perhaps better ways of accomplishing the same result? Would there be other and undesirable consequences in addition to the benefits?

Answers to these questions will sometimes comprise a major portion of a proposal. Anyone who proposes a course of action would be well advised to try to think of all the objections that might be raised, and to forestall those that seem most likely to give trouble. No one can provide a foolproof method of deciding which of the possible objections should be answered, and which should be ignored in order not to bring them needlessly into the focus of attention.

In anticipating objections we cannot overlook the fact that action on a proposal often involves more than the proposal itself and its obvious consequences. Incidental questions usually arise on such issues as the establishment of a precedent or the compatibility of such action with established policy. Some of these objections may grow out of valid considerations, but others grow out of human weaknesses. For example, a proposal from one supervisor might run into trouble not because it is unsound in the specific case but because a favorable decision could lead to similar requests from other supervisors, many of which might have to be turned down. Those in authority might well decide that improving performance in one area would not justify the damage to morale and hence to performance in other areas.

Unfortunately, the real reason that may underlie some objections does not always appear on the surface. An administrator who must be consulted about a proposal may offer objections on grounds that appear weak because, in the back of his mind, he has misgivings he does not care to state—for example, whether veterans on his staff would function well if forced to substitute new and strange methods for methods with which they are familiar.

The concealed objection is perhaps the hardest to overcome—provided, of course, that a proposal itself really has merit. When the real grounds for objections are held back, we do not have a chance to answer them directly even if we could do so. About all that one can do sometimes is to prepare the emotional ground for the proposal in advance, and perhaps try to see how, by minor changes, he can minimize the extent to which it treads upon anyone's toes. Such concessions to human weakness will at least give a proposal a better chance of surmounting, by real merit, the irrelevant obstacles that under ideal conditions would not exist.

Arrangement of Material. In arranging the content of the "conviction" portion of a proposal, the best principle is to place the strongest material first. If a reader is not favorably impressed by what he encounters first, he is more likely to look for weakness in what follows. For the sake of completeness and to forestall objections, unimpressive material may sometimes need to be included; but it should be held back so that when vital matters have already been covered, a reader may either skim over the rest or read it carefully, whichever he pleases. If the weaker material comes first, the reader may lose interest before he reaches the most favorable points.

Securing Action

Every part of a proposal is of course aimed at securing action, but the chances of success are increased if there is one part in which the idea of action is the definite focus of attention. What can we do in this connection? Certainly we cannot pressure our readers too strongly if they are people over whom we have no control because they are above us or operate in a different line of authority. Often we must proceed as if we felt sure that they would not need to be urged to act if they became convinced that our proposal was good.

We can, however, make sure that, so far as it is appropriate for us to define it, the specific course of action necessary to carry out our proposal is absolutely clear. Especially, we can make sure that the first step to be taken is easy to identify; and if there is a really important reason that action should begin soon, we can mention that reason.

Also, we can increase the chances that our bid for action will get attention by setting it apart physically from the rest of the proposal. This can be done by a heading, by leaving extra space above it, or by some change in the form of text such as deeper indentation and single spacing in a double-spaced manuscript. Sometimes we can make the action definite by a numbered list of steps that must be taken. Often we can clarify the picture by starting each item on our list in a manner that shows who must carry out that particular job, or by underlining the person or division concerned with each step so that people can locate at a glance the matters that concern them personally. Or, we can begin or end each step by indicating the date when it would have to be begun or completed. Unless a proposal is very short, we must prevent the section where the whole proposal is boiled down into terms of action from looking like a tag end—a final detail of no greater importance than the bulk of the material that precedes it.

Actually, it is often desirable, in the general statement at the beginning of a proposal, to tell the date by which action is necessary so that when a reader first glances at the proposals, the need of early action, if it exists, cannot escape his attention. Offering this information at such a time does not appear to be an undue effort to tell the reader what to do or when to do it; it merely gives him significant information and thus may bring about faster action by securing earlier attention for the entire proposal.

(Illustrative Specimens Follow)

SPECIMEN PROPOSAL *

The following proposal is brief but was produced with the same care that is given to the preparation of much longer proposals. It was provided with a handsome cover and consisted of a title page, three pages of text, and two appendixes. The appendixes have been omitted. One of them named personnel who might be assigned to the project and described their qualifications, devoting half a page to each person. The other consisted of a three-page list of the Research Division facilities that might be used as needed.

---

* Courtesy of Texas Instruments Incorporated.

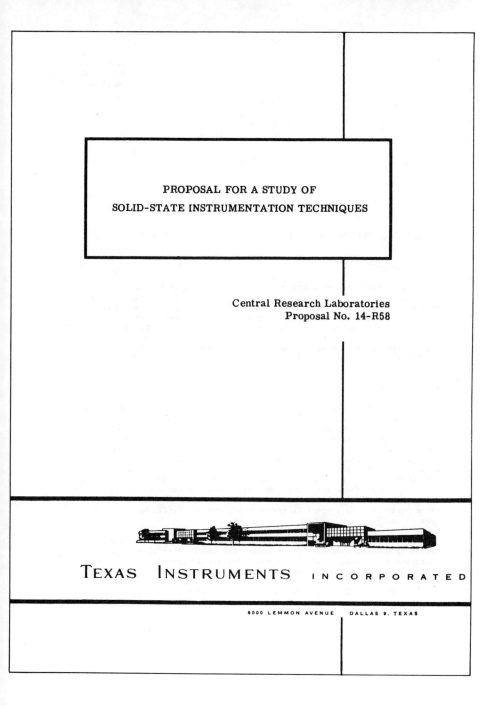

PROPOSAL FOR A STUDY OF
SOLID-STATE INSTRUMENTATION TECHNIQUES

Central Research Laboratories
Proposal No. 14-R58

TEXAS INSTRUMENTS INCORPORATED

6000 LEMMON AVENUE   DALLAS 9. TEXAS

TEXAS INSTRUMENTS
Incorporated
6000 Lemmon Avenue
Dallas 9, Texas

PROPOSAL FOR A STUDY OF
SOLID-STATE INSTRUMENTATION TECHNIQUES

Reference: Wright Air Development Center Purchase Request No. 56257

I.   INTRODUCTION

Texas Instruments is extremely interested in this project because it offers the opportunity to apply the company's years of solid-state experience to a problem which has tremendous military importance. However, Texas Instruments believes that the interests of the government would be better served by a modification of the exhibit. Division of the effort into an initial study phase is suggested, followed by a laboratory testing program based on the findings of the initial phase. This approach would provide for a more efficient application of effort than would a concurrent program.

II.   TECHNICAL DISCUSSION

The tremendous advances in propulsion systems in recent years, and the extremely wide range of environmental conditions under which these systems must operate, have largely made obsolete the classical Newtonian methods of measuring essential quantities such as pressure, temperature, and acceleration. Also, the transducers which have been developed to implement these measurements have been outmoded. This rapid increase in the need for exotic transducers has led to a "cross-pollination" of techniques and methods. This situation has produced a patchwork crop of transducers, developed under the stress of the moment, which are not necessarily optimum for the given application. Such hybrid devices often result from the interest of an individual in a specific measurement, and are hardly satisfactory for general use.

It is the combination of extreme environmental conditions imposed on modern propulsion systems which suggests the feasibility of solid-state materials for transducers. These materials are inherently less subject to physical failure under extreme environmental conditions than are less rugged conventional transducers. Solid-state materials have proven extremely reliable mechanically and electrically in devices such as diodes, transistors,

1

264

photoconductors, and many others. Texas Instruments is already producing a transducer of the same general family in the "Sensitor." It is a solid-state temperature-sensing resistor. This device has found wide application in fields ranging from geophysics to missiles. Although this device is not useful over the wide ranges required of the proposed transducers, it is indicative of the diversified interest in solid-state devices at Texas Instruments.

As we stand on the threshold of a new technique, it would be well to review not only the transducers but the methods by which the measurements are made. There are obviously certain ranges of the specific measurable parameters, made under certain benign environments, where conventional techniques and transducers possess desirable characteristics. At this time, it would hardly be reasonable to concentrate effort in these fields.

With this fact in mind, it would be well to review the state of the art giving particular attention to methods of measurement (variation in resistance, capacitance, inductance, etc.) and to limitations such as dynamic range, output level, linearity, hysteresis, size, etc.

III. PROPOSED PROGRAM

Texas Instruments proposes a six-month program consisting of two parts.

A.   Phase I, Transducer Evaluation

This phase will consist of an appraisal of present transducer technology, to determine in which fields semiconductor transducers promise to make the greatest immediate contribution.

The Industrial Instrumentation Division of Texas Instruments has had long experience in the measurement of physical phenomena to a high degree of precision. This experience would prove invaluable in making a support study such as the one here proposed.

B.   Phase II, Solid-State Evaluation

This phase would consist of an extensive literature survey and a thorough theoretical study of the response characteristics of known semiconductor materials to pressure, temperature, acceleration, and determination of heat-transfer rate throughout the ranges specified in the reference. This study would be carried out by personnel of the Central Research Laboratories of Texas Instruments.

IV.   ITEMS TO BE DELIVERED

Texas Instruments Central Research Laboratories will deliver monthly and final reports as specified in Exhibit WCLC-2-56257. The final report will

2

consist of a correlation of both of the studies, showing the areas in which semiconductor materials can make the greatest contribution to the transducer field and recommendations for future laboratory studies to implement devices utilizing these materials.

V.   CONCLUSIONS

Texas Instruments broad experience and demonstrated capability in the semiconductor field and the scientific background and ability of its technical staff assure that a thorough and productive research program will be conducted. It is believed that the study outlined above represents the most logical and efficient approach to the investigation of this important field.

/s/ _____

J. M. McMILLIN
Device Research

/s/ _____

R. L. PETRITZ
Director of Device Research

3

266

ASSIGNMENTS

Write a proposal (length to be specified by the instructor) called for in one of the following circumstances. If you use, with permission, a subject not on the list, it will be necessary to settle such questions as who makes the proposal and to whom it is made.

1. A department in your college wants permission to buy instruments and perhaps hire additional help so that it can test and adjust certain equipment now sent to the manufacturer for such service. (The aim would be to avoid delay and possibly to reduce expenses.)

2. A school or some large company has its own water system. It would like to connect its system with that of the community where it is located so that each will have a greater reserve to draw upon in emergencies.

3. Some division of either a university or an industrial establishment wishes to put into effect a systematic procedure for replacing obsolete or obsolescent equipment.

4. A small feeder airline is in the process of installing a different type of airplane that cannot, under unfavorable circumstances, land or take off at a certain municipal airport. It wants the municipality to extend the runways. If this is not done, the company may be forced to request government authorities to permit a reduction in service.

5. A company owns a tract of land that lies along a river. It is willing to make a gift to the city of a stretch of this tract closest to the river for use as a park if the city will protect that stretch, and therefore the land behind it, against floods.

6. The stores in a certain area are willing to lease some unused land for use as a free public parking area if the city will develop it and maintain it for such a purpose.

7. A trailer court owner wishes to have the city rezone a small tract of land now limited to residential use so that he can expand his court onto it.

8. The trees on a college campus or a city park are threatened with damage by disease or insects. A custom-spraying company would like to be hired to do the spraying necessary for protection. (This will make it unnecessary for the college or city to buy equipment, hire personnel, and do the job itself.)

9. A research institute or a university is conducting tests of various kinds of insulating material. A company whose product is not being tested believes that this newly developed product is superior to the others. It is willing to provide free specimens if the university will include them in its testing program.

10. A manufacturer of farm machinery has learned that an attachment for some type of machine is promising. This attachment has been designed and is being developed by a very small company. The manufacturer would like to help in testing and further development in return for being given the first opportunity to buy the attachment if it is successful.

11. A department of some company has been doing some job by oxy-acetylene welding. It would like permission and funds to study and try out arc spot welding, which might be superior, as a method for doing the job.

12. The authorities in charge of a safety program wish to increase the number of safety inspections in an area or on a job where accidents have been increasing. (As an alternative, the proposal could be that certain specific safety measures be adopted in the area.)

13. There are reasons that it might be desirable to split a certain department in your university into two departments. A committee has been appointed to study the question and recommend to the administration how the split shall be accomplished.

14. A small community would like to be the site of a new plant that a company intends to locate in the area, and wishes to demonstrate its suitability and offer incentives that will induce the company to come there.

15. The company referred to in assignment 14 is willing to come to the community if certain conditions can be met.

Part Three

BUSINESS
CORRESPONDENCE

13

GENERAL
PRINCIPLES
OF
BUSINESS
CORRESPONDENCE

If we regard the term *technical writing* as broad enough to include whatever writing you will be responsible for doing on the job, there can be no doubt that letter writing is an important part of the subject. Anyone who cannot write effective letters will be seriously handicapped in his career.

Study of letter writing is especially desirable because of the difference between letters and most of the other material written by those trained in technical professions. In many professions a person will spend much of his time thinking not about people but about things—about steel, or oil, or concrete; about transistors, or chemicals, or geological formations; about smog, or insecticides, or machinery. And when much of his writing deals impersonally and objectively with such subjects, he can profit by a reminder that there are times when writing is done for the sake of personal communication, and when different techniques are therefore desirable. A study of letter writing constitutes such a reminder.

To make it easier to visualize the finished product, attention is first centered on letter form. Next, the substance of letters in general is discussed. In following chapters, specific types of letters are considered, in order to illustrate how the general principles of letter writing work out in a variety of characteristic situations.

CORRECT FORM IN BUSINESS LETTERS

This discussion of letter form is not exhaustive, for covering every possible question of form would occupy too much space and would make it harder to identify and remember the points that are essential. If you need additional information on some points, you may find it in a special section in the best collegiate dictionaries. The information that follows, however, will answer most questions that arise in ordinary correspondence.

Identification of Parts of the Letter

The parts that appear in *every* letter are (1) the heading, (2) the address, (3) the salutation, (4) the body, (5) the complimentary close, and (6) the signature. The heading is the section that tells the address of the writer and the date; the address is the section telling whom the letter is addressed to; the salutation is the "Dear Sir" or its equivalent; the complimentary close is the "Very truly yours" or its equivalent; and the signature includes the longhand signature of the writer plus the typed material that accompanies the longhand signature. These and certain other parts that appear with varying frequency will be discussed later in more detail.

Miscellaneous Mechanical Details

Stationery. The stationery should be good, unruled bond paper, preferably white, 8½ by 11 inches large. If the first page of a two-page letter bears a printed letterhead, the second should match it in quality and color but should be blank. Smaller stationery is sometimes used for extremely short letters, but paper of standard size is usually preferred even for short letters because of the greater convenience for filing.

Placement of the Letter on the Page. To place a letter on a page so that the margins are well balanced demands either long experience or careful planning. The result aimed at should be approximately as follows: (1) there should be more white space at the bottom than at the top unless the length of the letter and the size of the letterhead makes this impossible; (2) the side margins should be approximately equal and should ordinarily be no larger than the bottom margin—often being smaller; (3) regardless of the length of the letter, the body should fall partly above and partly below the center of the page. A short letter will look better if slightly more than half the body is above the center of the page.

In spacing a letter it is helpful to remember that there are six lines of type to the inch, and either ten or twelve letters to the inch (usually twelve) in the line. Most writing averages about six letters to the word, including space between words. By utilizing these facts you can reduce the uncertainty about the space a letter will occupy if you must do your own typing.

When a letter is written on a blank sheet, the minimum margins all around are 1 inch—preferably 1½ inches at the top and bottom. The maximum margin at the top is about 2½ inches, and at the sides is 2 inches. The space between the heading and the inside address may vary from a double space in the longest letters to six spaces in the shortest. In the shortest letters, the bottom margin is obviously controlled by the length of the letter.

When the stationery bears a printed letterhead, the point to consider when setting the top margin is the first line of the inside address. *In the shortest letters* this may be as much as 3½ inches (21 lines) below the top of the page. This would normally leave room for six or seven lines of the body of the letter above the center of the page. The side margins would of course be the maximum for such a short letter. *For the longest letters,* the inside address may begin only a double space below the date line, which would itself be only a double space below the bottom of the printed letterhead. For shorter letters, the date line would be placed either (1) two spaces below the printed letterhead or (2) half way between the letterhead and the inside address.

Spacing Within the Letter. The best procedure, normally, is to single-space within the paragraphs of all business letters and to double-space between paragraphs. The space between the heading and the inside address varies. There should be a double space, however, between any other two parts of the letter, namely (1) between the inside address and the salutation, (2) between the salutation and the body, (3) between the body and the complimentary close, and (4) between the complimentary close and the signature if the first line of the signature is typed. More will be said later about spacing the signature.

Systems of Indentation and Punctuation

The heading, if a letter is on blank stationery, is in block style. (That is all lines begin the same distance from the left side of the sheet.) It may be placed so that all of its lines begin just to the right of the center of the page, or so that its longest line extends to the right-hand margin.

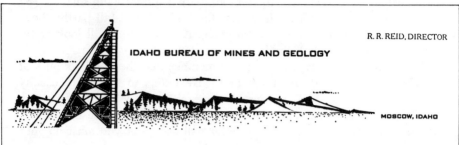

R. R. REID, DIRECTOR

IDAHO BUREAU OF MINES AND GEOLOGY

MOSCOW, IDAHO

September 5, 196_

Mr. Albert L. Wilson
Red River Route
Elk City, Idaho

Dear Mr. Wilson:

This will acknowledge your letter concerning feldspar. I believe that
the best source of the information that you need on this subject would be
the chapter on feldspar in the U. S. Bureau of Mines Bulletin 585, <u>Mineral
Facts and Problems</u>, published in 1960.

A reprint of the feldspar chapter may be obtained from the Superintendent of Documents, U. S. Government Printing Office, Washington, D. C. for
10 cents. The complete bulletin, bound in hard cover, sells for $6.00. It
is a book of over a thousand pages giving data on the occurrence, methods
of processing, and uses of virtually every mineral commodity used by man.

The principal uses of feldspar are in the manufacture of glass and
ceramic products. There are no rigid market classifications because most
buyers set up their own specifications for the material they use. In general,
the glass industry uses a granular product, which is virtually all -20 mesh,
with little or no dusty fines. Also, this industry can tolerate little or
no iron in its feldspar. The ceramic industries usually demand a finer
product, ranging from 120 to 325 mesh.

Prices paid for feldspar will vary from $10 or $12 per ton up to as
much as $25 per ton, depending on the grade of the material and on whether
it is bagged or shipped in bulk. An average price would probably be in
the range of $15 per ton.

I trust that this information will be of some help to you. If we
can be of further assistance, please let us know.

Sincerely yours,

Lewis S. Prater
LSP:em   Assistant Director

**Figure 15.   Letter of Approximately Average Length, Correct in Form and Well
Placed on a Letterhead.**

1819 Walton Street
Spokane, Washington
May 7, 196_

Mr. John A. Smith, Personnel Manager
Columbia River Construction Company
Box 308
Portland, Oregon

Dear Mr. Smith:

Thank you for your letter of May 4, offering me an
interview in connection with my application for a
position as a junior engineer.

I can easily arrange to be in Portland on the after-
noon of Thursday, May 19, which is in line with your
suggestion. I will telephone your office during the
morning of that date to inquire about the time that
you have set for my appointment.

The more I consider the matter, the more I find that
the prospect of working for your company appeals to
me. You may therefore be sure that the opportunity
to have an interview is sincerely appreciated.

Very truly yours,

Joseph A. Roach

Figure 16. Extremely Short Letter, Correct in Form and Well Placed on a
Blank Page.

The inside address is also blocked, with all lines beginning at the left margin. The salutation begins at the left margin. The beginning of each paragraph is indented either five or ten spaces. Terminology varies, but the form described is usually called the semiblock system. In the full block system, which some companies prefer, not only the paragraphs but also the date line (which is the only typed material in the heading of a letter on a letterhead), the inside address, the complimentary close, and the signature begin at the left margin. However, the most frequent deviation from the semiblock system consists of not indenting for paragraphs. This deviation is entirely acceptable if the letter is single-spaced but not if it is double-spaced.

The modern system of punctuating the heading and inside address is the open system. That is, no punctuation is used at the end of any line unless, of course, it is necessary to use a period after an abbreviation.

Figures 15 and 16 show business letters in correct form, well placed on the page.

Form for Individual Parts of the Letter

The Heading. If the stationery does not bear a printed letterhead, the heading contains from two to four lines, usually three. The first line, plus the second if necessary, tells the local address from which the letter was written; the next line tells the town and state; and the last line tells the date. The name of the writer does not appear in a typewritten heading. The heading is placed in the upper right-hand portion of the page. It may be placed so that its longest line ends at the right margin of the page, or it may begin slightly to the right of the center of the page, regardless of where this causes the lines to end. The top line of the heading is typed 1 inch to 2½ inches from the top of the page, the exact distance depending on the length of the letter.

If the letter is written on stationery with a printed letterhead, the typed heading consists of the date line only. This may be placed half way between the bottom of the letterhead and the inside address, far enough to the right so that it extends to the right-hand margin, or it may be centered and placed two spaces below the letterhead. A printed letterhead is often designed so as to provide a natural space for the date line.

Examples of Typewritten Headings

```
1316 Twenty-seventh Street        The Associated Engineers
Alameda, California               University of Idaho
May 15, 196_                      Moscow, Idaho
                                  February 20, 196_
```

Abbreviation, capitalization, and use of numbers are illustrated in the preceding headings; but since these are matters that apply to other parts of the letter also, they will be discussed as the final point under *Form*.

The Inside Address. The examples of inside addresses given later illustrate usage in the most common cases. As indicated, considerable flexibility is necessary to prevent some of the lines reaching an unwieldy length or to prevent the number of lines from becoming so great as to be awkward. Usually, however, three or four lines of reasonable length are sufficient.

When a letter is addressed to an individual, some title or the equivalent must always be used. To omit it is discourteous. The title *Mr.* is of course the most common, but it may be replaced by *Doctor, Captain, Professor,* or any other term one might use before the person's name if one were actually speaking to him. The terms *Honorable* and *Reverend* are sometimes used in place of titles. *Honorable* is appropriate when one addresses an important governmental official. *Reverend* is appropriate when one addresses a clergyman. (Full coverage of all the possible forms appropriate for all clergy may be found in many books.) It is also correct to indicate the reader's degree, for example, Ph.D. or M.D., after the name rather than placing a title before the name. There should be no duplication, however; *Dr. Ralph Morgan, M.D.* would be incorrect.

If your letter is addressed to a woman you may be uncertain about whether to call her *Miss* or *Mrs.* The following suggestions may be helpful:

1. If you have received a letter from the woman you are addressing, look at her signature. If you see nothing to indicate that *Mrs.* is called for, address her as *Miss.* (If *Mrs.* were called for, she would presumably have indicated that fact unless she assumed that you knew it already.)

2. If you are addressing a married woman or a widow, the correct form would be *Mrs. John R. Brown* rather than *Mrs. Mary Brown*, unless she herself uses the latter form in business.

3. If you are addressing a divorcee, the correct form is *Mrs. Mary Brown.* (This suggestion is based on the assumption that *Brown* was her married name. If she has resumed her maiden name, she is addressed as *Miss Mary Brown*, just as if she had never been married.)

4. The use of some other title (*Professor* or *Dr.*, for example) rather than *Miss* or *Mrs.* is entirely appropriate.

The Salutation. When a letter is addressed to an organization, the salutation should be *Gentlemen:* (or *Ladies:* if the organization is composed of women). *Dear Sirs* is out of date, except in a letter addressed to more than one individual. Though some companies omit all punctuation after the salutation, the vast majority use a colon.

For letters to individuals, note the following salutations, arranged in the order of decreasing formality:

Sir: (*too formal for most letters*)

My dear Sir: (*rather ceremonious*)

Dear Sir: (*very common*)

My dear Mr. Jones: (*often appropriate*)

Dear Mr. Jones: (*most widely used of all forms*)

It is often appropriate to replace *Mr.* by some other title, such as *Doctor, Professor, Captain, Governor,* or *Mayor.* It is more complimentary to refrain from using any abbreviation for a title, except *Mr., Mrs.* and *Dr.* The terms *Honorable* and *Reverend* are not titles, and though they sometimes replace titles in the inside address, they should not be used in the salutation. Many other terms, such as *Superintendent,* are sometimes erroneously used as titles. When there is doubt whether some particular term should be used as a title, it is advisable to refrain from using it.

As for the choice between the reader's name or *Dear Sir,* it used to be customary to use the name only when one knew the reader or at least had received a letter from him. In recent years this convention has been widely disregarded, for business letters are becoming less formal and more personal. To use *Dear Sir* may make a letter sound cold and remote. The modern trend is to use the reader's name unless his high rank or the occasion of the letter would cause informality to be in bad taste. The same situation holds true in a letter addressed to a woman. If her name is not used, the salutation is *Dear Madam.* There is a strong tendency, however, to avoid *Dear Madam* and use *Dear Mrs.* (or *Miss*) *Jones,* or *My dear Mrs. Jones.* In the last analysis, your own sense of appropriateness must determine your choice of salutations. There is no reason not to use the first name of a reader if you would use it in speaking to him personally and if there is no special reason informality would be unsuitable to the occasion.

The salutation must harmonize with the inside address. If a letter is addressed to an individual, the salutation must be to an individual and the same title must be used in both places. If the letter is addressed to an organization, the salutation must be to an organization. This holds true even when an "attention line" comes between the inside address and the salutation.

To show how inside addresses and salutations can be handled on many occasions, the following examples are provided:

```
Mr. David M. Jones, President        Western Testing Laboratory
Western Testing Laboratory           Olympic Building
Olympic Building                     South Bend, Iowa
South Bend, Iowa
                                     Gentlemen:
Dear Mr. Jones:


Mr. Walter S. Stevens                Messrs. William Smith and H. R. Brown
Secretary of the Chamber of          1148 Harrison Boulevard
  Commerce                           Twin Cities, Arkansas
Box 101
Caldwell, North Dakota               Dear Sirs:  (or Gentlemen:)

Dear Mr. Stevens:
```

Dr. Frederick C. Moore 1415 West Grant Street Tulsa 12, Oklahoma	Frederick C. Moore, M. D. 1415 West Grant Street Tulsa 12, Oklahoma
Dear Dr. Moore:	Dear Dr. Moore:
Dr. Walter C. Church Professor of Mathematics University of Kansas Lawrence, Kansas	Professor Walter C. Church Department of Mathematics University of Kansas Lawrence, Kansas
Dear Dr. Church:	Dear Professor Church:
Director of Personnel Hammond and Haskins Milling Company Fourth and Main Streets Sandpoint, Utah	American Association of University Women Cascade Building 761 Main Street Sandpoint, Utah
Dear Sir:	Ladies:
The Honorable John R. Doe United States Senate Washington 25, D. C.	The Honorable John R. Doe The House of Representatives Washington 25, D. C.
Dear Sir: (or My dear Senator Doe:)	Dear Sir: (or Dear Mr. Doe:)
The Honorable John R. Doe Governor of (State) (Capital City and State)	The Honorable John R. Doe Mayor of (City) (City and State)
Dear Sir: (or My dear Governor Doe:)	Dear Sir: (or My dear Mayor Doe:)

The Complimentary Close. The complimentary close is placed a double space below the final line of the body of the letter. It usually begins slightly to the left or right of the center of the page.

The form used most frequently is *Very truly yours. Yours truly* is more formal and somewhat less friendly. *Sincerely yours* is an extremely common variation which is completely correct, but many discriminating writers avoid wasting the extra assurance of sincerity on routine occasions and reserve *Sincerely* for letters in which the emotional tone is more intense than usual. *Cordially yours* is a gracious form if one is doing the reader a favor or in a position to do him favors, but it seems inappropriate in a letter soliciting a favor. *Respectfully yours* is used mainly when the reader's position entitles him to special respect or when one is formally submitting material to a person who outranks him in his own organization. It is too formal and too subservient for ordinary use. Participial endings—that is, *hoping, trusting,* and similar terms ending in *ing*—are out of date. The best attitude is to regard *Very truly yours* as standard and to use it unless there is reason for deviation.

The Signature. The place and contents of the signature are shown in the various examples following. Whenever a letter purports to be personally written, the name of the person who wrote it must be signed in longhand, even if the primary signature shows the letter to come from an organization. The name of the writer must always be typed, however, as well as signed in longhand.

The first example below indicates that the writer is acting merely as an individual; the second and third both show that the writer acts in behalf of an organization; the fourth shows the letter as being primarily from an organization, even though the name of the person who actually wrote the letter is also given. Note that in Numbers 2 and 3 the organization is not named, the assumption being that it was named in the letterhead. Otherwise, the name of the organization would appear in the signature. In all of the examples, the complimentary close is shown above the signature in order to show the relative positions of these two parts of the letter. At least a triple space would be left for the writer's longhand signature. If the first line under the complimentary close is typed, as in Number 4, a double space is used between the two.

(1)

Very truly yours,

John M. Jones

John M. Jones

(2)

Very truly yours,

John M. Jones

John M. Jones, Secretary

(3)

Very truly yours,

John M. Jones

John M. Jones
Production Manager

(4)

Very truly yours,

THE REED PAPER COMPANY

Robert L. Brown

Robert L. Brown
Sales Manager

The Attention Line. In a letter addressed to an organization, an attention line is sometimes used in addition to the inside address. By using it one can indicate the name, the position, or both of the individual from whom the leter should receive attention. Though there are several places where such a line can be placed, the two places illustrated below are probably the most common. Note that the salutation matches the inside address in spite of the attention line.

```
The H. C. Capwell Company
Broadway and Twentieth Streets
Oakland, California

Attention of Mr. H. L. Klarnet
Gentlemen:
```

```
The H. C. Capwell Company
Broadway and Twentieth Streets
Oakland, California

Gentlemen:                      Attention of the Credit Manager
```

The Subject Line. Only a very small proportion of business letters contain subject lines, for a good opening will identify the subject without a special line being necessary. Sometimes, however, a subject line is desirable, as, for example, when you have been requested to refer to a file number. It is most frequently placed to the right of the salutation and on the same line or a double space below. When it is not on the same line as the salutation, it either may be centered or may align with the paragraph openings. Note the following illustration:

```
The Prudential Insurance Company
The Paulson Building
Spokane, Washington

Gentlemen:                      Subject:  Policy No. 6,499,313

As you requested in your letter of July 23, I am sending you more
complete information on . . .
```

Stenographic References, Enclosures, Postscripts. When a letter has been transcribed by a stenographer, her initials and sometimes those of the person who dictated the letter are placed at the left margin, either on line with the bottom of the signature or slightly lower. If enclosures are to be sent with the letter, that fact is indicated either one or two spaces below the initials. The following illustration shows these details in one of the many acceptable forms.

282 BUSINESS CORRESPONDENCE

We shall hope to receive your consent in the near future.

Very truly yours,

THE CENTRAL ELECTRICAL COMPANY

W. I. Bowers

W. I. Bowers

WIB/lc
Enclosures: 2

If a postscript is added, it is placed a double space below everything else in the letter. It is typed in the same form that has been used for the paragraphs in the body of the letter. It may or may not be preceded by *P.S.* Obviously, it should be short.

As used in modern business letters, a postscript is not a means of adding some statement that has been omitted by accident, for letters should be written well enough that such accidents do not happen. Rather, it is a device used to throw emphasis on some matter of special importance, or else to add something that it seems desirable to mention but that is not really related to the main message of the letter. Since such a device loses its effectiveness if overworked, postscripts should be used sparingly.

Additional Pages. When a letter must consist of more than one page, the stationery used for all pages should be exactly alike except that as mentioned previously, only page 1 bears a letterhead. The side margins of extra pages should be the same as those on the first page. The top margin should be equal to the left margin. Often, in order that the second and later pages can be identified, the name of the person or organization addressed, the page number, and the date are typed at the top of the second and later pages. (This precaution, however, is not mandatory when common sense indicates that it is unnecessary.) The first line of the body of the letter comes three or four lines lower. Several forms may be used for this reference information, one of the commonest being as follows:

Dr. Irvin B. Steadman   -2-   October 3, 196_

Abbreviation, Capitalization, and Numbers

Abbreviation. In the body of a letter, the usage in abbreviation is the same as in any other writing. In all other parts of the letter, the main point to remember is to refrain from overabbreviating. The first rule is: in case of doubt, don't. Do not abbreviate the name of a person or organization unless the person or organization does so. Do not abbreviate months. Most organizations do not abbreviate the names of states (except that *N.Y.* and *D.C.* are customary), nor do they abbreviate such words as *Street* and *Avenue.* Most organizations write out such terms as *East* and *West* in addresses (2315 *West* Walnut Street). Some latitude is permissible if abbreviation is necessary to prevent a line being so long as to appear awkward. Yet even then you should use a consistent style in any given letter. That is, it would be wrong to abbreviate a term such as *Street* in the heading and write out the same term in the inside address.

As mentioned in the discussion of the salutation, it is more courteous not to abbreviate any title except *Mr., Mrs.,* and *Dr.* In the inside address, the terms *Honorable* and *Reverend* are sometimes seen abbreviated, but is more courteous to write them out. The compliment that you imply by using one of these terms is cancelled when you attempt to save time by reducing the term to an abbreviation.

Capitalization. In the body of the letter, capitalization is the same as in any other writing. In other parts of the letter, the examples that have been given are a sufficient guide.

Use of Figures or Words for Numbers. In the use of figures or words to express numbers, the body of a letter is no different from any other writing. One point however—the writing of dates—calls for comment. The best form is as seen in the example, *June 17.* The year would be added only if needed. You should not use such terms as the *seventeenth* or the *17th* unless the month has already been named in the body of the letter.

In other parts of the letter than the body, the best usage is as follows: A house number is written as figures. The number of a street is written out unless it consists of more than two words, in which case it is written in figures. Examples are: *Eighteenth* Avenue, *Forty-ninth* Street, but *114th* Street. (Some authorities permit the omission of the *th* when using figures, and write *114* Street.) It is permissible, also, to use figures for any street number if such a word as *East* or *North,* either written out or abbreviated, appears between the number of the house and the number of the street.

Years and days of the month are always expressed in figures. It is wrong, however, to use a figure to indicate the name of the month. (Correct: August 11, 1964. Wrong: 8/11/64.) The form *11 August 1964* is not widely used in the United States except in the armed services.

THE SUBSTANCE OF LETTERS

Learning how to use correct form is no more than a starting point in the study of letter writing. The real opportunity to profit by such a study comes when attention is turned to the substance of letters.

To be sure, some letters deal with routine situations and call for no special qualities beyond the completeness, clearness, and accuracy that are essential to any type of writing. Yet even a routine letter is a personal contact; and in letters that are not matters of mere routine, the personal element becomes extremely important. Thus it is well worth while to learn something about the attitudes and techniques that give letters the best chance of obtaining satisfactory results.

At the outset, you should understand the difference between a letter that merely is not bad and one that is really good. A letter may not be bad if it is correct in form, is free from serious errors in English or content, and does the obvious job without giving offense. A letter that is really good, however, is one *that exploits to the maximum, for the benefit of the writer or his organization, the contact that the letter represents.*

Standards of Appearance, Correctness, and Accuracy

You should make your letters neat for much the same reasons that you would try to present a neat appearance in a personal contact. The appearance of a letter influences its reception, for the reader forms some sort of impression before he even starts to read. A messy-looking letter can create an impression of carelessness that lessens the reader's confidence in the accuracy of its contents. Rightly or wrongly, the reader may subconsciously assume that your standards in other matters are comparable to your standards in your letters. If you have an opportunity to look at letters sent by successful American businesses, you will find that they invariably are neat and attractive.

Correctness involves both letter form and English. Correct form should become so habitual that it is taken for granted. And bad English in a letter, like bad English anywhere, is so damaging to prestige that it is not tolerated by modern American industry. The standards of correctness, however, should be those of liberal up-to-date authorities. These authorities base their judgment on the way language is actually used by literate people; thus many forms that were branded incorrect by textbooks years ago are now entirely acceptable except on extremely formal occasions.

Accuracy should include both the accurate reading of the letter you are answering, and accuracy in the information your own letter contains. A surprising amount of confusion, waste of time, and annoyance is caused by writers' failure to notice what is really said in the letters they attempt to answer. Frequently, an additional exchange of letters is the result. And as for making sure that their own letters are accurate—that is a matter that demands more care than most writers realize. Such matters as dates, amounts, the numbers of orders or statements, and file numbers demand methodical checking. Errors such as a reference to *Monday, May*

18, when May 18 falls on a Tuesday provide another example of the need for close attention to detail. For that matter, errors in ordinary words are almost as easy to make as errors in figures and can create confusion and sometimes ill feeling. If you write, "We are *not* making an exhaustive study of the cause of the trouble" when you intend to write "We are *now* making an exhaustive study," you convict yourself of a fault you have not committed. And again, if you write *"Neither* the manager *nor* the field agent would have been seriously concerned about this matter" when you intend to write *"Either* the manager *or* the field agent," you seriously misrepresent the facts and may lose a great deal of good will.

Language in Business Letters

The first point to realize about the language to be used in business letters is that there is no special language for business letters. However, many writers whose conversation is perfectly natural fall into an unnatural jargon as soon as they start a business letter. They use long, flowery expressions such as *I beg leave to inform you*. They use wordy phrases such as *at an early date* for *soon* and *at the present time* for *now*. They make excessive use of the passive voice, writing, for example, *Your letter has been received by us* and *It would be greatly appreciated by us* instead of *We have received your letter* and *We should appreciate it*. They use pomposities such as *It would be in accordance with our desires if* . . . for the simpler *We should like to have you*. . . .

A good way to avoid unnatural language is to ask yourself, "Would I feel ill at ease if I talked this way in a personal conversation with the man to whom I am writing?" It would be going too far to say that a letter should exactly duplicate the language of ordinary conversation, but it is certainly true that language which would sound pompous or unnatural in a conversation is bad style in a letter also.

Additional examples of undesirable business-letter jargon are:

> *beg to advise, state, inform, acknowledge,* etc.
>
> *your letter of recent date* (Refer to the date specifically; or if the date is not known and the situation does not justify looking it up, merely use *your recent letter*.)
>
> *same* (as in "Fill out the questionnaire and return *same* to us.")
>
> *party* (with the meaning of *person*. This use of *party* is appropriate only in legal documents.)
>
> *favor us with*
>
> *kindly* for *please*
>
> *enclosed please find a copy of* (Use *enclosed is a copy* or *a copy is enclosed*.)
>
> We wish to *take this opportunity* (unless the phrase has some mean-

ing. If you were mentioning something incidentally when writing upon another subject, the phrase would be appropriate, but most of the time it is entirely devoid of meaning.)

Sentences in Business Letters

Sentences in business letters tend to be shorter than sentences in most writing. This results from the fact that many letters must be dictated, or written rapidly and mailed with little if any revision. Under these circumstances, long sentences are likely to become jumbled and to slow up the process of writing. You should not form the habit, however, of making all sentences so short that you write in the "primer style."

Paragraphs in Business Letters

Because most business letters are not themselves very long, their paragraphs tend to be short. The first and last paragraphs are often single sentences and are seldom more than two sentences long. The other paragraphs characteristically run from two to four or five sentences. Unless a letter is longer than average, it is unlikely to contain any paragraph of more than 100 words. Single-sentence paragraphs are permissible if they do not become too numerous, but you should not fall into the habit of beginning a new paragraph with every sentence. Unless most of the paragraphs are longer than one sentence, there is no value in paragraphing at all except the psychological value of making the letter look easier to read. As a matter of fact, most long or medium-length letters that contain too many one-sentence paragraphs are found on examination to be poorly organized.

Though paragraphs in business letters are often too short to call for the use and full-scale development of topic sentences, paragraph unity is nevertheless important. The opening of a paragraph may cause a reader to form an instant impression about the topic that the paragraph concerns, and it is bad writing to mislead him by presenting information on other topics. In letters that are longer than average and are therefore likely to contain longer paragraphs, attention to paragraph unity is especially desirable.

Beginnings of Letters

The first paragraph of a letter, being mainly a contact paragraph, should usually be short—often consisting of a single sentence and rarely of more than two sentences. Nevertheless, it may need to (1) indicate the subject and purpose of the letter, (2) refer to previous correspondence if such correspondence needs to be borne in mind, and (3) establish a satisfactory tone. Obviously it is not always necessary to refer to previous correspondence, but the first and third of these functions always call for attention.

To say that the opening of a letter must always indicate the writer's subject and purpose seems to be dwelling on the obvious, yet this need is often overlooked. For example, a person inviting the reader to address some organization might tell about the organization for two or three paragraphs before coming to the point that concerns the reader—the fact that he is being invited to deliver an address. Therefore it pays to remember: make both the subject and the purpose clear at once so that the reader can see how *he* is concerned with what he is reading.

When you answer a letter you have received, you should immediately identify it by mentioning its subject and if necessary its date. Also, you should say enough to demonstrate that you have read it accurately. Such key facts as dates and amounts of money may well be restated, so that if any error has been made in the other person's letter it will be discovered at once. Though such errors are not frequent, they can occur often enough to justify the precaution. The manner in which facts are restated should not be crude and obvious. It is poor writing to say, "I have received your letter of June 15. In this letter you say that you would like to have me make reservations for you for July 17, 18, and 19." Rather, let the facts seem to be mentioned incidentally, as for example, "Thanks for letting me know, in your letter of June 15, about your need of reservations for July 17, 18, and 19." Ostensibly, the sentence was written to say "Thank you." Actually, its purpose was to repeat the dates.

Mention of your own previous letters on a subject is advisable because the reader may have forgotten them and because your present letter may not reach the same person who read the earlier letters.

The establishment of tone is especially important. This subject will be covered extensively later in the chapter. Here, suffice it to say that the reader's original impression influences his reaction to all that follows. If the tone of the beginning is offensive, it will be doubly hard for the material that follows to get a proper reception. Hence the opening should usually be friendly in tone, and should never, regardless of the circumstances, be harsh or sarcastic.

At the very beginning you should try to get in step with the reader. Even if it will be necessary, later, to include material that takes issue with him, the opening should be an attempt to suggest that you are not an opponent who is trying to defeat him in an argument, but a person who has approached the subject with an open mind. Even if a letter deals with a situation so serious that a display of friendliness would clearly be insincere, it is always possible to be completely courteous in the opening and to avoid any display of anger.

Some might feel that it is a nuisance to have to make the opening of a letter friendly. Yet when you adopt a friendly or at least a courteous tone at the beginning, you are merely opening your letter as a tactful person usually opens personal conversation.

Endings of Letters

The best method of ending a letter depends on whether you are attempting to secure some specific action. If not, the ending should be a final brief paragraph showing friendliness and good will. Here again, there is a parallel between a letter and a personal conversation. One usually tries to end even a business conversation in a friendly manner.

A typical letter not attempting to secure action might be one giving some information that had been requested. You might well conclude such a letter by expressing hope that the information will be useful and that the reader's project will be successful. On the other hand, if you had been unable to provide the information asked for, it would still be possible to express a hope that the reader would find it elsewhere and that you could be of some service to him in the future.

If the purpose of a letter is to secure action, the action desired should be suggested by the ending. The suggestion should be as specific as the circumstances permit. Sometimes the request for action may be in the form of a command: "Sign up today." Sometimes, tact would make it advisable that the command be veiled: "To make sure that you receive the accommodations you desire, make your reservations today." Sometimes it must be toned down still more: "We should appreciate it if you could let us know by April 1 the dates that you prefer." The degree of urgency must always be a matter of judgment. If you need immediate action when requesting a favor, it is especially important to be tactful. In such a case your letter is less likely to arouse a negative reaction if it tells why immediate action is important—for example, "If you accept this invitation, we are anxious to give your address plenty of advance publicity. Therefore we hope you will let us know your decision at your earliest convenience."

An ending aimed at securing action need not entirely neglect the element of good will. A skillful writer can usually phrase his request for action so that good will is apparent.

Whether a letter does or does not aim at action, one fundamental point about endings should never be overlooked: the ending of a letter should never dwell upon anything that you would not want the reader to continue thinking about. A reader tends to retain in his mind whatever he has read last. Suppose a letter ends by saying, "In closing, let me express once more my regret that, as originally written, my report did not contain all the information you needed." The reader's mind is thus focused on the fact that the original report was unsatisfactory. On the other hand, the letter might end, "In the version I am now sending, I am sure you will find the full information that you will need as you proceed with the project." The reader's mind is thus directed to the merits of the new version rather than to the faults of the old. Although there are many occasions when a letter must express regret, the end should, if possible, be optimistic.

Need of Planning before Writing

Unless a letter is to be extremely short, you should plan it before writing it. Your plan may be nothing more elaborate than rough notes, but it should at least indicate the points to be covered and the order in which you will cover them. As you make your notes, it will pay you to make sure that you have at hand all the facts that must be included, so that you will not have to stop writing or dictating while you look up some bit of information.

The time used in making notes will be short and will be more than compensated for later because you will be able to forge ahead with assurance when you write. Also, planning in advance will usually improve the quality of your letter. That is, it will ensure your putting related material in the same part of the letter, will result in better arrangement than you could achieve while struggling with questions of phraseology, and will permit you to concentrate on how to express each idea rather than being constantly preoccupied with the question of what you are going to say next.

To be sure, as you gain experience and deal with situations that have become familiar, you will eventually be able to base many a letter on a plan you have used on similar occasions in the past. Even so, it will usually be advisable to have in mind or on paper a checklist of points to be covered; and it will also be advisable, before you write even a routine letter, to pause long enough to make sure that a routine letter will really cover the situation. Nothing is more annoying to your reader than to receive a letter that ignores some of the relevant facts.

Arrangement of Material in Letters

In writing a letter, as in writing anything else, you will need to be governed by two considerations as you plan the arrangement of the material—the subject matter and the reader. Whatever may be the message of a letter, there are two basic methods of arranging the material. These might be called "the order of saying *Yes*" and "the order of saying *No*." In any specific situation, one or the other should definitely be preferable.

When you are saying "yes" to a request, you should say it at once —sometimes even in the opening sentence. This is appropriate because a reader who learns that his request has been granted is in a more receptive state of mind to hear anything else you wish to tell him. Perhaps he must be told that granting such requests cannot be made a regular policy, or that careful consideration was necessary before consent could be granted. Perhaps you need to explain the circumstances that gave rise to the whole incident. All such material should be held back, however, until the affirmative answer has been given.

Some writers neglect this principle. They tell all the reasons that might justify a refusal before informing the reader that his request is granted. Thus they make the reader antagonistic, or, at best, secure only superficial attention to this material while the reader skims down the page looking for the definite answer. Moreover, by delaying the consent too long, they seem to give it grudgingly, and thus lose the good will that the consent might otherwise have gained. In view of all this, when you intend to say "yes," you should say it at once and say it graciously, then offer any explanations that are necessary, and finally, bring the reader's attention back to the fact that his request has been granted.

When saying "no," however, you should not blurt out your refusal at the beginning, but should hold it back until you have given the reasons for the decision. Thus the decision seems to be the outgrowth of the facts. If the "no" comes before the reasons, the reasons seem to have been scraped together to justify an answer that had been decided upon at the outset. The proper method is to try to make the reader himself see that a negative answer is indicated by giving him the evidence and leading him to that answer gradually. When you make your decision known, you should do so as tactfully as possible. Although no letter should be long-winded, the very fact that you have taken pains to write a full explanation suggests that you have not rejected the request peremptorily.

Naturally, it is not possible to generate so much good will with a refusal as with a consent, but the arrangement of material recommended above at least makes the best of the situation. A refusal that is tactful will create much less resentment than one that is tactless.

Not every letter, to be sure, forces you to grant or refuse a request, but the basic principle can be applied in almost every situation. If your letter bears good news, let the reader know it at once; if the news is bad, break it gently; if it is partly good and partly bad, first tell the good news, then tell the bad news, and next direct the reader's attention toward whatever aspects of the situation are most cheerful.

As you apply these principles, it is a good idea to decide very early how you want a letter to end. You need not go to the extreme of writing the last sentence of a letter first; but it is only common sense to decide what idea you want that last sentence to express. If you do so, you can move toward that ending more smoothly. Also, you can avoid the misfortune of using, in the middle of a letter, the idea that would be the best possible ending—therefore having either to use an ending that is not as good as it might be or to repeat ideas that you have already expressed.

Negative, Neutral, and Positive Approach

When we say that a writer's approach to a letter is negative we mean that by the power of suggestion he creates in the reader's mind an undesirable impression about his (the writer's) attitude or about the way in which a situation should be interpreted. When we say that the approach is neutral, we mean that there is nothing in the writer's manner that creates either a desirable or an undesirable impression. When we refer to the approach as positive, we indicate that the power of suggestion operates in a favorable manner.

The difference between the negative, the neutral, and the positive approach can be seen in the following sentences, all of which convey the same basic fact.

1. I was surprised to discover in your letter of June 26 that you claim I have made an excessive charge for investigating your lighting needs.
2. I have received your letter of June 26 concerning my charge for investigating your lighting needs.
3. I have been glad to do as you requested in your letter of June 26, and look into the question of whether I have made the correct charge for investigating your lighting needs.

The first sentence sounds indignant; it suggests that the writer's purpose is to prove the reader's letter was not reasonable; it shows that he regards the reader as an opponent in an argument. The second is completely noncommittal as to the writer's attitude. The third, without implying that a concession is to be granted, makes it appear that the writer welcomes the opportunity to correct a mistake if one has been made or to explain how the charge was arrived at if it is correct. A positive approach is always best when it is possible, and in any event the negative approach can always be avoided.

One cause of the negative suggestion is the use of words with a negative flavor. For example, "We have received your letter in which *you claim* that the last shipment was improperly packed," implies that the writer questions whether the statements of the reader are accurate. (Even if such were the case, it would be undesirable to make that fact apparent at the outset.) Other characteristic negative terms are "you neglect," "you fail," "your complaint," and "your error."

The negative tone may also be a matter of basic outlook—a tendency to see the dark side of a situation rather than the bright side. One writer may write, "We regret to say that unfortunately we cannot comply with your request until . . . ." Another and better writer will say, "We shall be glad to comply with your request as soon as . . . ." The difference is that one sounds like a refusal and the other sounds like a consent. One stresses the fact that immediate compliance is not forthcoming; the other stresses the fact that eventual compliance is possible. Again, one writer may write, "My experience is limited, consisting of nine months as assistant to . . . ." Another writes, "My qualifications have been increased by nine months' experience as assistant to . . . ." The first suggests that the reader consider nine months as very slight experience. The second encourages the reader to think of how much a person may know at the end of nine months that he did not know before.

Finally, certain kinds of material may in their very nature be negative. Consider the sentence, "Now that it's fall and you're getting warm clothes for the children, hadn't you better make sure that your automobile chains are in good condition?" This is negative because it makes the reader think of other expenses, which may be so hard to meet that he will economize by making his old chains serve. Another example of negative material is this ending to a letter: "I hope that our decision will not interfere with the pleasant relationship that has always existed between our companies." The writer showed by this ending that he himself thought of the decision as one that *might* interfere with the pleasant relationship. He might better have written, "I believe that the reasons I have offered to explain our decision show it to be appropriate, and I shall look forward to a continuance of our pleasant relationship."

Tone

A discussion of tone is really an extension of what has been said about the negative, the neutral, and the positive approach, for it concerns the impression created in the mind of the reader about the writer's personal attitude. Just as in a personal conversation, this impression can either increase or decrease the likelihood of satisfactory results.

The tone of letters can be infinitely varied. A letter can sound friendly, cheerful, courteous, serious, formal, informal, cordial, hostile, ingratiating, blunt, sarcastic, indignant, flippant, whining, evasive—in fact it can suggest any attitude that can be suggested by a person's manner in a face-to-face conversation. It is possible, of course, for a letter to have a purely impersonal tone. The best that can be said for such a tone, even on a routine occasion, is that it does no damage. But on any occasion that is not entirely routine, there is often a danger that it will create a damaging impression of coolness and indifference.

Obviously some of the tones named above—sarcasm, bluntness, hostility—are undesirable. A warning against them is nevertheless called for because many a person who would agree that they are undesirable will, under the stress of emotion, write letters that possess them.

As for letters that sound apologetic or ingratiating, their tone is often the result of carrying such qualities as reasonableness and friendliness too far. No quality is so good that it cannot be overdone.

What tone, then, should you try for? So far as it is possible to generalize we might say: your letters should almost always sound friendly; and on the few occasions when friendliness would obviously be insincere, they should as an absolute minimum be entirely courteous. They should usually be cheerful. And the tone of modern letters is strongly in the direction of informality except when informality would suggest lack of suitable respect.

None of this means that a letter need be unbusinesslike or that it cannot be intensely serious when seriousness is called for, any more than a personal conversation would need to lack seriousness because one's manner is friendly.

How is such a tone achieved? Skillful letter writers, especially in letters that go outside their own companies, form a mental picture of the image they want people to hold of their companies, and they bear this image in mind as they write. Eventually it becomes practically automatic for them to adopt a suitable manner when they write letters. This is comparable to the way in which a person in military service automatically adopts a manner suitable to the occasion when he talks in the performance of his duties. It is comparable to a salesman's habit of talking to a prospect in a certain manner, regardless of his own state of mind at the moment. Unless you are fortunate enough to possess instincts that will always guide you to letter tone that is appropriate, you should keep reminding yourself to adopt a desirable tone until it finally becomes second nature for you to do so. If you fail to do this, you are likely to form habits that produce a contrary result.

The "You Attitude"

Almost every book on letter writing speaks of the "You Attitude." This phrase means merely that the writer attempts in every way possible to show that he has thought about the reader's interests as well as his own. A good example is one letter written by a manufacturer refusing to accept an order from an individual consumer. This manufacturer might have offered as his reason the nuisance it would be to handle such small orders. Instead, he stressed the advantage to the purchaser of being able to see the various sizes and colors and of obtaining products without delay, as he could do if he were served by a retail merchant.

This "You Attitude" can be achieved even in letters that would seem to offer little opportunity for it. For example, a letter written to collect back payments on a refrigerator purchased on the installment plan would have as its actual purpose the securing of the payment; yet the writer might indicate that he was writing because he did not want the reader to lose the refrigerator, as would happen if he did not make the payment; or he might stress how desirable it would be to the reader to protect his credit rating.

Good Will in Business Letters

Whatever its message may be, a letter should present that message in a manner that generates or retains as much good will as possible. The way to create or retain good will, so far as you can do so by means of writing techniques, is mainly to express good will. It is hard for a reader to remain unfriendly in the face of consistent friendliness on your part. It bothers him more to say "no" to someone who has been pleasant than to someone who has been indifferent or antagonistic. Showing good will pays off by making the reader want to see things as you see them.

Also, making good will permeate your letters is a sensible precaution for it can prevent inadvertently offensive remarks from doing damage. If a statement in a conversation is taken in an unpleasant way that you did not intend, you can notice the effect at once and correct your slip. Moreover, once said the remark passes by at once. But when a letter gives offense, you are not present to observe its effect and have little opportunity to set the matter right. Also, what you have said is there to be read repeatedly. Consequently, it is necessary, when you are writing, to take extra precautions to avoid giving offense unintentionally. There is no better way to do this than to make good will so evident that the reader will realize an unfortunate slip could not have been meant as it sounded.

The time when it is hardest to express good will is when you must answer an unpleasant letter from an angry reader. It is entirely natural to feel an impulse to answer such a letter sharply, but the impulse should be resisted. In refusing to lose your temper because the reader has lost his you are not necessarily giving evidence of weakness. And one point not to be overlooked is this: having blown off steam, your reader may no longer feel as belligerent as before. He may even feel a little ashamed at having lost his self-control. If you answer in kind, you relieve him of his worry about whether he has gone too far; but if you are courteous as well as firm in your manner—if you refrain from entering a contest in recrimination—you have a good chance of making him regret his remarks and wish to show that he is not quarrelsome and unpleasant. This may go far toward making him easier to deal with.

If you are tempted to regard anything said above as soft or emotional, remember that American industry is spending millions of dollars annually in the belief that good will is profitable. Expressing good will in your letters will increase the chance that they will be effective both in their immediate results and in their long-range contribution to a favorable image of you or your company. And just as it is worth while to include material for the sake of good will, it is often sensible to omit remarks that, though justified by the facts, are not really essential and would sacrifice good will. It is important to remember that you cannot assume every reader to be a fair-minded, unprejudiced judge. Therefore your manner and material should be determined not by what you would be *justified* in saying but by what will produce the result you desire. The satisfaction of "telling off" a reader who has been unreasonable is a luxury you cannot afford. Constant attention to good will is by no means sentimentalism. We may hope, of course, that it will usually be a sincere expression of your actual feelings; but it is definitely called for by intelligent self-interest.

EXERCISES

Exercise 1

Change the following addresses, salutations, and complimentary closes so that they conform to the best modern usage. Do not make unnecessary corrections. You may assume that where abbreviations appear in company names, the forms used are the correct official forms.

(1)

F. H. Palutho, Inc.
1618 Front Ave.
Salem, Arizona

Dear Mr. Palutho:

                Very truly yours,

(2)

Mr. Carl A. Simmons, manager
Northern Chemical Company
Box 834
Crescent City, Ohio

Gentlemen:

                Very truly yours,

(3)

Thurber Sand and Gravel Company
Seventh and Broad Streets
Preston, Ark.

Attention of Arthur Thurber, President

Dear Mr. Thurber:

                Very truly yours,

(4)

Hon. Floyd Collins Hunter
The House of Representatives
Washington, D. C.

Dear Hon. Hunter,

                Sincerely yours

(5)

Alfred O. Schultz
613 18th St.
Houston, Maine

Dear Sir:

Very Truly Yours,

(6)

Dr. Ralph M. Jackson, M.D.
Swanson Medical Bldg.
Salem, Kentucky

My Dear Dr. Jackson

Sincerely yours,

(7)

Curator Charles R. Cobb
The Pioneer Museum
1316 Post Ave.
Norman, Mo.

Dear Mr. Cobb;

Very truly yours

(8)

Mr. Clyde Montgomery,
Central Steel Company
Newport, Utah

Dear Mr. Montgomery:

Sincerely yours,

(9)

Prof. Herbert H. Howley
Dept. of Ag. Chem.
Bristol State University
Bristol, Alabama

Dear Prof. Howley:

Very truly yours,

(10)

Walters and Cochrane, Incorporated
Box 707
Cleveland, Ohio

Dear Sirs:

Very truly yours,

Exercise 2

Rearrange the following material so that each item is an inside address in acceptable form, with an attention line if one is indicated. Add a suitable salutation after each address.

    1. The purchasing agent of Campbell and Kelly, Inc. at Winchester, North Carolina.

2. The Central Steel Corporation, located at Pittsburgh, Pennsylvania, postal zone 30, at the street address 7th and Post streets.
3. Edgar D. Martin, an assistant professor of physics, at the San Francisco Technical Institute, San Francisco, California. He holds the degree of Ph. D.
4. The Pacific Marine Supply Company, 14 Harbor Drive, Seattle, Washington. Ask for the attention of the Sales Manager.
5. H. Walter Copeland of the Delaware Pump Company, 931 Division Street, Wilmington 6, Delaware. Mr. Copeland is assistant to the president.
6. Southwestern Agricultural College, El Segundo, Texas. Ask for the attention of the Director of the Research Bureau.
7. The Northern Division of the Universal Plastics Company located in Milwaukee, Wisconsin. The box number is 464.
8. The personnel manager of the Kettleman Pulp and Paper Company, Minneapolis, Minnesota. The address is 8137 State Street. The postal zone is 34.
9. The Business and Professional Women's Club, in the town of Creston, Colorado. The address is Box 523.
10. Two men, named Carl N. Curtis and Oliver Evans, whose address is Municipal Consultants, Inc., at 1909 Columbus Avenue, Schuyler, Ohio.

Exercise 3

Each of the following sentences occurred at or near the beginning or ending of a letter, as indicated. Most of them are faulty in some respect, either because they contain unsuitable ideas for the positions they occupy or because their tone, ideas, and language would be unsuitable regardless of their position. Write an improved version of each sentence that needs improvement. If it is necessary to interpret a situation more definitely or to supply additional facts, feel free to do so.

Beginnings

1. We have received your request for a replacement but because of the facts stated below, we cannot agree to grant it.
2. I have received your letter in which you claim that we have not done a satisfactory job in overhauling the motors that you sent to us.
3. Your order for 2000 brochures reached us this morning, but we are unable to do the job because you neglected to tell us your decision about the quality of paper you wish to have us use.
4. Though I realize that this inquiry reaches you at a time when you may be especially busy, I hope that your interest in the subject will induce you to answer the following questions:
5. As the operator of a feed lot you will be interested, we believe, in the damage that is threatened by the recent appearance of starlings in this area.
6. We have received your letter of December 10 in which you complain about the scuffing of the paint that we used on the concrete in your court.
7. We are sorry to learn that your compressor is giving you trouble. We will of course live up to our guarantee, but in order that we may de-

termine the extent to which it is still in force, we would appreciate your answering the following questions.

8. In closing let me again express our regret about the damage done to your lawn by our tree-trimming crew.
9. The motor that you sent us has been overhauled and is now in good condition. We are sorry that it burned out, but as we have indicated above, your maintenance men are to blame because they did not use a heat-resistant lubricant.
10. I hope that what I have said will result in our receiving faster service, for if this complaint does not get results we will have our work done elsewhere.
11. I hope that this letter, which lets you know how seriously we regard the situation, will result in substantial improvement so that we can continue to use your service in the future.
12. We hope that this incident will not destroy your confidence in our ability to give you good service in the future.
13. We hope that you send word, in the near future, that this offer is accepted so that we can arrange a work schedule that will permit us to give you immediate service.

Exercise 4

Study the following letters to discover the respects in which the principles explained in this chapter have not been applied. Try also to think of *ideas* that might, if added, increase the letters' effectiveness. Criticize or rewrite any letters designated by the instructor.

(1)

Dear Sir:

This is to acknowledge receipt of your letter of June 10 in which you claim that a pea crop on your property was damaged as a result of our using a brush-killing spray along the railroad right of way.

You have been misinformed about our brush-killing activities. On the date when, according to your account, the carelessness of our crew is supposed to have done the damage, we did no spraying at all along the stretch of track that runs past the field you refer to. The crew merely stopped to examine the condition of the brush there, which had been sprayed two weeks earlier. If the damage had been caused by the spraying at the earlier date, it would have been noticeable long before the time when you say it became apparent.

Since the facts do not bear out your statement that your crop was harmed by us, we naturally will not pay for the damage that it suffered.

Yours truly,

(2)

Dear Sir:

Thank you for your letter inviting me to come for an interview on May 11. Unfortunately, I cannot get away on that date because I must attend a meeting held that morning.

I could come on May 12 and would appreciate your letting me know whether you would be able to talk with me then instead of on May 11.

I would be pleased if you would also give me a little more information that would affect my decision if you offer me a position. I would like to know whether you would consider reimbursing me for the expense of moving. Also, could you let me know whether I would be asked to move very often if I enter your employment?

You expressed an interest in when I could start work if I am employed. I believe that September 1 would be the earliest date when I should offer to do so, for I would wish to give reasonable notice to my present employers if I leave them.

In addition to the information requested above; I would also be interested in knowing a little more about your community. In particular, do most of the people on your staff consider it necessary to send their children to private schools, or may I assume that the public schools would be satisfactory? And is it likely that I could find a suitable residence within a reasonable distance of the office?

I shall hope to hear from you soon so that I can know whether to plan on coming to see you on May 12. If that would not be a satisfactory date, May 13 and May 19 are other dates when I could come if they would suit your convenience better.

Very truly yours,

(3)

Dear Mr. Jones:

I have received your letter of December 1 telling me of your concern about your son's midsemester grades and asking whether I can find tutors to help him with his studies. I am glad that you wrote to me, for it gives me an opportunity to discuss your son's attitude toward college.

As you know, the note that informed John of his low grades suggested that he should come to see me. He has not followed this suggestion—probably because other matters of greater importance than his grades have occupied his time and attention.

In this connection, the enclosed clipping from the student newspaper will probably interest you. It shows that your son broke a national record by staying under a shower for twenty-four hours. I do not suppose that this record-breaking performance has been injurious to your son's health, but it certainly must have left him too fatigued to study effectively afterward. And it certainly shows that he is not very much interested in using his time in a manner that contributes to academic success.

I will see whether I can find tutors for your son if you wish, but I do not feel that lack of tutoring is the cause of his difficulties. Perhaps if you could persuade him that he should not waste time in trying to excel in useless activities, he could do satisfactory work without the assistance of tutors. I would attempt to persuade him of this myself if he would follow the suggestion that he come to see me.

Very truly yours,

(4)

Gentlemen:

We have received your letter telling us that you accept our offer to move the heavy equipment from your old science building to the new building that is nearing completion.

We shall be glad to do this work for you, but cannot possibly complete it by September 15, which is the date you specify. As we indicated in earlier correspondence, moving this equipment will be a four-week job. The earliest date when we could begin it would be September 4, and there is a strong likelihood that the date might be from one to two weeks later. Consequently, the earliest date when we could guarantee to have everything moved would be October 15.

If you will review the case, you will not blame us for this delay. We submitted our offer on June 15, and on July 1 we wrote to ask that you hasten your decision. After waiting ten days we took on another job and went to work on it on July 20. We cannot do both jobs at once, and cannot hope to complete the one we are now working on before September 1.

We realize the importance to you of getting moved before the opening of the school year, but since it took you six weeks to reach your decision, we can hardly be blamed for not being able to start work only two weeks after you did so. We would have liked to give your job top priority, but we could not risk having the idle time that would have existed if we had not accepted the other job when it came along.

There are not many outfits in this area who are really competent to move heavy scientific equipment, and we doubt that you will find any of them able to serve you on such short notice. We would like to do the job for you and know that we can handle it to your satisfaction. We therefore hope that you will let us know immediately whether our offer to do it beginning some time in the first half of September and completing it by October 15 is acceptable.

If the acceptance is long delayed, we might again be forced to take on other work and be tied up during the dates that are now open in September and early October. We therefore hope to hear from you soon.

Very truly yours,

14

SPECIAL
TYPES
OF
LETTERS

Not every letter can be classified according to type, and the inclusion of this chapter is not intended to imply that such is the case. Rather, its purpose is merely to show how the general principles apply in a number of characteristic situations. No effort is made to include all the types that are generally recognized. Credit letters, for example, are omitted because they are unlikely to be written by anyone in a position that calls for technical writing. Sales letters are omitted for the same reason, though some of the sales letter techniques are explained in the discussion of letters urging action. The types included justify the attention they receive not only because they illustrate the application of general principles but also because you may some day occupy a position where any of them may have to be written.

INVITATIONS

Though invitations of a social nature are beyond the scope of this book, there are many times when invitations

301

are essentially business letters. For example, anyone who is active in a professional organization may need to write an invitation to attend or participate in a meeting.

In writing an invitation, make the purpose of your letter clear very early. Don't leave your reader wondering, as he reads, why you are telling *him* whatever it is you are saying. Also, in or immediately after the opening, include something to catch his interest. One good way to do this is to refer to something he himself has done or something you have read or heard about him.

Try to persuade your reader that the expenditure of time involved in the acceptance of your invitation will be justified. The importance of the occasion, the number expected to attend, facts about the organization, names of others who will be present—any such information can be useful in this connection.

Make a subtle appeal to self-interest if you can plausibly do so. Many a person accepts an invitation, partly at least, because he hopes to gain good will or publicity for the organization he is associated with. Of course care must be taken not to be crude and obvious in appealing to self-interest. Your tone should make it clear that though you hope your reader will somehow benefit from accepting your invitation, you consider that basically he will be rendering a service.

Make sure that you include all the facts your reader will need in making his decision—especially the date, the time, and the place of meeting. Make it clear what you expect or hope he will do—deliver a major address, participate in a panel discussion, attend social events—in general, make him feel confident that he has the complete picture. If he is to deliver a major address, give him some idea about how long he will be expected to talk, and either suggest a subject or let him know that you will leave the choice of a subject to him. (One possibility is to mention something you would be glad to hear him talk about, but indicate your willingness to let him use either that subject or one of his own choosing.) If the occasion calls for any comment on financial matters, say what is necessary.

When all these points, or as many of them as seem appropriate, have been covered, end an invitation by suggesting action, that is, by referring to your hope to receive a letter of acceptance. The main difficulty in writing the ending is the question of how to induce the reader to write soon without seeming to rush him unreasonably. (In this connection, be considerate. Don't delay so long in sending your invitation that you must ask your reader to answer in haste.) Perhaps the mildest way to request early action is to use the phrase, "at your earliest convenience," which is not jargon, because it is the simplest way of expressing the idea. If it is necessary to ask for action by a specific date, mention the reason—for example the need of printing a program or beginning publicity.

Make your ending pleasant, in fact make the letter pleasant, by showing a desire to be hospitable and to make the occasion enjoyable for the person you are inviting. An offer to make hotel reservations or to meet him at the station or airport is one way of showing hospitality and consideration. In any event, your ending can easily be written so as to be complimentary as well as being a request for action.

Though all the preceding suggestions are worth considering, you should not try to follow so many of them in one letter that the letter grows unusually long. Usually, a letter from two-thirds to three-quarters of a page is long enough. If the reader accepts and needs further information, you can supply it later. In the original invitation it is better to select the ideas that best suit the occasion rather than to try to use every device you can think of.

The following letter illustrates the application of these principles.

Dear Professor Ward:

I have learned from Rodney Kelly of the Kramer Manufacturing Company that you will be in Fort Wallace from April 21 to April 25 for the purpose of talking with technical writers in his company.

It happens that on the evening of April 23 there will be a meeting of the Fort Wallace chapter of the American Society of Technical Writers and Editors. It will begin at 8:00 o'clock and will be held in the small lecture room of Blewett Implements, Inc. I would like to invite you to attend this meeting.

I believe you would find it interesting and worth while to spend the evening with us. Our program will consist of a panel discussion on some aspect of technical writing yet to be chosen, followed by a general discussion of questions raised by the audience. Afterward, refreshments will be served and informal conversation will go on as long as anyone cares to remain.

The attendance usually runs from thirty to forty, and the employers of those in attendance include at least six or seven companies. I am sure that if you can come, you will meet people whom you would be glad to know. I am also sure that many of those in attendance will be glad to get acquainted with you and to hear what you have been learning about technical writing problems in your visits to companies in other areas.

If you are free to spend the evening with us, we shall be glad to provide you with transportation to and from your hotel. I hope that you can accept this invitation, for I believe we can offer you an interesting evening and I know that you would receive a cordial welcome.

Very truly yours,

LETTERS GIVING INSTRUCTIONS

Letters giving instructions, as we will discuss them here, are those primarily intended to tell the reader that he is to do certain things and to explain, if necessary, how to do them.

The first requirement, if those who receive instructions are to follow them properly, is absolute clarity. As a Prussian general once remarked, "Anything that can be misunderstood will be misunderstood." True, it may take extra time to make instructions unmistakably clear; but the extra time devoted to clarity is usually less than the amount of time it takes to repair the damage caused by having things done wrongly.

Clearness is partly, of course, merely a matter of writing. Everything about clearness said elsewhere in the book, especially in the discussion of style, applies to clearness in writing instructions. Completeness is also an element in clearness. In giving instructions you will find the time well spent if you think the subject through, visualize every contingency, and cope with it if you think it might arise and cause uncertainty. And in dealing not with contingencies but with regular essentials, you will have to use good judgment in deciding which details would be useful and which can be omitted.

Usually instructions will be clearer if at least a minimum amount of information is provided about the situation that makes them necessary. A reader who is aware of reasons and purposes will usually grasp instructions faster, remember them better, and follow them more intelligently than would be likely if he were expected to follow them blindly. But the actual orders should stand out sharply and distinctly rather than merging with the explanatory matter.

A letter of instructions can often be improved by the use of mechanical devices such as numbering, headings, and extra indentation. These devices were discussed in Chapter 5, in the section dealing with instructions. To be sure, a letter is seldom long enough to permit the use of very many mechanical devices, and also they may take more time to work out than it is practical to spend on a letter to a single individual. But they should not be overlooked in a letter that goes to a number of people.

Finally, tone can be important in a letter of instructions as in other letters. Instructions are not always given exclusively to subordinates. For example, instructions on such matters as safety procedures, accounting methods, or use of cars from a company car pool might be issued to people in other lines of authority. And even in giving instructions to subordinates, a pleasant and courteous tone increases the chance of securing willing cooperation.

Following is a letter giving instructions.

> Compressor Department Correspondents:
>
> For a long time it has been a problem to keep track of the exact location and status of the numerous drawings produced in connection with each job that is done by this department. In an attempt to cope with this problem we have produced a new form for keeping records and will begin using it on July 1.
>
> This form will make it easy for everyone concerned with drawings to keep accurate records and to obtain the information he needs. Also, it will permit the production department's transmittal state-

ments to the district office to be used as the district office's statement to the customer. This latter feature should do away with the need for retyping and thus prevent delay in the district office.

A copy of the new form is enclosed and an ample supply will be sent to you soon. It should be used as follows (the first four steps being necessary only when the drawing is transmitted for the first time):

1. As a first step, if you are the one to originate one of these "Drawing Transmittal" sheets, insert the customer's name in the top left box.

2. Enter the job or project number in the box below the one where you placed the customer's name.

3. Enter the district office address in the center box, under the name of our company.

4. Enter the type of equipment to be produced and the name of this department in the top right box.

5. In the main part of the sheet, enter the number of each drawing and a descriptive title identifying it in the appropriate columns at the left side of the page.

6. Note that there are four identical sets of columns. One column in each set indicates whether the drawing is transmitted for the first, second, third, or fourth time. The others indicate the date it is transmitted, its status (whether "for approval," "final," etc.), and the date when it was received if it has already been transmitted once. As the drawing is sent out more than once, these sets of columns can be used consecutively without its being necessary to retype the number and title. When you transmit a drawing, enter the appropriate facts in the first set of columns that has not yet been used.

7. In the first space provided at the top of the page, enter *in pencil* the date when the drawings must be returned. (If the space has already been used, erase the old date and enter the new one.)

8. Send the sheet and the drawing to the person or company supposed to receive them.

When you examine this form you will see that on a single line it keeps an orderly record of the location and status of each drawing while it is sent out and returned as many as four times, and that on a single sheet it keeps this record for as many as 22 drawings. Thus one can usually at a glance tell the location and status of all the drawings for a job.

Please study this sheet so that you can use it efficiently on the date mentioned, July 1. I am confident that when we have all become familiar with it, we will all find it extremely helpful because it will give us better records and will reduce the time spent on keeping them.

Very truly yours,

INQUIRIES AND ANSWERS TO INQUIRIES

Letters of Inquiry

The task of writing letters of inquiry may fall to the lot of a person in almost any position. When an inquiry is sent to a person or organization that has a responsibility for supplying information—for example, a chamber of commerce or a governmental bureau—it poses no special problems. The same is true when the receiver may have a chance to profit by supplying information because he increases his chance of selling goods or services. But when it goes to a recipient who is under no obligation to answer and who does not profit by doing so except in good will, it must be written with more care. Most organizations, to be sure, answer legitimate inquiries as they answer other correspondence. But whether they supply the desired information depends in part on whether the writer succeeds in making them really want to be helpful and in making the answer as easy as possible to write. Our discussion will concern mainly inquiries to be sent when the circumstances call for tact and care.

The resemblance of one such inquiry to another is great enough that the following instructions may be applied in most occasions.

1. Open your letter by making it clear that your purpose is to obtain information, and identify the subject that the information concerns. Don't leave your reader wondering why he should be concerned with the situation that you are dealing with.

2. Tell your reader why the information is needed. Though your explanation should not be long-winded, it is neither courteous nor reasonable to ask your reader to use his time for your benefit unless you let him see that your purpose is neither trivial nor contrary to his own interests.

3. Unless it is obvious, let him know why he or his organization has been chosen as a source of information. As you do this, you will often be able to say something complimentary that will increase your reader's desire to be obliging.

4. Ask the questions that you hope your reader will answer. These questions, of course, are the actual reason for your letter's existence and will be discussed below in more detail.

5. Offer to return the favor by supplying similar information to your reader, or perhaps by supplying information on the results of your investigation if you are writing to a number of other people. Of course no such offer should be made if it would be an empty gesture, but there are many times when a mutual exchange of information is natural among individuals or organizations engaged in similar activity.

6. End with a tactful suggestion of action combined with the assurance that you will appreciate whatever help you receive. In expressing your appreciation it is best to avoid saying "Thanks in advance," either directly or by implication, unless your personal relationship with the reader justifies your taking his assistance for granted. There is a real though subtle difference between saying "I shall appreciate whatever information you send me" and saying, "Thank you in advance for answering these questions" or "Thank you for this information."

The action requested should be made as easy as possible to perform.

For example, you might encourage your reader to jot down his answers at the bottom or in the margin of your letter, and enclose a stamped and self-addressed envelope. If you do this and if your reader can answer your questions without looking up the information, he may answer you at once rather than waiting until some time when he is writing letters.

The actual questions, as mentioned above, are the heart of the letter. Unless your needs are so simple that you are asking only one or two questions, both courtesy and self-interest dictate that your questions be worked out carefully. They should be well organized, with those dealing with a single aspect of the subject placed consecutively. Each question should be as brief as clarity permits. The answers called for should be brief facts or estimates rather than general discussions, for a discussion is likely to be vague and to be filled with hedging and qualifications.

If there are several questions, it is advisable to number them. When there is room, it may be desirable to make them stand out as a single block of material by widening the side margins. The numbers make it easy for the reader to check up on precisely what facts he must have in order to answer. Also, they make it impossible for him to overlook any questions by accident. And finally, they cause him to arrange his answers in the exact order of the questions, which is a great help if you are tabulating the answers from many persons.

Though an inquiry should request information mainly by asking specific questions, it is usually advisable, also, to invite the reader to add his own comments or other information that he might consider relevant. Especially, he should be invited to supply any additional information that affects the interpretation or the significance of the answers he has supplied.

Closely related to an inquiry is a questionnaire, which of course would be accompanied by a covering letter. In fact, a questionnaire is merely the result of removing the questions from the letter, placing them on a separate page, and providing room for answers. Unfortunately, though a questionnaire must be used when questions are numerous, many people who answer straight inquiries disregard questionnaires. If a questionnaire seems necessary, the letter that accompanies it should merely be a brief, normal letter of inquiry without the questions. The page bearing the questions should contain enough information, however, to be answerable if separated from the letter.

A letter of inquiry follows.

Mr. Joseph O. Hurley
Columbia Power Company
Portland, Oregon

Dear Mr. Hurley:

I have heard with interest about your address at the Northwest Institute of Real Estate Appraisers last month. Would it be possible, since I have been unable to obtain a copy of this address, for you to provide me with some of the data it contained? If so, I am sure that it would be useful in one or more of the information leaflets that we distribute each year.

The particular facts I have in mind are related to the use of electric power in the production of metals, and consist of answers to the following questions:

1. What increase has occurred during the last five years in the production capacity of electric steel furnaces in the Northwest?

2. What increase seems probable during the next five years, as indicated by the expansion programs under way or announced by producers?

3. How much has the use of electric power increased as a result of the increase in production of steel mentioned above?

4. What increase in the use of electric power will result during the next five years if the anticipated increase in the production of steel occurs?

5. How much did you estimate that the power requirements for the production of nonferrous metals will increase in the Northwest during the next five years?

I hope and believe that you can answer these questions without difficulty, for I understand that the information was contained in your address. I wish very much that I could have heard you speak, but this was not possible. When your address is published, as I understand it will be eventually, I intend to obtain a copy immediately for I am sure that it contains a great deal of other information that we can utilize.

Meanwhile, I shall greatly appreciate it if you can send me the specific figures requested above. You may count upon our always being glad to return the favor by sending any information we obtain about the present conditions and probable developments in the power industry.

Very truly yours,

John Doe
Director of Public Relations
Inland Gas and Electric Company

Answers to Inquiries

The following suggestions apply when the answer to an inquiry is sent to a reader who is not a potential customer for goods or services. The answer to a potential customer is essentially a sales letter and is therefore beyond the scope of this discussion.

When your answer to an inquiry contains most or all of the information requested, the opening should make it clear that the reader's request is being complied with, and of course it should cover all the points that must be covered in any opening. Then should come the information requested, as far as it can be provided. If part of the information cannot be provided, a statement to that effect comes next, accompanied by a suitable expression of regret and whatever explanations are called for. The ending is usually an expression of good will. For example, it can be a statement of your hope that the reader's project will be successful or an offer to provide additional information if such an offer is suitable.

When your answer to an inquiry does not provide the information requested, its contents should be arranged in the pattern suggested for all refusals. (See page 290.) Rather than blurting out the fact that the request is being refused, you should first attempt to show that you would like to comply with it. Then should come a brief statement of the reasons that you cannot do so, leading to a tactful but not evasive statement that the information requested cannot be supplied. In stating reasons you should not be unduly apologetic but should avoid bluntness.

After the actual refusal you should include at least one or two sentences so that the reader's final impression will be your good will rather than your refusal. You can create such an impression by saying that you hope he can find the information elsewhere, that his project will be successful, or that you can be of service to him in the future. Many times, when you cannot answer his exact questions, you may be able to send printed material or suggest other sources of information. A well-written refusal can at least prevent the reader from feeling rebuffed.

The following letters are examples of how the answer to an inquiry may provide information or may say that the information requested cannot be provided.

Dear Professor Smith:

I have received your pleasant letter of October 20 in which you inquire about my recent study of the kinds and frequency of errors made by students of technical writing.

I am preparing an article in which I will give a full description of my method of investigation and my findings, but since it is not yet in print, I am glad to provide the following answers to your questions:

1. The 36 students whose writing I studied were all required to take the course in which they did the writing. Twenty were juniors and 16 were seniors.

2. The writing that served as a basis for my conclusions consisted of five papers by each student. The total length of the papers by each student was a minimum of 6000 words.

3. I have classified the weaknesses of the students' writing under five headings: Mechanics (that is, weak writing in general), Form (use of figures, headings, equations, etc.), Organization, Style, and Content.

4. I found that once the students became aware of the standards they were expected to meet, those who were originally weak in the first three areas improved rapidly at first and gradually thereafter. Improvement in style was usually slower but was steady. Improvement in content was erratic, seeming to depend on the student's

maturity and on his job experience. The students with practical experience were better able to judge what material to include and what to omit.

I believe that the most significant point to emerge from my study is the need of constantly encouraging the student to think of writing as a matter of meeting the specific needs of specific readers. The erratic nature of the improvement in content is responsible for my conviction that consideration of the reader's needs cannot be overemphasized.

I hope that this information is useful to you. If you would like to receive a more extensive report about my work, I suggest that you write to me again in June. By then I will have extra copies of my article and will be glad to send you one. Meanwhile, you may be sure that I am gratified by your interest.

Very truly yours,

Dear Mr. Johnson:

I have received your inquiry of September 4 containing several questions about capability and cost data for the projects that comprise the Cascade Regional Power System.

It is true, as you may have heard, that a report containing information of the kind requested has been made to the Administrator. If it were possible, I would be glad to give you this information. I am prevented from doing so, however, because the report is limited to government use only.

Actually, the figures in the report cannot be considered final. They have been gathered together for staff members to use when they appear at Congressional hearings. Many of them involve complicated relationships among several factors and could not be expected to convey an accurate picture unless accompanied by a careful and sometimes lengthy explanation.

Though I cannot release the precise figures that you request, I have selected three or four pamphlets that I think it likely will interest you and am enclosing them. If I can be of further assistance, please let me know.

Very truly yours,

COMPLAINTS AND ADJUSTMENTS

Complaints

A letter of complaint is one of the types most likely to be badly written. It is likely to be written by a person who is irritated—perhaps justifiably—by both the facts to be complained about and the necessity of writing the letter; and with the reader at a distance, the temptation to write a harsh, angry letter may be hard to resist. Many a person who would be moderate if he were face to face with someone throws restraint aside and is unpleasant in a letter.

The purpose of a letter of complaint is not to relieve your emotions. Rather, it is to affect the attitude and perhaps the actions of the reader.

Thus, even if harshness would be justified, you defeat your own purpose by being harsh, angering the reader, and rendering him incapable of passing fair judgment on the merits of your case. All in all, you are unlikely to gain any desirable result by a display of irritation that you could not gain without it and yet retain good will.

A letter of complaint should, at the least, be completely courteous, and it is often more effective if the tone is friendly. You should address the reader as if you consider him a fair and reasonable person. Thus your letter will seem intended to make sure he becomes clearly aware of certain facts and realizes their significance—facts that you would presumably wish to know if the case were reversed.

This does not mean that you need to be weak and apologetic, nor that you need to minimize the seriousness of a serious occasion. But, it is possible to be direct and intensely serious without being quarrelsome or sarcastic. Even when a situation is so serious as to call for a clear warning that drastic action may become necessary, the warning can be phrased so that it does not sound like a threat. In keeping with the "You Attitude," it can be expressed in such a way as to show your desire to avoid an action that presumably would be to his disadvantage.

Another attitude to guard against is self-righteousness. Though it may be desirable to present yourself as fair and reasonable, you are not likely to secure the reaction you desire if you seem convinced that you are perfect and your reader is highly reprehensible.

One may hope that in avoiding personal unpleasantness in a complaint you are not falsifying your feelings; but whatever your feelings may be, your letter should not be written to express them. It is written to produce a desired effect on the reader, and a letter along the lines recommended is most likely to secure the effect desired.

When a complaint must contain a request that a reader take some specific action—for example, grant an adjustment—you should assume that he accepts his moral and legal responsibilities, tell him the facts on which your request is based, and ask him to do what you think the situation calls for. The tone of such a letter is improved by an expression of regret that the request is necessary. The conclusion should of course be the specific request for action.

Following is a letter of complaint.

Gentlemen:
Last week a shipment of several pieces which I had turned over to your Enfield agent was delivered to my home in Alturas. I am writing to let you know of the inconvenience I was caused by the manner in which the shipment was handled.
I had been told by the Enfield agent that delivery could not be made before August 18 at the earliest. Instead, the shipment arrived on August 16. It was merely a stroke of luck that I was there to re-

ceive it. As a matter of fact, I had not yet prepared a place to put it, and as a result I have been forced to handle everything twice.

The truck arrived at 7:15 a.m., and I was still in bed at the time. The driver asked me to pay $68.50 for shipping charges before he would unload the shipment. He would not accept my check, saying that he was not permitted to do so. I did not have that amount in the house, and was forced to borrow cash from three neighbors—a necessity that was both inconvenient and embarrassing.

If you will imagine yourself in my position, you will realize how I feel about this experience. I feel that those who use your services should be able to rely upon the statements of your agents, and I feel that if you expect payment to be made in cash, the customer should be warned so that he can make sure he has the necessary cash available. I wonder what would have happened if I had been out of town, or if I had been unable to obtain the cash for payment before the bank opened at ten o'clock.

You are constantly advertising the excellence and convenience of your service on radio and television. If you make such claims about your ability to satisfy your customers, I believe you should welcome this information about my dissatisfaction, and should adopt policies that will prevent such occurrences in the future.

Very truly yours,

Answers to Complaints and to Requests for Adjustments

Three kinds of letters are covered in the following discussion: answers to complaints that have not asked for any specific adjustment, answers that refuse adjustments, and answers that grant adjustments. All three have a good deal in common; in fact, everything that is said about the first applies to both the others.

Answers to Complaints Not Involving Adjustments. The key to writing a good answer to a complaint is the same as the key to success in writing anything else: form a clear picture of the result you hope to accomplish, and write in a manner designed to accomplish that result. You will find it is easy to forget this, however, in answering a complaint. The complaints you will answer will not always be justified, and whether justified or not they will sometimes be unreasonable or unpleasant. Consequently, you will be tempted to say, and even be justified in saying, things that it would be better to leave unsaid. You may constantly have to remind yourself that you are not writing to express your emotions or to win an argument. You are writing in order to affect your reader in a certain manner, usually to make him feel less injured or antagonistic. The tone and content should be settled upon with this definite purpose in mind.

This general advice is outlined in the following suggestions:

1. Even if you are answering an angry, unreasonable letter, your tone should be pleasant, or at least completely courteous. This does not mean that your letter must be subservient, but only that it should be a calm, reasonable attempt to reach an understanding.

2. You should avoid the role of an opponent who is trying to defeat the reader in an argument. To accomplish this result it is well to mention very near the opening some point or principle on which you and your reader will agree.

3. Detailed restatement of the complaint refreshes the reader's memory of his original annoyance and revives his anger. Therefore you should limit your restatement of the complaint to the minimum that is necessary to show you have read it with care and understand it correctly.

4. If the complaint contains misstatements, do not repeat them for the express purpose of proving that they are false or erroneous. Of course you must state the facts as you know them to be, but it is better to refrain from calling attention to the fact that what you are saying contradicts what the reader said. In doing this you give him a chance to back down with a minimum of embarrassment.

5. Expressions of regret should be proportionate to the seriousness of the occasion. They should be neither so perfunctory as to suggest indifference nor so excessive as to magnify a small matter into a large one.

6. Explanations should not be too long and involved. To have them so creates a risk of seeming unduly apologetic or unduly argumentative. If the tone creates a satisfactory impression, a simple explanation of what went wrong will usually be sufficient.

7. The ending should not revert to the cause of the complaint. It should be based on the assumption that the matter at hand has been cared for and that all will be well in the future.

Some of the preceding suggestions picture your reader as a person whose complaint has been unpleasant or immoderate. This emphasis is justified by the fact that unpleasant complaints are the hardest to answer. Your problem will of course be simpler when you answer a complaint that is free from a quarrelsome tone. The opening should make it clear that you are glad your reader let you know he was disturbed. It should show him that you have been glad to look into the case open-mindedly and are anxious to set matters right if you have been at fault. (There is no reason, however, that on every occasion blame must be fastened upon someone.) Include whatever explanations seem relevant and express an appropriate degree of regret. If his complaint called for action, say what you have done or propose to do. End as recommended in the suggestions above.

The main consideration here is to convince your reader that you are really concerned about whatever it is that has disturbed him. It is possible, of course, to magnify a small matter into a large one; but even a moderate complaint should not be answered in such a perfunctory manner that you appear indifferent.

The following letter is an answer to the complaint that appeared earlier.

Dear Mr. Jones:

I can understand your feeling as you do about the way in which your shipment from Enfield to Alturas was delivered, and am extremely sorry about the inconvenience that was caused you.

Our drivers are not supposed to make deliveries at any residence before 8:00 a.m., even if it means a loss of time to wait until then. We will emphatically notify the driver at fault that he is to wait until the proper time in the future.

I do not personally have the authority to change the policy of asking that payment for a shipment be made in cash. However, I can and will bring the problem that this policy created for you to the attention of the company officials who make the policies on such matters. Our agents have been instructed always to notify our customers of this policy, but we will re-emphasize this fact in the next bulletin that we send to them.

It is somewhat unusual for a customer to find it inconvenient when service is faster than he had anticipated, but I can see that in the case of your shipment, early delivery was not desirable.

We really do make a sincere effort to give the good service that we promise in our advertising, and we appreciate your letting us know your experience. We hope that we have a chance to serve you again, for we would like to demonstrate that we can do so to your satisfaction.

Sincerely yours,

Letters Refusing to Make Adjustments. Included in Chapter 13, on business correspondence in general, was a discussion of the order of saying "no." What was said in that discussion applies, as might be expected, to a letter refusing to make an adjustment.

In brief, the order of saying "no" calls for holding back the actual statement of a refusal until the facts and reasons for refusing have been presented. This arrangement conveys the impression that the request was received by a person who was willing to consider it with an open mind and grant it if the facts showed that an adjustment was due. Having the actual statement of refusal precede the statement of reasons conveys the impression that the writer decided to refuse and then looked for reasons to justify his decision. This, plus the fact that being refused does not put the reader into a receptive state of mind, makes it undesirable for the refusal proper to be placed near the opening.

The opening of a refusal to make an adjustment should of course acknowledge the letter you are answering and should include enough facts to show that you understood it correctly. It should convey the impression that your first reaction was, "Let's look into this matter and see whether we should grant an adjustment." Even if you know before you start writing, as of course you will, that you are not going to comply with the request, you can open your letter by saying that you are glad your reader felt free to bring the case to your attention, or that you are sorry he has encountered trouble. Often it will be useful if you state the principle on which you base your decisions on matters of the kind in question. For example, you might mention your willingness to make repairs without charge if the product you had sold developed trouble within the guarantee period and had been used for the purpose intended.

Next should come the facts that you consider relevant and perhaps your reasoning as you considered these facts. In refusing to grant a request that is based on incomplete or inaccurate statements, present the facts that justify your decision but do not go out of your way to prove that the reader is guilty of misstatements. Nothing is gained by making your reader feel embarrassed. If you show up the weakness of his case too devastatingly, he may dislike dealing with you in the future, or may become angry at you in order to escape a low opinion of himself. Likewise, in trying to demonstrate that you are not to blame for something that has gone wrong, do not make a point of putting the blame on the reader. Most of the time, the less said about blame, the better.

Having stated the reasons for your decision, you may logically go on to state the decision itself. Be tactful as you do so. Avoid the word *refuse* if possible. It would be better, for example, to avoid such phraseology as, "We must therefore refuse to grant your request for a reduction of our charge from $275 to $200" and say instead, "We believe that in view of these facts, our charge of $275 is correct." The effort to be tactful should not be carried so far, however, that it makes your answer unclear or evasive.

When your decision has been stated it is usually desirable to add a few lines turning attention to the future. You can say that you look forward to a continuance of pleasant and mutually rewarding relations, that you would like to be of service in the future, or whatever else the specific circumstances permit you to say. Of course, any idea or attitude can be carried too far, but the general principle of ending a letter on a cheerful, forward-looking note is sound.

It is possible, of course, that a letter constructed along these lines may not have the desired effect; but after all, letters cannot achieve miracles. Sometimes no amount of skill in saying "no" can prevent the reader from feeling resentment. But when refusal is necessary, the method explained should hold resentment to a minimum.

The letter that follows is an example of a well-written refusal to make an adjustment.

Gentlemen:

We have received your letter asking that we repaint certain parts of your experimental poultry building at our own expense, and have been glad to review the case so as to see whether we should consent to do so.

As you know, we have already sent our men to look over the condition of the paint job. They agree that the paint is flaking badly, and you are right, of course, in feeling that paint should not flake off after only two years.

Our records show, however, that only part of the job was done by our crew. Instead of having us prepare the building for painting as well as paint it, you had the preparation done by your own employees.

The service that paint will give depends on the condition of the surface that is painted as well as on the paint and the way in which it is applied. Our foreman remembers that he was uneasy about the condition of the wood when his crew did the job, and tells me that he mentioned this fact to you.

So far as we have learned, the paint has not begun to peel off from any building we painted at the same time if we were permitted to do the preparation as well as the painting. We therefore believe the peeling you mention is caused by the preparation rather than because of inferior paint or workmanship and cannot agree to bear the expense of repainting.

We should be glad, however, to repaint the places that are peeling at the lowest possible charge that would permit us to do the job as we feel it should be done. We will guarantee our work if you use a paint we can recommend and permit us to do the preparation as well as the painting.

If you would like to proceed on such a basis, let us know and we will estimate the charge immediately.

Very truly yours,

Letters Granting Adjustments. Sometimes you may need to grant an adjustment on an occasion that is important enough to call for more than a routine consent. In this event, the letter differs from a refusal in one important respect: the action being taken should be indicated extremely early in the letter. Thus the letter will contain: (1) an acknowledgment of the complaint (though the term *complaint* would not be used); (2) a statement that the request for an adjustment is being granted (these two parts may be combined); (3) whatever expressions of regret are called for unless regret has already been expressed in the opening; (4) whatever explanation seems necessary; (5) an attempt to turn the reader's thoughts away from the occasion for complaint and focus them toward the future.

This order is psychologically sound. The reader will listen to explanations more understandingly after he has learned that the request has been granted.

When as a matter of policy you must grant an adjustment to which you do not feel the claimant is entitled, you should grant it graciously. Some writers will offer all the reasons that might justify a refusal before finally saying that an adjustment has been granted. By adopting this grudging, argumentative method, they sacrifice the good will that they are making the adjustment in order to retain. A letter will not have the desired effect if it shows the reader that though his request is being granted, he is considered unreasonable to have made it.

The letter that follows is an answer to a complaint in which an adjustment was granted.

Gentlemen:

Thank you for letting us know about the trouble that developed in the tires we recently retreaded for you. We are sorry that you have had reason to be concerned, and we will of course live up to our guarantee of giving satisfaction.

We believe we know what probably caused the bond between the casings and the tread to weaken. A factory service expert who visited us last month to make a routine check on our equipment discovered that the gauges which record the temperature during the cure were out of adjustment. He replaced them immediately, and as a result of his visit we feel confident that the work we are now doing will be completely satisfactory.

I suggest that you telephone us at our expense so that we can settle upon a time for us to do the job over again, without charge, on the tires where the bond has loosened. We will make a point of doing the work promptly and feel sure that when we return the tires to you, they will give you good service.

Sincerely yours,

LETTERS URGING ACTION

Many letters written for the purpose of urging action do not fit into any of the types discussed elsewhere. There are letters intended, for example, to urge the reader to contribute to some fund, to join a program for smoke or erosion control, or to join some organization. The writing of such letters may be demanded of men in any business or profession.

Letters of this type resemble sales letters closely enough that they can often be based on the sales letter pattern. This pattern involves four steps: (1) attracting attention and securing interest; (2) arousing desire; (3) convincing the reader that the act he is urged to perform will satisfy that desire; (4) securing action. The key words are *interest, desire, conviction,* and *action.* Though the lines that mark off one step from another need not be sharply drawn, the four functions must always be performed in any letter that attempts, under one cover, to persuade the reader either to make a purchase or to perform an action of some other kind.

To obtain *interest* it is best to get the letter under way with a minimum of the preliminaries that usually occur at the opening. The reader should immediately encounter something that he himself is concerned with rather than material that concerns the writer. If the opening can suggest that the reader's own welfare is involved, or the welfare of his organization, so much the better.

One of the poorest openings encountered recently was in a letter by a social fraternity attempting to raise funds. It read: "It seems as though every time we write to the alumni we are asking for something." This showed that the writer himself was uncertain of the appropriateness of his request. Moreover, it put the reader on guard and warned him to steel himself to refuse. The writer should have aroused enthusiasm about the fraternity and its project before letting the reader realize that he was about to be asked for money. In other words, he should have adopted the "You Attitude."

In attempting to arouse *desire*, remember one fundamental point. You do not attempt to *create* desire. Rather, you try to think of some desire that the reader already feels, fan it into intensity, and then associate the action aimed at with its satisfaction. Technical writers can profit by seeing how advertisers use this principle. For example, a person may not desire an air-cooling system; but he does desire comfort, so his desire for comfort is exploited in a letter selling an air-cooler. Similarly, a man may not desire membership in an organization, but be eager for professional advancement; or a company may be induced to join a smoke-control program not so much to provide smoke control as to obtain good will. The starting point in arousing desire is to ask yourself, "What are some of the desires that the reader already feels?" and then, "How can I connect the idea I am trying to sell with one of those desires?"

This is not to urge you to attempt anything specious or far-fetched. The connection you attempt to show should really exist. In fact, if the connection between the act you try to obtain and the desires the reader feels is not genuine, the letter has little chance of success.

In arousing desire you do not emphasize every idea you can think of. You should make one single "appeal" dominate. Other possible appeals may be mentioned but should be kept subordinate. If a second letter is sent, a different appeal may be emphasized; but in any single letter, one incentive is emphasized and the others are kept in the background—visible, perhaps, but not conspicuous.

To secure *conviction,* simply use whatever evidence is best suited to the occasion. No generally appropriate methods can be suggested, as have been suggested for attracting interest and arousing desire. Whatever evidence you offer, you should carefully avoid an argumentative tone. Try to make it appear that you and your reader are both following certain facts to their logical conclusion.

In the effort to secure *action,* three points must be borne in mind: (1) The action suggested should be complete and specific. Rather than "Let us know your decision," you should write, for example, "Check the enclosed card to indicate your decision." (2) The action should be made as easy as possible. For example, it might be helpful to supply an envelope or card that is already stamped and addressed, or perhaps you can supply blanks to fill in rather than forcing the reader to write a complete letter. (3) There should be an effort to make the action immediate, even if delay would do no harm. Once the reader starts postponing action, he is likely to do so indefinitely, for his impulse to act is stronger at the moment he finishes reading the letter than it will be later, when its contents have faded from his memory. Therefore it is well to offer some plausible reason he should act at once, preferably some benefit to him if he does so.

Certain final cautions are needed in regard to a letter aimed at action. First, the opening paragraph should be brief. This will make it look easy to read and thus encourage the receiver to start reading. If your action letter is a form letter, the hardest problem, quite often, is to induce the reader to read it at all. Second, the length of the letter needs careful consideration. If it is too long, a reader may not complete it—in fact may not even start it; but if it is too short, he finishes reading it before it has time to make any impression on him. Finally, you should not discuss any expense that you are asking the reader to incur until you have aroused his enthusiasm about the project concerned. Talking about expenses too early arouses the reader's defenses and dampens his enthusiasm.

An example of a letter urging action is in the section that covers form letters.

FORM LETTERS

Everyone is familiar with form letters, yet they pose some problems in writing that you may not realize when reading them.

A form letter is reproduced in quantity by such methods as ditto, mimeographing, printing, or automatic typewriter. Obviously it is less impressive than a personally written letter, for the reader immediately realizes that the message is of no more concern to him than to many other people. This is a disadvantage it is frequently necessary to accept, however, when the same message must in fact be sent to many people and when the time and expense of individual letters would be prohibitive. Moreover, the disadvantage can be somewhat reduced by obtaining a good reproduction job on a good grade of paper and by sending the letter as first-class mail in a sealed envelope. Sometimes, also, individual addresses and salutations can be inserted by typewriter, so that the effect is less impersonal. As any of these measures is considered, its expense must of course be taken into consideration.

Unless individual inside addresses and salutations are inserted with a typewriter, they are the parts of a form letter that pose the first problem. Sometimes it is possible to improvise two or three lines to replace the inside address, as for example:

To the Officers and Advisors of
Student Chapters of
The American Society of Civil Engineering

Gentlemen:

More frequently, however, the inside address is omitted, and except for the heading, the letter begins with the salutation. This can be *Dear Sir* or *Gentlemen* unless the letter reaches both men and women. Sometimes, instead, you may be able to use more specific salutations such as *Dear Purchasing Agent, Dear Subscriber, Dear Member, Dear Motor User,* or *Dear Friend.* These variations should be carefully chosen, however, for they are in danger of seeming too coy. Still another device is to replace the salutation with such a line as: *To All Users of Drafting Instruments:* or *To All Users of Power Saws.*

The only other question of form arises in connection with the signature. Sometimes, in form letters, an effort is made to make the letter seem more personal by reproducing the writer's handwritten signature by mimeograph or in print. Often, however, the primary signature (that is, the first line below the complimentary close) is typed, usually capitalized throughout.

There is no reason that the body of your form letter really needs to differ from the body of individual letters, either in form or content. However, since a form letter is not likely to be dictated and sent without revision, you can often spend more time planning its layout. For example, you can emphasize a paragraph by widening the margins, or you can use the device of having the first paragraph end with three double-spaced periods in the middle of a sentence, and thus tease the reader into the second paragraph. Sometimes these eye-catching devices help to offset the disadvantage a form letter suffers in comparison with an individual letter, but they should not be so extensive that they make a letter look cluttered.

The soundest way, however, to compensate for these disadvantages is to take more care with a form letter than it is possible to take with most individual letters. Having more opportunity to revise, and being free to write a form letter when you can do it justice, you can often produce a much better letter than you can dictate as part of the day's routine.

One more caution is needed: The message of a form letter must be so expressed that it is appropriate for *every* person who will receive it. For example, if some of the receivers are in universities and others in business, or if some have been members of an organization and others are not yet members, the phraseology must be appropriate for either group. And if the letter is to be sent at different times of the year as need arises, it must avoid seasonal allusions.

The letter on the following page is a form letter urging action.[*]

---

[*] Courtesy of Cecil Hathaway.

LATAH COUNTY
HIGHWAY DISTRICT NO.2

Moscow, Idaho

July 30, 196_

Highway and Good Roads
    District Commissioners

Gentlemen:

    The 36th Annual Meeting of the Idaho Association of Highway and Good
Road Districts will be held in Moscow on the University of Idaho campus
on November 15 and 16 (Friday and Saturday).

    To make this meeting a success, we have to meet two requirements:

        1. A large attendance, representing ALL Highway and Good Roads
            Districts.

        2. A program dealing with interesting subjects.

    You can help us on both scores. You can swell the attendance by
coming yourself, urging other commissioners to do so, and bringing the
District Foreman or Clerk. The expense of the trip can reasonably be
charged to your district, and we will make every effort to present a program that will justify the expense.

    You can help us to arrange a program by telling us what the re-
presentatives in your district would like to hear discussed. Listed on
the attached sheet are some suggested topics. If you think of something
that would interest you more, there's a place below the list for you to
jot it down. Then, under the priority number, write "1" beside the topic
of greatest interest, "2" beside the second most interesting, etc. We'll
try to find qualified speakers on the subjects that are most in demand.
And well in advance of the meeting you'll receive a tentative program.

    Of course if this program is to be in line with your references,
we'll need to hear from you soon. Why not look over the list right now
while it's handy, indicate your preferences, and get it off your mind by
mailing it today?

    We hope you'll do this--and then begin laying plans to be on hand in
November.

                      Sincerely yours,

                      Cecil Hathaway
                      Latah County Highway District No. 2

ASSIGNMENTS

In writing the letters called for in the following assignments, make up headings, addresses and signatures. When such an assumption is reasonable, assume that a letterhead occupies the top two inches of the page and use only a dateline as a heading. If you type your letter, place it properly on the page.

In developing details of a situation, you may need to assume that the date is different from the date when you actually write the letter. You may also need to make up additional details. However, you should *not* make up facts that would change the essential nature of the problem.

In particular, do not yield to the temptation to imitate the specimens that appeared earlier in the chapter, but rather, try to develop your own skill.

1. You are connected with a school, business, or governmental unit. Construction of something such as a building, stretch of road, or bridge, has been practically completed. There is to be a dedication ceremony. It is your responsibility to invite some important person to participate in the ceremony. (He may be a speaker, a guest who sits on the officials' platform, or a participant in any other way you wish.) Write a letter of invitation to be sent to him.

2. Write a form letter to be sent to numerous people inviting them to attend a ceremony of the kind described in Assignment 1. If you prefer, you may make this an invitation to attend a banquet, but not as guests whose tickets are complimentary. Though this is a form letter, it is presumably to be typed separately for each recipient, so it should have an individual address and salutation. (If study assignments have not already included form letters, you should study the section on that type before writing this assignment.)

3. Assume that you have received the letter called for in Assignment 1, but are unable to accept the invitation. Write an answer. If it seems appropriate, offer to arrange to have someone else in your organization come in your place. (How definite such an offer should be would depend on the role you have been asked to play.)

4. Assume that the fieldmen in some company with which you are connected have grown careless—or at least reports have been received to that effect—in some process of inspection, testing, or securing samples to send to the laboratory for testing. Write a letter of instructions to all fieldmen telling them just how the process is to be performed. Remember that the letter will reach some men who have been using proper methods; and though you must attempt to improve the practices of those who are careless, you do not want to antagonize the others. Suggested activities about which to give instructions might include field sampling; various field tests; mixing, batching, or curing of concrete; inspection of welding jobs; preparation of metal, wood, or masonry surfaces for painting; inspection of lumber to see whether it is the grade that it should be; moisture determination in soils; field testing of aggregate; or care and adjustment of any type of equipment.

5. Write a letter of instructions telling the receiver to conduct an investigation and submit a report on his findings. Make clear to him why the investigation is needed, what ground it must cover, and when the report is due. Tell him as much as the circumstances call for

about the methods he is to use in obtaining information. If any instructions about expenses are necessary, they should be included.

6. Write an inquiry asking an organization that has been using some product, machine, or equipment about whether it is receiving satisfaction. You wish to know because your own organization is contemplating purchase of the same product or equipment. Though you invite general comment, write an inquiry that includes several specific questions.

7. Rewrite the following ineffective letter of inquiry.

Gentlemen:

In a recent issue of Food Engineering I encountered a reference to your endorsement of a new type of package for frozen whole eggs —a package that consists of a polyethylene bag within a paper carton.

Would you be able to tell us whether eggs in these packages can match the flavor of fresh eggs? Also, we are interested in knowing whether sanitation problems are more difficult than those encountered in using the 30-pound can that is now the standard container for frozen eggs.

We are interested because like others who market frozen eggs we have found that the 30-pound can has certain shortcomings. We would like to be able to market our product in 10-pound packages. Would the new method make this possible? And would its use offer any savings in time, labor, and storage costs?

We would specially like to know how long it takes to defrost the product in a 45 to 50 degree refrigerator, and whether quick defrosting is possible.

We shall appreciate it if you can answer these questions, and would be glad to receive any other information you can send us. You mention that several egg brokers and distributors in your area are now using the method. We would be glad to know the names of these companies if you would care to send them.

Thank you in advance for your assistance in getting the information that we need.

Very truly yours,

8. In answer to an inquiry, write a letter in which you provide most of or all of the information requested. This may be an answer to a letter you have written or assume has been written, as called for by Assignment 6, or to some other inquiry that you have the information to answer.

9. In answer to an inquiry, write a letter that contains little or none of the information requested. The inquiry that you answer may be any of those suggested in Assignment 6.

10. You are connected with some organization that has placed an order for one article or more to be shipped a considerable distance with shipping costs prepaid. When you had originally asked that a price be quoted, you asked that it include the cost of shipping. Both the bid you received and your purchase order specified that shipping costs were covered in the price quoted. You have now received a bill in which they are added. Write to the seller asking that he make a suitable adjustment and that he submit a statement showing he has done so.

11. A certain local company has an annual contract for cleaning and repairing typewriters or some other type of equipment used by your organization. This company has done good work but has sometimes not come for several days when notified that a machine needs attention. Also, after picking up machines they have often waited a few days before working on them. When you have complained, they have customarily offered the excuse that they were extremely busy. As a result, you have been caused considerable inconvenience. Write a letter making it clear that you will not renew the contract, which has sixty days to run, if you have further cause to complain. You can point out that there is no reason to pick up a machine until they are ready to work on it, and that if they are too busy to give prompt service, you will turn for help to someone who isn't too busy to do your work promptly.

12. You are a private citizen living in a residential district. Some company has a repair crew working close to your home on a job such as installing new equipment or gas mains, or cutting back trees that interfere with power lines. Members of this crew have customarily talked loudly and used bad language—language that has been offensive to women in the area and has added objectionable terms to the vocabulary of your children and their playmates. Write a letter to the company asking it to put an end to this objectionable behavior. See if you can write a letter that is not apologetic yet does not brand you as a prude.

13. Answer the letter called for by Assignment 12. Let it be assumed that the complaint has been brought to the attention of the foreman of the crew, orders having been given to put an end to its cause. Without losing your sense of proportion, let your reader see that you don't blame him for his feelings. Let him know that you want him to inform you if he has further cause for complaint. In general, do what you can for the sake of good will and in the interest of a desirable company image.

14. The company that you represent has sold some piece of equipment covered by a guarantee. The article in question has given trouble and the purchaser has complained, asking you to make repairs at your own expense. You have sent a service man or inspector, and he has found that something about the way the equipment was used has caused the damage. (This could be such misuse as overloads or failure to follow instructions about lubrication.) Write a letter telling the reader what has been found to be the cause of the trouble. The situation is one in which the guarantee is void. Try to make the reader see that he should meet the expense of repairs himself. Urge him to follow instructions about maintenance, lubrication, etc. in the future and try to create confidence that if he does so he will receive satisfaction.

15. You are connected with a company that had hired a commercial weed-killing company to apply weed killer on an area heavily infested by noxious weeds, especially Canadian thistle. You find that not all the Canadian thistle have been killed. You knew when the land was treated what chemicals were being used. These did not include a weed killer called Metadandon 3T (imaginary name), which you have recently read is particularly effective on Canadian thistle. Write a

letter expressing your discontent about the way the job turned out and raising the question about whether the most effective weed killers were used. (A new or partly developed subdivision might be an area where such a problem could arise.)

16. You are connected with the company that did the weed-control job described in Assignment 15. Answer the letter that Assignment 15 called for. Metadandon 3T is more powerful than any chemical you used, so powerful that if even a mild amount of drift occurs, it is likely to damage broad-leafed plants of many kinds. Also, it moves in the soil, and even when it does not drift, may affect plants beyond the area where it is used. Governmental agencies have not yet cleared it for use in agricultural lands. You could not use it without risk of damage in areas adjacent to the one that you were treating. You used the most powerful killers it was safe to use. The weather just after you did the job was unfavorable to the best results, but the kill (you have inspected the area) was good for a single treatment. One more treatment should probably kill the thistle that remain. This will be lighter and less expensive than the first treatment. Suggest that you be permitted to apply a second treatment as soon as the weather is right, which could be at any time.

17. Write a form letter 250 to 300 words long in which you try to convince the readers to perform some action such as coming to a meeting for a cause of common interest, joining in some program such as weed control or control of a tree disease in the area, attempting to obtain some municipal improvement, or joining some organization. As an alternative you might solicit pledges or contributions to support some program or activity. The subject should be a matter of lively interest in your home or college community, or in the profession for which you are training.

The date may be assumed to be different from the date on which you actually write the letter. Those who receive the letter should all have something in common, such as being farmers, lumbermen, stockmen, engineers, sportsmen, people in organizations interested in public health, or parents. Supply an inside address that would be suitable for all who receive the letter. Unless the sort of group to which the letter is sent is clear from the letter itself, add a note giving this information to the instructor.

15

LETTERS CONCERNING EMPLOYMENT

For a person about to graduate from college, the process of securing employment has changed considerably in recent years. Large corporations and governmental units are now sending representatives to colleges and universities for the purpose of recruitment to such an extent that a letter of application is not always the first contact between the employer and the prospective employee. On the contrary, when a graduating senior writes a letter in connection with employment, he often has been interviewed already, has received an application blank, and may have filled it out and submitted it. As a result of the interview a company representative will have formed and recorded his impression about the applicant's appearance and personality to supplement the facts about qualifications which he obtained from the applicant and from other sources.

Under such circumstances, the traditional instructions about how to write a letter of application are not entirely applicable. Rather than starting from scratch and writing a full-scale application, the applicant will base his letters on the way he sizes up the situation as a result of the interview and on any leads he may have picked up regarding what he should emphasize among the many things he may feel justified in saying about himself.

Still, the full-scale letter of application is not a matter to be neglected. There are still numerous occasions when it may be written by students seeking their first employment after graduation, and it is as important as ever to the person who already has a position but wants to apply for something better in a different company. Therefore this chapter will first cover the traditional letter of application, because even those who do not need to write the full letter may need to use parts of the material it contains. Next, attention will be centered on letters written after an applicant has been interviewed. And finally, some concrete suggestions that apply to letters written under either circumstance will be presented.

THE CONVENTIONAL LETTER OF APPLICATION

The Opening

When you write a conventional letter of application for a specific position, start with a short paragraph indicating the position you are applying for and telling, perhaps, where you learned that the position was open. If necessary, identify yourself—for example, as a graduating senior or as the occupant of whatever job you hold. Make it clear that your letter is definitely an application, if such is the case, rather than just an expression of interest that includes some facts about yourself to justify a request for information. In general, let your opening paragraph merely establish contact and provide the information that will enable your reader to judge your qualifications without having unanswered questions in the back of his mind.

Try to put something that will arouse your reader's interest either in the first paragraph or in the opening of the second paragraph if you can think of anything that will serve such a purpose. This might be, for example, a reference to some extraordinary qualification or to an unusual combination of qualifications. Not everyone is fortunate enough to be able to include such a bid for interest, but if you can somehow, at the outset, set yourself apart from the run-of-the-mill applicants, what follows is more likely to receive attention.

The Central Section

The central section should follow smoothly after the opening. Its contents will often fall naturally into sections on education, experience, personal information, and references, but there is no reason to regard this pattern as mandatory, nor to arrange the sections in this particular order.

The best arrangement is one in which the strongest points are placed first. It is easier to convince a reader that you are a strong candidate at the beginning than it would be later, when the first sections have already created the impression that your qualifications are about on a par with those of other applicants.

Education. As a minimum, name the higher educational institutions that you have attended and the degrees you have earned or are about to earn. If you have an outstanding academic record, mention it. Do not hesitate to name your extracurricular activities, for they help to round out the impression about the kind of person you are.

The amount of detail about education should be governed by the amount of other information you expect to present, the strength of your scholarship, and the extent to which your academic training is directly related to the work you would do on the job. Facts about education that one applicant should mention—for example, courses taken—might well be omitted by an applicant whose other qualifications are stronger.

Experience. Nothing is better evidence of your fitness for a job than successful experience in a job of similar nature. If you have had such experience, mention it early. Do not feel, however, that experience in a job of any kind is unimportant. In almost any kind of work, you have had a chance to demonstrate good or bad personal qualities, and it is a well-known fact that personal qualities are often a decisive factor in an employee's success or failure. In general, the picture of your experience should be complete. If anything is omitted, there will be noticeable gaps of time in your record, and these will make a reader wonder whether you have something to conceal.

Personal Information. As a minimum tell your age, place of birth, weight, height, health, and marital status. It might be desirable also to mention freedom from physical handicaps. Reference to leisure interests will sometimes help the reader to think of you as a person. Additional facts about your background help to make the picture complete and are especially likely to be valuable if your background is in any way related to the field you are seeking to enter. Of course the value of personal information, like the value of any information, is relative. Whether certain facts are worth including may depend on how much else you have to say, and it might be helpful for one applicant to include information that another could omit.

References. You should usually name from two to four references, preferably former employers or instructors. If you are just completing your work in college, include at least one reference from the institution that is awarding your degree. The number of references should of course depend on how many are necessary to confirm what you have said in your letter. Courtesy and self-interest make it advisable to secure the consent of anyone whom you name as a reference. And by all means make sure that you have the name (spelling included) and position of each reference absolutely correct. Unless it is obvious, make sure that the reader knows why a person whom you name as a reference is qualified to judge your fitness for the job you are seeking.

Though the logical place to list references is the latter part of the letter, do not hesitate to mention an especially important reference early—even in the opening paragraph. The name of an important person or of a person whom the reader knows personally is effective in arousing interest.

The Ending

Because a list of references does not make interesting reading and because the references are usually named near the end of the letter, you will improve your letter if you can say something to give it a lift at the end. A single-sentence summary of your qualifications might serve the purpose. Another possibility would be a comment on the work you have done to qualify yourself for such a job and the effort you will consequently put forth to make good. Whatever you may say to strengthen your ending must be the outgrowth, of course, of material that your letter has included, and it is therefore impossible to offer a formula for your guidance.

The major function of the ending is to suggest action. This action may be the offer of a job, the invitation to come for an interview, or a letter providing information or telling you what to do next. You will need to appraise the situation, decide what action is the next likely development, and phrase your suggestion accordingly.

Try to phrase your effort to secure action in such a manner that it avoids negative suggestion. When you write, "*If* my qualifications are of interest, I shall be glad to come for an interview," you imply uncertainty whether he will be interested. Though you should not appear to take too much for granted, you might avoid this implication by writing something such as, "I shall appreciate your consideration of my qualifications and shall be glad to come for an interview on any date that you suggest." Such an offer gets rid of the *if* without seeming overconfident.

Unless your potential employer is hard-pressed for help, it is best to refrain from trying to hasten his action. If it is essential, however, that you secure an early response and if you are tactful, you might be able to speed matters along without giving offense. No resentment would be aroused, for example, by such a sentence as, "Since I shall be leaving town for one month on June 10, I should appreciate it if I might have an interview before that date." Most employers are normally considerate and are not likely to resent a reasonable request tactfully made. But pressure must be applied with care or your effort to obtain early action may reduce the chances that action will be favorable.

The Use of a Resume

When, for the sake of completeness, you must include so much material that your letter is in danger of becoming too long, and when you have not been given an application blank to fill out, you may find it advisable to use a resume. Such a sheet should not be used, however, when it would cause needless repetition or would make the letter itself too scanty.

The resume is a complete picture of the facts, in tabular form. It should bear your name and address (future as well as present address if a change is imminent), should be dated, and should indicate the position you are applying for. It should contain the routine personal information that would otherwise be placed in the letter, and should give full information on education, experience, and references. More details can be included in the resume than it is usually advisable to place in the letter itself.

There is no standard form for the resume, but it should be a tabulation rather than a discussion in sentences. The major headings are likely to be *Personal Information, Education, Experience,* and *References,* under which may be used any subheadings needed. To decide on the system of headings, jot down as rough notes all the facts to be covered, and then work out a plan of headings to cover them. Arrange the material on the page so it has a pleasant appearance, and make it as neat and accurate as the letter itself.

A clear understanding of the relationship between the resume and the letter is important. The function of the resume is to free the letter from certain routine information that is uninteresting but necessary for completeness. In the resume you provide the full record. In the accompanying letter you focus the reader's attention on the particular facts that are most important, and bring out their full significance.

A resume cannot perform all the functions of a letter; rather, it performs the functions of an application blank. However completely the resume may present the facts, it remains for the letter to create a personal interest, for it is only in the letter that you seem to be talking to the reader personally.

LETTERS FOLLOWING INTERVIEWS

As mentioned earlier, for a student who is about to earn a degree in a large or middle-sized institution, the routine of obtaining a position may begin with an interview on the campus and filling out of an application blank. If he writes a letter at all, it will be only to supplement the considerable information already in the hands of the potential employer, or to cope with some later development. The person who writes under these circumstances may be able to apply some of the preceding instructions but his letter will not stand independently as the major instrument for obtaining employment.

Many authorities feel that after an applicant has been interviewed he can help himself by writing a letter even if he must use his imagination to create a pretext for doing so. One possibility is a letter ostensibly written just to say "Thank you for the interview," but expanded by the addition of anything else that the writer thinks would be helpful. The conditions that can exist after interviews are so varied that it would be impossible to generalize on the question of whether an applicant's chances would be helped by a letter written on mere pretext. An applicant has to use his own judgment about whether to write a follow-up letter. The decision should certainly be based in part on the atmosphere that developed during the interview.

Assuming that you face this problem and do decide to write a follow-up letter (either because of a concrete development or on a pretext you have decided would be plausible), what kind of material can you use? Some of the possiblities are as follows:

You can answer or supplement your earlier answers to questions that were not entirely settled.

You can describe the growth of your interest in some matter that you had not thought about intensively before the interview—for example a kind of work that is different from what you had had in mind.

You can dwell upon facts about the company that increase its appeal to you.

You can say that you have been giving additional thought to what qualifications you can offer in some particular respect, and supplement what you said earlier on that point.

You can say that you have been thinking a great deal about some remark made by the interviewer, and review some aspect of the case in the light of this added consideration.

Admittedly it takes imagination to translate these general ideas into definite, concrete terms. There is no guarantee that every applicant can produce a letter that will help his prospects. But it is probably true that most job seekers, after an interview, think of things they wish they had said, or wonder whether they made themselves entirely clear on certain points, or think of questions they wish they had asked. The exercise of ingenuity will often make it possible to use some such afterthought as a point of departure for a letter.

And what can such a letter do for you beyond supplying concrete facts not supplied before? The answer to this question depends largely on your adroitness as a writer. Assuming that you write it skillfully, such a letter can help you to gain credit for initiative, originality, imagination, and aggressiveness. It can convey the impression of a lively interest in the company, beyond the fact that you need a job.

Also, it can demonstrate your literacy and your skill in writing—a skill that improves your potential value in any large organization. Just as there are some people who write badly but make a good personal impression, there are others who can present themselves better when they write than when they talk. If you are one of these, your letter may help to counterbalance your conversational shortcomings. And even if you are fortunate enough to make a good impression in a conversation, you will strengthen that impression by showing that you write well in addition to talking well.

Of course if you are weak in writing, there is no reason to feel that you can help your prospects by writing when it is not essential to do so. The best policy under these circumstances is to keep every letter as simple as possible and at least to avoid the pitfalls that are pointed out in the remainder of the chapter.

GENERAL SUGGESTIONS

Neatness

Neatness is a must. Before the person who receives your letter can begin to read it, he forms an impression about you on the basis of its appearance which affects his reception of its contents. If sloppiness and carelessness are qualities of your letter, he associates you, at least subconsciously, with those qualities, and you are handicapped from the outset.

Further, a failure to make your letter neat is not very flattering to those to whom you send it. You force your reader to conclude either that you regard him and the position as unimportant or else that you are satisfied to turn in an inferior performance on an important occasion. You can hardly expect him to believe you will do your utmost to serve the interests of his company if you are careless even when working directly in your own interest.

In view of these facts you should no more send a slovenly looking letter than you should appear for an interview with uncombed hair and a dirty shirt.

The "You Attitude"

Don't let your desire for a position make you overlook the fact that a potential employer is less interested in your anxiety for the job than in the question of whether you can become a valuable employee. Your tastes, ambitions, and desires are irrelevant unless they will cause you to do better work. Sometimes, to be sure, they will improve your work. The fact that a job is in line with your long-range ambitions might make you try harder to do it well. Your liking for a certain region might re- duce the likelihood that you would resign because of a desire to live elsewhere. Still, you are wasting space if you talk about such matters without relating them to the way you will function as an employee.

In this connection, if you are applying for one specific position, you can sometimes help your chances by making it clear that you have care- fully considered the demands of the job as well as your own qualifica- tions. This must be done carefully; if you do it crudely, you will appear to be trying to tell the reader what he wants. But if you do it well, you suggest that before you decided to apply, you carefully considered the question, "Is this the right kind of job for a person with my qualifica- tions?" Every one of us knows things about himself that no one else knows. Your potential employer realizes that try as he will, he cannot discover all of your limitations. If you can convince him that you your- self have coolly analyzed your strong points and your weak points and are applying for the job that your abilities qualify you to perform, he will take your application far more seriously.

Objectivity

Keep your letter objective. You will gain nothing from making un- substantiated claims that you are self-reliant, dependable, tactful, and the like. Possibly you are, but such claims are just as likely to appear in the letters of applicants who have no justification for making them. Anyone who has had much experience in hiring employees knows this, and nothing will lose his interest faster than claims that are not sup- ported by objective evidence.

Tone

A satisfactory tone is usually the result of striking the right balance between extremes. You should aim to appear self-confident but not con- ceited; obliging but not ingratiating; earnest but not pompous.

The tone of your letter will result in part from your choice of lan- guage. Many a person whose manner in a conversation is entirely normal becomes stiff and pompous when he writes a letter of application. Phrases such as *earnest desire, intense determination,* and *it is my wish to* are unlikely, however, to increase your chance of obtaining a position. On the contrary, they suggest that you are so eager to be impressive that you have been unable to express yourself in a natural manner. Every- thing said about the language of business letters in Chapter 13 applies with special emphasis to letters of application; and if it is not fresh in your mind, you would do well to review the section dealing with that point.

Excessive Use of "I"

Since you are telling about yourself when you write a letter of application, you will probably find it difficult to avoid using "I" at the beginning of every sentence, and thus making your letter monotonous. It is better, however, to use *I* liberally than to try so hard to avoid it that your sentences become involved and unnatural, or that you sacrifice parallel structure where it might be appropriate. The best way to solve this dilemma is to write the first draft of your letter without worrying about how often *I* appears and then, as you revise it, change a sentence here and there until the use of *I* is no longer conspicuous.

Discussion of Salary Expected

Much of the time you will know whether a position pays an acceptable salary before you apply for it; and even when this is not the case, you are usually in a better strategic position if you let the employer be the first to bring up the subject. If you feel it necessary, however, to mention the salary you would expect, the place to do so is near the end of the letter. Your first job is to convince your reader that your services would be of value, for until he is convinced of this, he is not interested in what it will cost to secure them.

Making Sure All Questions Are Answered

Before you consider your letter complete, make sure that it will not leave any unanswered questions lurking in the reader's mind and making him uneasy. For example, make it easy for him to see that there are no substantial periods of time left unaccounted for in your history. Also, unless it is apparent that the position you apply for is an advancement, let him know why you prefer it to the one that you already hold. If you are not working, let him know the reason unless it is obvious, as it will be of course if you are just finishing school.

Failure to make the picture complete by the inclusion of such information may delay a decision about whether to hire you until there has been another and needless exchange of letters, or may even result in the job going to someone else who seems to be qualified and who has provided all the desired information.

Seeing Things as the Reader Sees Them

One final suggestion is in order. When you are keenly interested in a job and sincerely convinced that you could do it well, you will be strongly tempted to make statements about yourself that sound less impressive to someone else than to you. You will probably feel that these statements are justified, and you may be right in thinking so. The reader, however, does not see things through your eyes. It is therefore a good idea to put yourself in his position. Imagine yourself receiving the letter—from someone whom you do not know any more about than the reader knows about you. Ask yourself, "If I were the reader, would these statements impress me as I hope they will impress the man I am writing to?" If you are capable of using your imagination in this manner, you may eliminate some lines that sounded good to you when you wrote them, but by doing so you will produce a letter that is not diluted by ineffective material and will therefore be more likely to carry conviction.

(Illustrative Specimens Follow)

SPECIMEN LETTERS OF APPLICATION

Following are two letters of application, one of which is accompanied by a data sheet. These letters are in line with the principles described in the preceding discussion; but they are specimens, not models. If a letter of application is assigned, do not borrow phraseology from the specimens.

There is no reason, however, that you should not adapt the specimen data sheet to your needs, for a data sheet is merely a tabulation of facts and makes no pretense of being a personal communication.

Terrace Gardens Trailer Court
Moscow, Idaho
April 10, 1966

U. S. Bureau of Public Roads
914 Jefferson Street
Boise, Idaho

Gentlemen:

    I have learned from the University Placement Bureau that you have openings for several junior engineers. Since I shall receive my University of Idaho degree in Civil Engineering early in June, I should like to apply for one of these openings.

    In addition to the qualifications represented by my degree I can point to a record of eighteen months of experience as an employee of the Idaho State Department of Highways. This experience includes two summers as a surveyor and one year (September, 1964 to September, 1965) as an inspector.

    My education in engineering has all been obtained at the University of Idaho, where my grade average at the end of seven semesters is 2.7. I have taken courses in Timber Structure, Concrete Structure, and Steel Structure Design; but even though design is my special interest, I am willing to start out in some other field if that is where the Bureau needs to place me.

    Since I was raised in this area and like it, I would be glad to work in the Northwest permanently. I am willing, however, to move to some other location if that is where I am needed.

    As for personal information--I was born in Nampa, Idaho and am 23 years old. I am five feet seven inches tall, weigh 130 pounds, have perfect health, and am free from physical handicaps. My dependents are a wife and one child. My leisure interests are swimming, archery, and golf.

    My references, named by permission, are as follows: (1) Professor C. E. Moore, Head of the Department of Civil Engineering, University of Idaho, Moscow, Idaho. (2) James M. Bell, Associate Professor of Civil Engineering, University of Idaho, Moscow, Idaho. (3) Roy Thayer, Idaho Department of Highways, Boise, Idaho.

    I would like to make highway engineering my permanent occupation, so you may be sure that if I have a chance to work for the Bureau, I shall spare no effort to give satisfaction. I can come to Boise at any time, and I would be very much pleased to do so if you will suggest a date when it will be convenient to grant me an interview.

Sincerely yours,

John R. Doe

Figure 17. Well Written Application, Used without Resume.

U.S.S. Providence (CLG-6)
FPO, San Francisco, California
April 15, 1966

Mr. V. S. Casebolt, Director of Personnel
Washington Water Power Company
Spokane, Washington

Dear Mr. Casebolt:

Since I was raised in Spokane, where my father is engaged in the practice
of law, I know enough about the Washington Water Power Company to believe
that you often have openings for electrical engineers. If there is likely
to be such an opening next fall, I should like to apply for it.

My qualifications consist, in brief, of a degree in electrical engineering
from Stanford University and of almost two years service as an officer in
the engineering department of a guided missile cruiser in the U. S. Navy.

While at Stanford, where I spent four years, I concentrated on electronics
design and took fifteen units of electronic laboratory courses. During my
senior year I worked as a technician for the Department of Physics on
electronic instrumentation for nuclear physics projects. This involved
some design work and also repair and construction of such instruments as
pulse height analyzers, metering equipment, and amplifiers.

In the Navy, as division officer in charge of the electrical distribution
system and auxiliary machinery, I directed the work of about thirty-five
men. I hold the rank of Lieutenant (Junior Grade) and am the administrative assistant of the engineering officer.

I am especially interested in a position with your company because I believe it offers an electrical engineer a better opportunity for a career
than he could find elsewhere in the Spokane area, and because I should
like to return to that area and remain there permanently.

I shall be glad to fill out an application black if you will send one;
but in order that much of the information such a blank would call for
will be available to you immediately, I am enclosing a resume that provides it.

When my naval service ends, which will be on July 31, I shall come to
Spokane and would welcome the opportunity to appear for an interview.
I would be glad to wait until September 1 before going to work, but will
do so either before or after that date if you so desire. I shall appreciate any information you can send me about my prospects and to provide
any further information that you desire.

Sincerely yours,

John R. Doe

Figure 18. Well Written Application, Used with Resume.

QUALIFICATIONS OF JOHN R. DOE
Applicant for a position as an electrical engineer

Address: U.S.S. Providence (CLG-6)   Date: April 15, 1966
          FPO, San Francisco, California

PERSONAL INFORMATION

Age - 25   Health - excellent
Place of birth - Auburn, Washington Physical handicaps - none
Weight - 180   Marital status - married, one child
Height - 5 feet 10 inches   Leisure interests - radio, photography

EDUCATION

Central Valley High School, Spokane. Graduated in 1959
Stanford University, Stanford, California. Graduated in 1963
   Degree: Bachelor of Science in Electrical Engineering
   Academic record: 2.8 (3.0 is "B" average)
   Special emphasis in university: Electronic design
   Activities: Member and for one year secretary, American Institute of
                Electrical Engineers (student chapter)

EXPERIENCE

Experience related to electrical engineering

9 months (part time) technician for Stanford Department of Physics
   Duties: Work on electronic instrumentation for nuclear physics projects.
            Some work on design and considerable work on construction and
            repair of pulse height analyzers, metering equipment, and amplifiers.
2 years in Engineering Department of a guided missile cruiser in U.S. Navy
   Duties: Responsibility for distribution system and auxiliary machinery,
            with 35 men to supervise.
   Present rank and position: Lieutenant, J.G. Administrative assistant of
            engineering officer.

Experience - General

Service Station Attendant, East Bay Oil Company, summer of 1960
Clerk, Cardinal Motel, Palo Alto, California, summers of 1961 and 1962

REFERENCES

William L. Wardner, Ph. D.   Carl E. Dennison
Associate Professor of Physics   Professor of Electrical Engineering
Stanford University   Stanford University
Stanford, California   Stanford, California

Commander Floyd O. Todd, U.S.N.   Everett McGregor, Manager
U.S.S. Providence   Cardinal Motel
FPO, San Francisco, California   Palo Alto, California

Figure 19. Specimen Resume   (To be sent with letter shown in Figure 18.)

ASSIGNMENTS

Assignment 1

Write a letter of application setting forth your own qualifications for a position that you might plausibly apply for. Let it be assumed that you definitely know that an opening exists and that the reader knows little if anything about you until he reads your letter. In stating your qualifications limit yourself to facts except that if the instructor permits, you may assume that you are about to complete or have just completed the course you are taking. Obviously, this assumption would include your having gained any experience you are likely to gain before graduation. Use your own judgment about whether to send a resume sheet. Do not make unrealistic offers, such as an offer to travel farther for an interview than you would really be willing to travel under the circumstances.

Assignment 2

Assume that you had been scheduled for an interview with some potential employer's representatives who were on your campus or in the town where you are located. For some reason, such as an attack of influenza, you were forced to cancel the interview. You have learned that in the near future a representative of this employer will be holding interviews in some other city perhaps fifty or one hundred miles away. Write to him asking him if he will interview you there.

You may assume, if you like, that you have already submitted an application blank or, if you prefer, that you are sending it with your letter. If other assumptions would make the assignment more plausible in your particular case they are also permissible. The basic situation, however, should remain unchanged. In this letter you are attempting to demonstrate your interest in the company concerned and seize the opportunity to say enough about yourself to arouse interest.

Assignment 3

You have been negotiating with a potential employer and have reason to believe that the offer of a position is likely. Another employer with whom you have also been in contact makes you a definite offer. You feel that a position with the first employer mentioned would be preferable, but the one you are offered is good enough that you do not wish to lose your chance for it.

Write a letter to the employer who made the offer. You should probably tell him that you have been negotiating for another position but the major purpose of your letter, at least ostensibly, should be to ask some questions you would like to have answered before you make a definite decision.

Assignment 4

Under the same conditions described in the preceding assignment, write a letter to the potential employer who has not offered you a job, telling him about the offer that you have received. Without letting your letter sound like a threat, let him know that you will soon have to accept or decline the offer you have received. Try to make your reader understand that though a position with his company would be your first choice, the other position is good enough that you are reluctant to turn it down unless you can feel confident of something better. Try in a tactful manner to obtain a definite decision as soon as possible, or at least to obtain definite information about when a decision will be made.

Assignment 5

Assume that you have been interviewed by the representative of a potential employer four or five days ago. Write a follow-up letter of the kind described in the chapter.

Part Four

HANDBOOK
OF
FUNDAMENTALS

PARAGRAPHS

General Comment

The following discussion is concerned mainly with the ordinary, run-of-the-mill paragraphs that comprise the bulk of most writing, technical or otherwise. It also contains brief comments on paragraphs of isolated statement. To be sure, there are other kinds of paragraphs: introductory, transitional, and concluding paragraphs, and paragraphs of dialogue; but the first three of these four kinds do not give rise to much trouble and the fourth is rarely seen in technical writing.

The function of a paragraph is to group together sentences that concern the same topic and combine to form a thought unit. Some of the points to bear in mind in producing paragraphs that perform this function are as follows:

1. Effective paragraphs do not result from merely beginning a new paragraph whenever the one you are writing has grown long enough, nor even from merely beginning a new paragraph whenever you take up a new topic. Your paragraphs will be effective only if you know, each time you begin one, what point you intend it to make or at least what ground it will cover. That is, as you begin a paragraph you should have a definite idea about where you will be at its end.

2. A paragraph is likely to be more effective if its basic idea is expressed in a topic sentence. A topic sentence is usually most useful near the beginning of the paragraph, but it may be placed at the end; occasionally, for the sake of emphasis, it may be placed at the beginning and restated at the end in different words. Wherever it appears, it should dominate the paragraph, and the rest of the paragraph should serve mainly to develop it.

3. "Developing" a topic sentence means providing the additional facts and ideas that are needed to make it clear and acceptable, and possibly to indicate its importance. If a sentence does not need such development, then either the idea it conveys is not big enough to form the basis of a paragraph or else—much less frequently—it should stand alone as a single-sentence paragraph. If an idea cannot be developed in a paragraph of reasonable length, then it should be broken up into ideas of paragraph size.

4. If the topic sentence is merely implied and the reader must grasp the point of the paragraph from the details themselves, the first sentence should never fail to create an accurate impression about the topic and the basic idea of the paragraph. A reader who is skimming rapidly should not be misled about the contents of a paragraph when he looks at its first sentence.

5. Sometimes it is necessary, for the sake of fairness and completeness, to include material that runs counter to the main point of the paragraph. This material should not be placed at the end, for the end should strengthen, not weaken, the impression the paragraph is supposed to make. If some facts in a paragraph amount to concessions, the best pattern is likely to be: (1) a topic sentence making the main point clear, (2) the facts that must be conceded—introduced in a manner that shows them to be concessions, and (3) the material that establishes the main point of the paragraph despite the concessions.

6. If it is necessary to use transitional material to bridge the gap between two paragraphs, such material should open the second of the two rather than close the first. Such placement avoids weakening the emphasis of the first, and helps to introduce the topic of the second. Also, since most writers do place transitional material at the beginning of the new paragraph, that is where the reader will expect it to be.

Length of Paragraphs

One need only look at contemporary writing to see that paragraphs vary widely in length. The special kinds that were mentioned at the beginning of this discussion are often extremely short. The same can be said of the paragraphs in popularized treatments of technical subjects, and of paragraphs in publications with columns so narrow that long paragraphs would appear difficult to read.

Nevertheless, normal paragraphs serve their purpose best when they contain from three or four to seven or eight sentences—which would be from 75 to perhaps as much as 200 words. Experience has shown that paragraphs of such length usually present the material to the reader in thought units that he can grasp most effectively at one time. Occasionally it may be desirable to have a paragraph consist of only one or two sentences, but when a substantial piece of writing consists mainly of one-sentence paragraphs, the reader receives no help in determining which sentences are related to the same topic.

Paragraphs of Isolated Statement

Paragraphs of isolated statement are statements that do not need to be expanded upon but do not merge into the development of a single larger idea. For example, in presenting a series of conclusions each consisting of a single sentence, it is often desirable to treat each item as a separate paragraph. The same treatment is often suitable for some instruction material and for various other kinds of material, including much of the material in this Handbook.

Writing paragraphs of isolated statement obviously does not call for any special technique. They should be recognized as a distinct and acceptable type, but their existence should not be regarded as justifying the excessive use of one-sentence paragraphs when the subject matter calls for related rather than independent statements.

CORRECTNESS IN GRAMMAR

The following discussion has only one purpose—to help you to avoid the errors in grammar that occur most frequently. Consequently its contents are limited to the information that will best serve that purpose. A definition of grammatical terms appears later in the Handbook.

There are times, of course, when literate people disagree about whether some form is right or wrong. Many a usage that was once considered incorrect is now acceptable to liberal authorities. The point of view in this book is liberal, but in many cases both sides are presented when a form is disputed. This has been done on the grounds that if there are still many literate people who consider something to be an error, those who use this book are entitled to be warned. In this connection it is interesting to note that many a liberal authority concedes—in fact takes pains to point out—the acceptability of forms that he avoids in his own work.

Case of Nouns and Pronouns

Nouns and pronouns may be nominative, possessive, or objective in case. Nouns are identical in nominative and objective cases, but change form when they become possessive. (See pages 375-6.) Pronouns vary in form as shown by the following list:

Nominative	Possessive	Objective
I	my, mine	me
you	your, yours	you
he	his	him
she	her, hers	her
it	its	it
we	our, ours	us
they	their, theirs	them
who	whose	whom

All pronouns except those listed above and others derived from them, for example *whoever*, which becomes *whomever* in the objective case, are identical in nominative and objective cases and form the possessive, if at all, just as nouns form it.

The possessive forms *your*, *its*, and *whose* should not be confused with *you're* (you are), *it's* (it is), and *who's* (who is).

The three cases are used in accordance with the following rules:

1. The nominative case is used for the subject of a verb.

> VIOLATION: We shall hire *whomever* applies.
> CORRECT: . . . *whoever* applies. (The word in question is the subject of *applies* rather than the object of *hire*. The object of *hire* is the entire clause *whoever applies*.)
>
> VIOLATION: *Us* draftsmen need better light.
> CORRECT: *We* draftsmen . . . (*We* is correct, for it is in apposition with *draftsmen* and thus is a subject of *need*.)
>
> VIOLATION: He is older than *me*.
> CORRECT: He is older than *I*. (*I* is correct for it is the subject of the implied verb *am*.)

2. The nominative case is used for a subjective complement.

> EXAMPLES: It is *I*. It was *we* workers who objected.
>
> VIOLATION: It was *him*. It was *me* whom you saw.
> CORRECT: It was *he*. It was *I* whom you saw.

Note: In spite of the rule, such forms as "It was *me*" and "This is *him*" are widely used in conversation even by literate people, because the forms that are formally correct sometimes sound stilted. It is still best, however, to follow the rule in any piece of writing where formal style is called for; and even in conversation many discriminating people try to phrase their remarks so that they do not need to choose between stiffness and violation of the rule.

3. The possessive case is used to indicate possession.

> VIOLATIONS: A violation of this rule almost always results from the fact that the possessive and some other form are pronounced exactly alike. (Examples: *it's* and *its*, *who's* and *whose*, *ladies* and *lady's*. *It's* is correct only for *it is*, and *who's* for *who is*. *Ladies* is plural, not possessive.) Thus the errors do not indicate ignorance of the need for the possessive case, but rather ignorance of (or carelessness about) how the possessive case is formed. Information on forms that are correct for the possessive case appears in the list of pronouns at the opening of this discussion and in the discussion of the apostrophe on pages 375-6.

4. The possessive case is used for a noun or pronoun that precedes and modifies a gerund.

> VIOLATION: They objected to *him* altering the records.
> CORRECT: They objected to *his* altering the records.

Note: When a pronoun has no possessive form, for example *this* or *that,* Rule 4 must of course be disregarded. It is also disregarded if the presence of other words between the noun or pronoun and the gerund modified would make the possessive sound unnatural.

> CORRECT: There is no record of *this* being done before.
> CORRECT: The chance of *anyone* in the vicinity wanting to buy the property is slight.

5. If a noun or pronoun stands for something inanimate, the possessive case should be avoided, if possible.

> UNDESIRABLE: The *furnace's* grates; the *street's* surface.
> PREFERRED: The grates *of the furnace;* the surface *of the street.*

Note: There are many exceptions to this rule, especially when the noun in question involves time, as "an *hour's* work," or a *day's* pay." Exceptions are also permissible to avoid awkward constructions.

6. The objective case is used for the object of a verb, verbal, or preposition.

> DIRECT OBJECT OF VERB: The letter encouraged *him.*
> INDIRECT OBJECT OF VERB: The letter gave *him* useful information.
> OBJECT OF VERBAL: *Whom* do you intend to hire? (*Whom* is the object of the infinitive phrase *to hire.*)
> OBJECT OF VERBAL: Answering *him* was difficult. (*Him* is the object of the gerund *answering.*)
> OBJECT OF PREPOSITION: Three of *us* were chosen. (*Us* is the object of the preposition *of.*)
>
> COMMON VIOLATIONS: They offered my partner and *I* a good contract. (*Me* would be correct, for the term is used as the indirect object of *offered.* This type of error results from excessive concern about avoiding *me* as a subject, as in "John and *me* are going." Uncertainty as to what form to use after *and* can be settled quickly by eliminating *and* along with the term that precedes it. "They offered *I* a contract" would obviously be wrong.)
>
> All of *we* draftsmen were questioned. (*Us* would be correct, for *us* along with *draftsmen,* is the object of the preposition *of.* The subject of the sentence is neither *we* nor *draftsmen,* but *all.*)
>
> He is a man *who,* in spite of his youth, we can trust. (The parenthetical phrase *in spite of his youth* obscures the fact that the objective *whom* rather than the nominative *who* is needed, for the term is the object of *trust.*)
>
> *Who* do you give the answer to? (*Whom* would be correct, for the term is used as the object of *to.*)

Note: In conversation and in informal writing there is a strong tendency to permit *who* at the beginning of a sentence despite the rules. In formal writing, however, it is still desirable to follow the rule.

7. The objective case is used for either the subject or object of an infinitive.

> CORRECT: They expect *him* to do well. (*Him* is the subject of the infinitive *to do*. The object of *expect* is not *him*, but the entire infinitive phrase, *him to do well.*
>
> CORRECT: We knew *him* to be competent.
>
> CORRECT: We knew it to be *him.*

Agreement of Verb and Its Subject

A verb must agree with its subject in number, person, and gender.

Practically all of the violations of this rule have to do with disagreement in number. Person and gender will therefore not be discussed here. Rules involving agreement in number are as follows:

1. When the subject of a verb is compound and its parts are joined by *and,* it ordinarily takes a plural verb.

> EXAMPLE: The time and the place *are* uncertain.

2. When the subject of a verb is compound in form but singular in meaning, it takes a singular verb.

> EXAMPLE: Blue and gold *is* a pleasing color combination.

3. When the subject of a verb is compound and its parts are joined by *or,* it takes a singular verb if its parts are singular and a plural verb if its parts are plural. If its parts differ in number, it agrees with the part that is closer.

> CORRECT: Either the oak or the elm *is* to be removed.
> CORRECT: Either the chairs or the tables *are* to be refinished Monday.
> CORRECT: Either the cow or the pigs *are* to be slaughtered.

4. The word *number,* numerical quantities, and fractions take either singular or plural verbs according to their meanings.

> The number of complaints *has* been increasing.
> A number of changes *have* been made.
> Three days *is* a long wait. (*Three days* refers to a single period of time, even though *days* is plural in form.)
> Three days *have* passed since your letter was mailed. (Each day is conceived as a unit rather than as part of a single period of time.)

5. A collective noun takes a singular verb when the group it refers to is regarded as a unit, but takes a plural verb when the statement concerns the members of the group as individuals.

> The crowd *was* breaking up.
> The crowd *were* going to their homes.
> The committee *has* adjourned.

The committee *have* taken their seats.

Note: when you feel that following the rule would result in an awkward sentence, revise the sentence. For example: "The *people* in the crowd (rather than *the crowd*) were going to *their* homes."

6. Some nouns that are plural in form take singular verbs when singular in meaning—especially nouns ending in *ics*.

> CORRECT: The *news is* encouraging. *Mathematics is* difficult. *Tactics wins* battles.
> BUT: Our *tactics are* proving successful.

Note: For an excellent discussion of this subject, see the entry under *ics* in *Webster's Seventh New Collegiate Dictionary.*

7. Intervening words should not be allowed to interfere with the agreement of a verb with its subject. Many of the errors in agreement are caused by intervening words.

> CORRECT: Good management plus favorable economic conditions *was* responsible for the improvement. (The phrase introduced by *plus* is not part of the subject.)

8. A verb agrees with its subject even though a subjective complement that follows is different in number.

> EXAMPLE: The border *was* shrubs of several species.

Note: When you feel that following the rule would result in an awkward-sounding sentence, revise the sentence. For example: "The border *was composed of* shrubs of several species."

Agreement of Pronouns with Antecedents

The Rules. The basic rule is that a pronoun and its antecedent should agree in person, number, and gender. When a pronoun has a compound antecedent the following additional rules apply:

1. If the antecedent consists of two or more nouns connected by *and*, the pronoun should be plural.

> The table and the chair showed *their* age.

2. If the antecedent consists of two nouns connected by *or*, the pronoun should be singular if both nouns are singular, and plural if both nouns are plural. If the nouns differ in number, the pronoun should agree with the nearer.

> You may pay the bill if the manager or the auditor will give *his* permission.
> You may use either bolts or screws if *they* are large enough.
> Either the bolts or the clamp must have been loose in *its* place.
> Either the clamp or the bolts must have been loose in *their* places.

3. If the antecedent is two or more nouns connected by *nor*, the pronoun should be singular if both nouns are singular, but *plural if either noun is plural.*

> Neither the manager nor the auditor gave *his* consent.
> Neither the bolts nor the screws had fallen from *their* places.
> Neither the employer nor the employees were willing to change *their* attitudes.
> Neither the employees nor the employer were willing to change *their* attitudes.

The Errors. When a pronoun does not agree with its antecedent, the disagreement, almost always, is in number. The error does not usually result from ignorance of the rule, but from uncertainty about whether the antecedent itself should be treated as singular or plural. Numerous though the errors are, a surprisingly large proportion of them result from one of three conditions. Any person who can master these three conditions will thenceforth have little trouble with the reference of pronouns: (1) when the antecedent is a *collective* noun; (2) when the antecedent is *a noun of common gender;* (3) when the antecedent is not a noun but *an indefinite pronoun.*

1. *Reference of a pronoun to a collective noun:* A collective noun is sometimes treated as singular and sometimes as plural. It is treated as singular when the statement where it appears applies to the group as a group, and plural when the statement applies to the members of the group as individuals.

> CORRECT: The board of directors makes *its* report.
> CORRECT: The board of directors took *their* seats.

The forms that are wrong or at least undesirable occur when a writer first treats a collective noun as singular, then as plural—usually making it the subject of a singular verb and the antecedent of a plural pronoun.

> DOUBTFUL: The orchestra *waits* with *their* instruments ready.
> DOUBTFUL: The team *was* photographed wearing *their* new uniforms.
> IMPROVED: The orchestra waits with instruments ready.
> IMPROVED: The team was photographed wearing new uniforms.
> IMPROVED: The members of the team were photographed wearing *their* new uniforms.

2. *Reference of a pronoun to a noun with common gender:* Writers sometimes make the error of using a plural pronoun because of uncertainty about whether to use a pronoun of the masculine or the feminine gender in referring to a noun such as *spectator, student,* or *employee.* The correct form to use, in case of doubt, is the masculine.

> WRONG: A person should be able to rise above *their* environment.

CORRECT BUT STILTED: A person should be able to rise above *his or her* environment.

CORRECT: A person should be able to rise above *his* environment.

3. *Reference of a pronoun to an indefinite pronoun:* Sometimes the antecedent of a pronoun is not a noun, but an indefinite pronoun. Most of the indefinite pronouns are listed below. Each word on this list is treated as singular, even though some of them are plural in meaning. Hence any pronoun referring to a word on this list should be singular in number.

Indefinite Pronouns

one	everyone	somebody
anyone	anybody	nobody
someone	everybody	each
no one		

All the words on the list are common in gender. Hence, in an effort to achieve agreement in gender, writers use the plural *their,* which can be common gender, in order to avoid *he* or *she.*

This tendency is intensified by the fact that some of the words, for example *everyone,* are actually plural in meaning. Nevertheless, all the words listed are treated as singular (no one would think of writing "Everyone *are* here"), and except as noted below are not to be referred to by the plural *their.* Unless the feminine singular is known to be appropriate in the individual case, the masculine singular (*he, his,* or *him*) should be used. *His or her* is of course correct but is so stilted as to be undesirable.

DOUBTFUL: No one should neglect *their* responsibilities.
CORRECT: No one should neglect *his* responsibilities.

DOUBTFUL: Everyone should pay *their* bills promptly.
CORRECT: Everyone should pay *his* bills promptly.

WRONG: Each of those hired will be required to supply *their* own tools.
CORRECT: Each of those hired will be required to supply *his* own tools.

Exceptions. The rules just explained apply to writing that is formal in style, and many people who are careful with their language follow them even when writing or speaking informally. There is a contemporary tendency, however, to relax the rules. Some of the more liberal modern authorities would regard it as correct to use *their* when the indefinite pronoun referred to is plural in meaning. At least one president and more than one senator, speaking on television, have been heard to use *their* when the antecedent was *everyone.*

Agreement of a Demonstrative Adjective with its Object

A demonstrative adjective (*this, these, that,* and *those*) should agree with the word it modifies.

> WRONG: *These* (or *those*) kind of brakes may give trouble.
> CORRECT: *This* (or *that*) kind . . .

Note: In the error illustrated, the demonstrative adjective agrees with a closely related plural noun when it should agree with the singular noun that it actually modifies.

Adjectives and Adverbs—General Comment

1. An adjective may modify a noun or pronoun directly (in which use it is called an attributive adjective) or as a predicate adjective. Used as a predicate adjective, it applies to a noun or pronoun by assistance of a verb.

> The *old* building should be abandoned. (Attributive modifier. *Old* modifies *building.*)
> The building is *old.* (Predicate adjective. *Old* relates to *building* by assistance of the verb *is.*)

2. An adverb is used to modify a verb, an adjective, or another adverb.

> The snow had melted *rapidly,* so what might have been a *very* difficult trip was made *quite easily.* (*Rapidly* modifies the verb *melted; very* modifies the adjective *difficult; quite* modifies the adverb *easily*—which itself modifies the verb *was made.*)

3. Use of an adjective instead of an adverb to modify a verb is usually a serious error.

> WRONG: The car runs *good.* (The adjective *good* should not modify the verb *runs.*)
> CORRECT: The car runs *well.* (*Well* is correctly used as an adverb. In some meanings, *well* is also an adjective; but *good* is never correct as an adverb except when the phrase *as good as* appears in such a sentence as "He was *as good as* elected.")
>
> WRONG: I can do it *easy.*
> CORRECT: I can do it *easily.* (*Easily* is the adverbial form of easy.)
>
> WRONG: I can do it *easier* than he can.
> CORRECT: I can do it *more easily* than he can.
>
> WRONG: Among all those who protested, he talked the *angriest.*
> CORRECT: Among all those who protested, he talked *most angrily.*

Note: The error of using an adjective to modify a verb is especially prevalent, as shown in the last two examples of errors, in the comparative and superlative degrees. (For discussion of degree, see Rule 7 below.)

4. Use of an adjective to modify another adjective or an adverb (as

contrasted with an adverb modifying a verb, discussed in Rule 3) is not formally correct, but sometimes may pass as colloquial rather than being considered a serious error.

> WRONG: The car was running *considerable* better. (*Considerable* is an adjective and should not modify the adjective *better*.)
> WRONG: The next day, I felt *some* better. (*Some* is an adjective, not an adverb. It should be replaced by the adverb *somewhat*.)
>
> WRONG: It was *real* nice of you.
> CORRECT: . . . *very* nice of you.
>
> WRONG: It was made of *pretty* good material.
> CORRECT: . . . *rather,* or *quite,* or *fairly* good material.
>
> WRONG: He was late *most* every morning.
> CORRECT: . . . *almost* every morning.

Note: Real, pretty, and *most* might be regarded as colloquialisms above, but it would be better, except on an extremely informal occasion, to replace them by words that are recognized as adverbs. There is no way, except by familiarity with the specific word, to determine what adjectives are considered merely colloquial rather than actually wrong when used as adverbs.

5. Adverbs are rarely misused for adjectives as direct modifiers, but use of an adverb when a predicate adjective is needed is an extremely common error. A predicate adjective follows the verb but does not modify it. Rather, it relates to the noun or pronoun used before the verb as a subject. This use should not be confused with the use of an adverb to modify the verb. A predicate adjective characteristically follows a "linking" verb such as *be, become, seem, appear, smell, feel, look, sound, taste.*

> CORRECT: The glue is *sticky.* (Predicate adjective. *Sticky* refers to the noun *glue* rather than modifying the verb *is.*)
> CORRECT: The man looked *angry.* (Predicate adjective. *Angry* describes the man rather than changing or adding to the meaning of the verb *looked.*)
> CORRECT: The man looked *angrily* at the intruder. (Adverb modifying verb. *Looked,* in this sentence, has a different meaning than in the example above. It is not used as a linking verb, but indicates an action. *Angrily* tells the manner in which the action was performed.)
> WRONG: The dinner smells *well.* (*Well,* except in the sense of healthy, is an adverb, not an adjective. An adjective is needed here, for *smell* does not indicate an action and *well* tells a quality of the dinner rather than modifying *smells.*)
> CORRECT: The dinner smells *good.* (Predicate adjective.)
> CORRECT: The dog smells *eagerly* at the bone. (Note the different meaning of *smells,* and note that *eagerly,* an adverb of manner, modifies *smells.*)

CORRECT: The clerk felt *bad* about his error. (Predicate adjective.)
CORRECT: The motor was running *badly*. (Adverb modifying verb.)

Note: Those who make this type of error do so because they have been corrected for such errors as "The motor is running *bad*," or "He reads *good*." In an effort to avoid using an adjective when an adverb is needed, they are reluctant to use an adjective after a verb, even when an adjective is correct. One use of *badly,* however, calls for special comment: There is a strong tendency at present to accept "The clerk felt *badly* about his error" as correct despite the rule. *Bad,* of course, is also correct; in fact, it is preferable.

6. When the question of whether to use an adjective or an adverb has been answered, it may still be necessary to determine whether the particular word one wishes to use is an adjective, is an adverb, or may be used as either. Often, the adverbial form of a word may be distinguished from the adjective form because of its *ly* ending, as in *strong, strongly; clever, cleverly; sure, surely.* The *ly* ending, however, is not always a means of identification, for there are some adjectives that end in *ly* (*friendly, manly*) and many adverbs that do not end in *ly.* In case of doubt, it is advisable to consult a dictionary to determine the part of speech of the word in question.

7. Most adjectives and adverbs may be positive, comparative, or superlative in degree. The change in degree is achieved by more than one method, as illustrated in the following examples:

Adjectives

Positive	*Comparative*	*Superlative*
easy	easier	easiest
large	larger	largest
curious	more curious	most curious
good	better	best
bad	worse	worst

Adverbs

Positive	*Comparative*	*Superlative*
slow or slowly	slower or more slowly	slowest
easily	more easily	most easily
quickly	more quickly	most quickly
well	better	best
badly	worse	worst

Note: Some terms, such as *perfect* and *unique,* cannot logically be used in the comparative or superlative degrees. *More perfect* is a contradiction in terms, as are *more unique, more empty,* etc. It would be logical, however, to use such expressions as *more nearly* perfect, unique, full, or empty.

The comparative rather than the superlative degree must be used to indicate comparison of two objects. The superlative degree is used when three or more objects are compared.

> WRONG: His was the *best* drawing of the two drawings that were submitted.
> CORRECT: His was the *better* drawing of the two that were submitted.
> CORRECT: His was the *best* of the three drawings that were submitted.

UNITY AND COHERENCE IN THE SENTENCE

Unity of Thought

In this discussion we are concerned only with the declarative sentence—the sentence that makes a statement. Such a sentence may lack unity either because it fails to include all the material needed or because it contains extraneous material. The first of these two weaknesses may be prevented by the avoidance of primer style (pages 13-14). The second may be guarded against by being alert to the question of whether all the material in the sentence really merges to make a single statement. Consider, for example, the sentence, "Mack trucks, which are now being produced in three foreign countries, would be the best kind for us to buy for hauling logs and lumber." There is no clear reason for placing the fact about foreign production in a sentence with the purpose this one seems to have. There are many times, of course, when certain facts may be presented as either one sentence or more than one; but this does not justify inserting into a sentence facts that are not related to its purpose.

Sentence unity also demands that we do not end one sentence and begin another at an illogical place. Consider these sentences:

> The Ellsworth machine has ample power and those who have used it say it is easy to operate, but it is extremely noisy. Also, it is somewhat bulky.

The first of these two sentences names two good features and one bad. The second mentions another bad feature. If we assume that two sentences are desirable, sentence unity would be improved by telling the good features in one sentence and the bad in the other. A general rule to follow is: for the sake of sentence unity, construct your sentences so that they draw together the facts that are most closely related.

Unity of Structure

When a sentence lacks unity of structure it may be faulty in either of two respects: 1. It may be a mere fragment because it lacks some element necessary for grammatical completeness. 2. It may contain the error variously called a "comma splice," "comma fault," or "comma error." (A "run-on sentence" is basically the same error as a comma splice and is covered under that heading.)

Fragment Treated as a Sentence. A declarative sentence, to be complete grammatically, must contain a subject and a finite verb. Thus a participial or gerund phrase, a prepositional phrase, or a dependent clause is not a complete sentence, regardless of its length or complexity. Actually, it should not be necessary to subject a sentence to grammatical analysis in order to determine whether it is complete. If it is read attentively, a fragment may be distinguished from a complete sentence by the simple fact that it does not actually make a statement.

The error may usually be corrected by either of two methods: joining the fragment onto a sentence with which it is naturally connected, or changing it so that it may stand by itself as a complete sentence. The following examples show how fragments may be joined to other sentences or rewritten so that they are structurally complete. Whether the corrections indicated would be the best corrections possible would depend on the context.

> FRAGMENT: The volume grew lower and lower. *Finally becoming so slight as to be inaudible.* (Participial phrase rather than sentence.)
> CORRECT: The volume grew lower and lower, finally becoming so slight as to be inaudible.

> FRAGMENT: He was employed by the government for six years. *First in Washington, and later in New York.* (Prepositional phrases.)
> CORRECT: He was employed by the government for six years, first in Washington and later in New York.

> FRAGMENT: The company was losing money steadily. *Although sales were as high as in previous years.* (Subordinate clause rather than independent clause.)
> CORRECT: The company was losing money steadily even though the sales were as high as in previous years.

> FRAGMENT: Some of the expenses were increasing. *Overhead, for example, and the cost of raw materials.* (The italicized expression has no verb; it is used in apposition to *some of the expenses* in the preceding sentence.)
> CORRECT: Some of the expenses were increasing. Overhead, for example, and the cost of raw materials were higher than before.

Note: Skilled authors do sometimes use incomplete sentences as a device to secure special effects. Dickens, for example, wrote: "Dogs, indistinguishable in the mire. Horses scarcely better; splashed to their very blinkers." But this incompleteness was no accident. Until you are skillful enough never to violate the rules of grammar accidentally, however, you should not violate them on purpose to secure a special literary effect.

The Comma Splice. When a sentence contains two independent clauses, the punctuation between them must be a semicolon unless they are joined by a coordinating conjunction. Use of a comma instead of a semicolon on such an occasion is the error variously called comma splice, comma blunder, or comma error. It is more than a mere mistake in punctuation; it is a serious error in sentence structure—an indication that the writer does not know when he has completed a statement.

The only coordinating conjunctions are *and, but, for, or, nor,* and sometimes *so* and *yet.* These should be distinguished from conjunctive adverbs such as *however, moreover, therefore, consequently, further- more,* and many others. A handy rule of thumb for avoiding the comma splice is found in the fact that a conjunctive adverb may be buried within the clause that it introduces. Thus, if a connective word might come elsewhere than between the clauses it connects, a semicolon rather than a comma is necessary. For example:

> I have inspected it, *but* I shall be glad to inspect it again. (*But* could come only between the clauses.)
>
> I have inspected it; *however,* I shall be glad to inspect it again. (*However* might, if one desired, be placed after *glad* rather than at the beginning of its clause; thus it is a conjunctive adverb, and a semicolon must be placed between the clauses.)

There are various ways in which a comma blunder may be corrected. The simplest but not always the best is to replace the comma by a semi- colon or a period. Another possibility is to change the conjunctive adverb to a coordinating conjunction. Often, however, it is better to change one of the independent clauses to some other form.

> COMMA SPLICE: We shall be forced to find a new route, the grades on the one suggested are too severe.
>
> CORRECT: We shall be forced to find a new route; the grades on the one suggested are too severe. (Correction by change in punctu- ation.)
>
> CORRECT: We shall be forced to find a new route, for the grades on the one suggested are too severe. (Correction by using a co- ordinating conjunction.)
>
> CORRECT: The grades on the route suggested are so severe that we shall be forced to find a new route. (Correction by change in con- struction.)
>
> CORRECT: The severity of the grades on the route suggested makes it necessary to find a new route. (Correction by change in con- struction.)

Coherence

If writing is to be clear, every sentence must be coherent; that is, it must hold together. The relationship of every part to every other part and to the entire sentence must be unmistakable. To achieve this result it is necessary to consider the order of the parts, their structure, and the connectives that indicate their relationship. Lack of coherence often results from failure to apply the following principles:

1. Similar parts of a sentence should be expressed in parallel form so far as their contents permit.

> NOT PARALLEL: Wood was used for some of the parts, but others were made of metal.
> PARALLEL: Wood was used for some of the parts, and metal for others.

> NOT PARALLEL: Students in the night school learn auto mechanics, and are also taught drafting.
> PARALLEL: Students in night school learn auto mechanics and drafting.
> PARALLEL: Students in night school are taught auto mechanics and drafting.

(a) There should be no unnecessary change in the subject or voice. (Change in one frequently results in change in the other.)

> NOT PARALLEL: While the mechanic was tuning the motor, the tires and battery were checked by his assistant.
> PARALLEL: While the mechanic was tuning the motor, his assistant checked the tires and battery.

> NOT PARALLEL: Washing the equipment was one of his duties, and he was also expected to keep the supply bins filled.
> PARALLEL: He was expected to wash the equipment and to keep the supply bins filled.

(b) The elements of a series should be parallel in form.

> WRONG: A technician must learn the *use, upkeep,* and *how to repair* equipment.
> CORRECT: A technician must learn the *use, upkeep,* and *repair* of equipment.

If *the* is used before any element in a series except the first (in which case it applies to all the elements), it must be used before every element.

> WRONG: Information is needed about the length, the width, thickness, and weight of the sample.
> CORRECT: Information is needed about the length, width, thickness, and weight of the sample.

If *a* or *an* rather than *the* is the suitable word to precede any element in a series, it should usually be used before *each element where it would be suitable.* This is especially necessary if some elements are plural.

> EXAMPLE: We must bring nails, screws, *a* hammer, *a* chisel, and glue.

When the elements of a series cannot be made parallel in form without producing an awkward result, the phraseology should be changed so as to make it clear that a series is not intended.

WRONG: The chips are mixed with liquor and steam, fed into the apparatus, and the cooking process takes place as the mixture moves through the tubes.

CORRECT: After the chips are mixed with liquor and steam, they are fed into the apparatus, where the cooking process takes place as the mixture moves through the tubes.

(c) The elements that follow correlative conjunctions (*either . . . or, neither . . . nor,* etc.) should be parallel in form.

WRONG: It can either be shipped by freight or by express.

CORRECT: It can be shipped either by freight or by express.

2. Connectives should clearly and accurately indicate the thought relationship of the elements that they connect. The connectives that give most trouble are *as* and *while*.

(a) *As* is sometimes ambiguous because it might indicate either time or cause.

AMBIGUOUS: *As* the mixture was heated, its color changed.

CLEAR: When the mixture was heated, its color changed.

CLEAR: Because the mixture was heated, its color changed.

(b) *While* has two legitimate meanings, "during the time that" and "although." (Unfortunately, it is also loosely used in place of *and*.) As a result, many a sentence in which it appears is ambiguous. Unless the context makes its meaning instantly clear, it should be used sparingly for *although* and not at all for *and*.

AMBIGUOUS: *While* his breathing was becoming more rapid, his fever had fallen.

CLEAR: *Although* his breathing had become more rapid, his fever was falling.

CLEAR: At the same time that his breathing was becoming more rapid, his fever was falling.

AMBIGUOUS: Their truck tires are good, *while* their passenger car tires are even better.

IMPROVED: Their truck tires are good, *and* (or *but*) their passenger car tires are even better.

3. Reference of a pronoun to its antecedent should be clear and unmistakable.

(a) There should be only one word to which a pronoun may plausibly refer.

AMBIGUOUS (BECAUSE OF INDIRECT DISCOURSE): The manager notified the foreman that *he* was being transferred. (Manager or foreman?)

CLEAR: The foreman received notice of his transfer in a conference with the manager. (*His* has been related to *foreman* before the manager is mentioned.)

CLEAR: The manager, as he mentioned to the foreman, was being transferred.

Note: It is often suggested in textbooks that unclearness caused by indirect discourse be eliminated by changing it to direct discourse. This is rarely appropriate, however, in technical writing.

> AMBIGUOUS: Dairy workers should not be allowed to care for cows when *they* are ill.
>
> CLEAR: When dairy workers are ill, they should not be allowed to care for cows.
>
> CLEAR: Dairy workers should not be allowed to care for cows that are ill.

(b) Reference of a pronoun to a "weak" antecedent should be avoided.

> WEAK REFERENCE: The engineers must give special consideration to the smokestacks. *They* must be sturdy enough to withstand earthquakes. (Engineers or stacks?)
>
> IMPROVED: The smokestacks must be sturdy enough to withstand earthquakes, so the engineers must give them special consideration.

(c) A pronoun should not be used when its antecedent must be inferred by the reader because it has been expressed in some other form than a noun.

> VAGUE REFERENCE: An employee who is injured should receive first aid even though *it* may not be serious. (*It* has as an antecedent the idea of *injury;* but the idea is not present as a noun and must be inferred from the verb *injured.*)
>
> CORRECT: An employee who is injured should receive first aid even though *his injury* may not be serious.

(d) Vague use of *it* or *they* when a specific noun could be used should be avoided. (This rule would not prevent the use of *it* as in "*It* is raining," or "*It* is apparent that . . . .")

> VAGUE REFERENCE: *It* says in the report that the method is efficient.
> EXPLICIT: *The report* says that the method is efficient.
>
> VAGUE REFERENCE: In restricted areas, *they* require that visitors be identified.
> EXPLICIT: *The company* requires that in restricted areas, visitors be identified.
> EXPLICIT: In restricted areas, visitors must be identified.

(e) Use of *which* or *this* to refer to the general idea of a preceding clause or phrase rather than to a specific word is condemned by some textbooks but indulged in by many reputable writers. When this use can be avoided easily, it should be avoided.

> VAGUE REFERENCE: He has been studying every night, *which* should increase his value to the company.
>
> IMPROVED: He has been studying every night, so his value to the company should be increasing.
>
> IMPROVED: The study he has been doing every night should increase his value to the company.

(f) Use of *you* for *one* is often inappropriate. Unless you are using an informal style, do not write *you* unless you mean the reader. If *one* sounds stiff, change the sentence.

> INFORMAL: The factory is interesting, but *you* are not allowed to enter without permission.
> FORMALLY CORRECT: The factory is interesting, but *one* is not allowed to enter without permission.
> CORRECT: The factory is interesting, but *visitors* are not allowed to enter without permission.

(g) Use of the same pronoun to refer to two different antecedents should be avoided.

> CONFUSING: Although *it* is less crowded on the second floor, *it* is not strong enough to support the heavy machinery. (The first *it* is indefinite in meaning; the second refers to *floor*.)
> CORRECT: Although the second floor is less crowded, it is not strong enough to support the heavy machinery.

4. Modifiers (words, phrases, or clauses used to change or limit the meaning of other words) should be as close to what they modify as it is possible to place them without awkwardness. No possible doubt should exist as to what is being modified.

(a) Certain adverbs are especially likely to be put in the wrong position. These adverbs are *even, hardly, nearly, scarcely,* and especially *only* and *not.*

> MISPLACED MODIFIER: We *only* tried three times.
> CORRECT: We tried only three times.
>
> MISPLACED MODIFIER: Every small business can*not* grow large. (This is literally a statement that *no* small business can grow large.)
> CORRECT: Not every small business can grow large.
>
> MISPLACED MODIFIER: The boat *almost* seemed ready to sink.
> CORRECT: The boat seemed almost ready to sink.
>
> MISPLACED MODIFIER: It *hardly* felt as if it were heavy enough.
> CORRECT: It felt as if it were hardly heavy enough.

(b) Phrases and clauses, as well as words, should be placed as close as possible to what they modify.

> MISPLACED MODIFIER: It made a good impression on the inspectors carrying a full load.
> CORRECT: Carrying a full load, it made a good impression on the inspectors.
>
> MISPLACED MODIFIER: After it was repaired, it was given a trial run by a testing laboratory that lasted one week.
> CORRECTION BY CHANGE OF STRUCTURE: After it was repaired, it was given a one-week trial run by a testing laboratory.

MISPLACED MODIFIER: The factory reopened after a one-month shut-down on June 1.

CLEAR: After a one-month shut-down, the factory reopened on June 1.

MISPLACED MODIFIER: It was given an overhaul by a crew of expert mechanics that was long overdue.

CORRECT: It was given an overhaul that was long overdue by a crew of expert mechanics.

(c) "Squinting" constructions should be avoided. (Squinting constructions are those in which a modifier is placed between two objects, either of which it might modify.)

SQUINTING: The smoke jumpers who had been flown in *immediately* put out the fire.

CLEAR: The smoke jumpers, who had immediately been flown in, put out the fire.

CLEAR: The smoke jumpers who had been flown in put out the fire immediately.

(d) Though split infinitives are no longer regarded as a serious error, they are frequently awkward. Therefore one should not *unnecessarily* split infinitives in an effort to place a modifier nearer to its object.

AWKWARD: They decided *to quickly complete* the repairs.

IMPROVED: They decided to complete the repairs quickly.

(e) In attempting to place modifiers near their objects, one should not needlessly interrupt the smooth flow of thought through subject, verb, and complement.

AWKWARD: The crew extinguished, after a long and difficult struggle, the fire in the slashings.

IMPROVED ARRANGEMENT: After a long and difficult struggle, the crew extinguished the fire in the slashings.

5. Comparisons should be logical and complete.

(a) Objects that are compared should be similar in nature.

ILLOGICAL: The power of the diesel is greater than the steam engine.

LOGICAL: The power of the diesel is greater than that of the steam engine.

LOGICAL: The diesel engine is more powerful than the steam engine.

(b) Illogical use of *any* should be avoided.

ILLOGICAL: The first design was simpler than *any of the designs.*

LOGICAL: The first design was simpler than any of the later designs.

(c) If a comparison is not completely expressed, the words that are omitted must be clearly and unmistakably implied.

INCOMPLETE AND AMBIGUOUS: The manager trusts him *more than the superintendent.*

COMPLETE: The manager has more trust in him *than in the superintendent.*

COMPLETE: The manager trusts him *more than the superintendent does.*

INCOMPLETE: The highway is *as rough, if not rougher than* the side road.

COMPLETE BUT AWKWARD: The highway is *as rough as, if not rougher than,* the side road.

COMPLETE: The highway is as rough as the side road, if not rougher.

6. Use of mood and tense should reflect a consistent point of view.

INCONSISTENT USE OF TENSE: The production of grade "A" milk *required* the use of methods that *meet* official standards.

CONSISTENT: The production of grade "A" milk *requires* the use of methods that *meet* official standards.

INCONSISTENT IN MOOD: If you *would give* me an extension of time, I *shall* appreciate it.

CORRECT: If you *would give* me an extension of time, I *should* appreciate it.

INCONSISTENT IN MOOD: If the generated voltage *drops* below "E," current *would flow* through and help to rotate the armature.

CONSISTENT: If the generated voltage *drops* below "E," the current *will flow* (or *flows*) through and help to rotate the armature.

CONSISTENT: If the generated voltage *were* to drop below "E," the current *would flow* through and help to rotate the armature.

7. Dangling participles and gerunds should be avoided. A participle is a verb form used as an adjective. A gerund is a verb form used as a noun. (See Definition of Grammatical Terms.) When a participial or gerund phrase comes at the beginning of a sentence, it should be followed immediately by some term indicating who performed the action indicated, so that the action will not be attributed to the wrong agent.

In respect to meaning, a dangling participle or gerund is undesirable because it is likely to be wrongly interpreted when first read. In respect to grammar, it is wrong because it is a modifying element with nothing to modify—thus the term *dangling*—and has no grammatical connection with the remainder of the sentence.

DANGLING PARTICIPLE: *Having thought the case over carefully,* my opinion was unlikely to be changed.

CORRECT: Having thought the case over carefully, *I* was not likely to change my opinion.

CORRECT: *Since I had thought the case over carefully,* I was not likely to change my opinion.

DANGLING PARTICIPLE: It can be built with either one or two doors, *depending on the wishes of the buyer.*

CORRECT: It can be built with either one or two doors, *whichever the buyer wishes.*

DANGLING GERUND: *By rotating the crystal,* the light is directed so that only the desired wave length is reflected back to the absorption cells.

CORRECT: By rotating the crystal, *one* directs the light so that only the desired wave length is reflected back to the absorption cells.

8. Dangling infinitives should be avoided.

DANGLING INFINITIVE: *To conduct the test properly,* the motor must run at a constant speed. (It sounds as if the motor were conducting the test.)

CORRECT: To conduct the test properly, *one* must keep the motor running at a constant speed.

CORRECT: *If the test is to be conducted properly,* the motor must run at a constant speed.

9. When elliptical clauses or phrases are used, a sentence should be constructed in a manner that does not permit the reader to form a false impression. (An elliptical clause, phrase, or sentence is one from which something is omitted, being implied by what is expressed.)

MISLEADING ELLIPSIS: *While looking for a suitable location,* the truck broke down.

CORRECT: While *we were* looking for a suitable location, the truck broke down.

MISLEADING ELLIPSIS: *When working on the barn,* the problem of protecting the cattle hindered them.

CORRECT: When working on the barn, *they were hindered by* the problem of protecting the cattle.

PUNCTUATION

The major function of punctuation is to make writing clearer and easier to read. The rules, except for those that are mere conventions, have come to be what they are because experience has shown us how punctuation can best contribute to clearness. Thus there is no fundamental clash between the idea of punctuating for the sake of clearness and punctuating in accordance with rules. The best way to assist clearness through punctuation is usually to follow the rules.

To be sure, the existence of rules has not caused usage in punctuation to be completely uniform. The rules are flexible enough to permit a writer, on many occasions, to exercise his judgment in deciding between equally correct alternatives. The lack of uniformity does not result from widespread disagreement about the rules themselves, nor from general disregard of the rules. Most of the rules are generally agreed upon by authorities, and the occasions when well-educated writers violate them are not frequent.

Three marks are especially important to anyone who has difficulty with punctuation: the period, the semicolon, and the comma. Even though familiarity with the other marks is desirable, you will find that if you can learn to use these three marks correctly—especially the comma—most of your problems with punctuation will be solved.

Finally, it should be emphasized that even though punctuation may be valuable, there is a limit to what it can accomplish. Punctuation is not a substitute for smooth, easy-flowing sentence structure. There are many times when a writer who is worried about how to punctuate a sentence should rewrite it rather than punctuating it, for difficulty in punctuation may well result from awkward writing.

The following rules are generally agreed upon for ordinary writing. They are not intended to cover footnotes, bibliographies, or the technical parts of letters. The punctuation of these special forms is illustrated where the forms themselves are discussed.

The Period

1. Periods are used at the ends of all sentences except those that are interrogative or exclamatory.

2. Periods are used after abbreviations.

> a.m., a.d., Fig., i.e., R.F.D., U.S.
>
> EXCEPTIONS: Many abbreviations made up of the first letters of words that comprise the names of organizations are written without periods (NATO, UNESCO, TVA, NAM, UNNRA). Periods are often omitted, also, after abbreviations that are peculiar to technical style. (See page 49.)

3. To indicate the omission of words, three spaced periods are used. If the omission occurs at the end of a sentence, a fourth period is added to mark the end of the sentence.

> The survey . . . covered 174 of the 192 colleges now accredited in this field.

The Comma

The comma is used more than any other punctuation mark; in fact, it is probably used and misused more than all other marks combined. It is the main device by which the grouping of words, phrases, and clauses within the sentence is indicated, and hence it is of special importance.

1. A comma is ordinarily used between two independent clauses that are joined by a coordinating conjunction. The coordinating conjunctions are *and, but, for, or,* and *nor.* (*Yet* and *so* may also be treated as coordinating conjunctions when this rule is applied.)

> The trees had been damaged by fire, and the wild life had been destroyed.
> The building is old, but it has been kept in good condition.

Note: When both clauses are extremely short and simple, the comma may be omitted.

It was damaged but it still is usable.

Note: If a comma is used *within* one or both of two independent clauses, the comma between them is sometimes replaced by a semicolon. (See Semicolon, Rule 5.)

2. An appositive or a term of direct address is set off by commas.

The original factory, an old stone structure, still is standing. Your answer, Mr. Smith, is satisfactory.

Note: No comma is used when a noun and its appositive are so closely related as to join in expressing a single idea.

The invasion was led by my brother John.

3. An adverbial clause preceding its principal clause, or an adverbial phrase at the beginning of a clause, is usually set off by a comma.

After the achievement tests had been completed, the results were tabulated.
On all floors except the second and the fourth, the fire hazards have been removed.

Note: If an adverbial clause or phrase is extremely short, and if omission of the comma could not cause confusion, the comma may be omitted.

When he arrived he was admitted immediately.
During July the plant will be closed.

4. Independent elements, participial phrases, gerund phrases, and other such constructions at the beginning of a sentence are set off by commas.

No, the shipment has not yet arrived.
Worried by the complaints, we began an investigation.
The contract having been broken, no payment was due.

5. A conjunctive adverb (*however, moreover, therefore,* etc.) is usually set off by commas when it comes *within* the clause to which it applies. When it comes at the beginning of a clause, it may or may not be followed by a comma but will always be preceded by a period or semicolon. (See Semicolon, Rule 2.)

His objection, therefore, was ignored.
I had heard the rumor before; consequently, I did not believe it.

6. Any mildly parenthetical element is enclosed in commas if it seems desirable to set it apart from the rest of the sentence. A writer is called upon to use his best judgment in applying this rule, for too many commas will make a sentence jerky and hard to read.

The newer strains, to be sure, will survive the blight.

The answer, when received, was unsatisfactory.
The central section, for example, was undamaged.
The frame, they insisted, was too light.

7. A term such as *namely* or *that is,* used to introduce an example or a list, is usually set apart from that example or list by a comma. (The mark that precedes such an expression depends on the sentence structure.)

The usual crops—that is, wheat, peas, and alfalfa—are in good condition.
Three species of tree were observed, namely, pine, fir, and cedar.

8. Nonrestrictive clauses are set off by commas. Restrictive clauses, however, are not set off.

The south side, which has been exposed to the sun, was badly faded.
He moved to Arizona, where the climate was not so moist.

but

The road went to pieces where the permafrost had been disturbed.
All motorists who drive recklessly should be fined heavily.
I have never been there when the legislature was in session.

Note: In the first two examples, the clauses introduced respectively by *which* and *where* merely add some additional facts. If they were omitted, the meaning of the remainder of the sentence would be unchanged. Hence they are nonrestrictive. The clauses introduced by *where, who,* and *when* in the other three examples are restrictive. Each is used to limit—to *restrict*—the meaning of the main statement, which would be radically changed if the clause in question were omitted.

Sometimes a sentence does not make sense unless a clause is interpreted in a single way—restrictive or nonrestrictive. When this is true, an error in punctuation merely increases the difficulty of reading. There are times, however, when restrictive and nonrestrictive interpretations are equally reasonable. When this is the case, an error in punctuation leads a reader to misunderstand the meaning. Note how the meaning of the two sentences that follow depends on punctuation:

The elms which stand on the south side are to be cut down.
The elms, which stand on the south side, are to be cut down.

9. When a sentence contains a series, the elements in the series are normally separated by commas.

Cattle, sheep, and hogs are now selling for higher prices.
New deposits have been found in Canada, in Africa, in Central America, and in Alaska.

Note: If a comma is used *within* any element in a series, it is often better to use semicolons rather than commas *between* the elements.

Note: Opinions differ over whether to use a comma before a conjunction (*and* or *or*) that precedes the last item in a series. In technical and scientific periodicals and in material published by the United States Government, use of the comma is predominant. In journalistic and popular publications usage is divided. Sometimes a comma is essential for clearness because of *and* or *or* being used within one of the items. For example:

> The panels were painted red, green, yellow, and black and white.

Without the comma after *yellow,* it would be impossible to know whether *black* belonged with *yellow* or with *white.* In view of this, it seems advisable to regard the comma as normal punctuation rather than trying to check each series to see whether a comma is needed for clearness.

10. Two or more adjectives preceding a noun are ordinarily separated by commas. The comma before the last adjective is omitted, however, if that adjective is so closely associated with the noun that the two seem to merge into a single thought unit.

> A big, powerful truck is needed.
> He has a modest, unassuming manner.
> It was housed in a large wooden structure.
> The watchman was a feeble old man.

11. A word or phrase that is placed in an abnormal position in a sentence should be set off by a comma or commas.

> To a trained accountant, the problem would look easy.

12. A comma is sometimes used to indicate the omission of one or more words.

> July will be devoted to writing; August, to revision.

13. A direct quotation is set off by a comma or commas.

> "The tires are threadbare," he asserted, "and will blow out at any moment."
> He asked me directly, "Will September delivery be acceptable?"

> EXCEPTIONS: A quotation that blends into the regular structure of the sentence is not set off by commas. A title in quotation marks is not set off by commas unless some other rule makes commas necessary.

> The poet's prophecy about "airy navies grappling in the central blue" has become an unpleasant reality.
> The rhythm of "The Raven" is very striking.

14. Commas are variously used to separate items in dates, places, and numbers as illustrated in the following examples:

> IN DATES: Payment shall be made on September 15, 1956, at the main office of the company.

IN PLACES AND ADDRESSES: San Francisco, California, is an important shipping point.

The company is located at 70 Fifth Avenue, New York 11, New York.

TO SEPARATE ADJACENT SETS OF FIGURES: In 1950, 675 men were added to the payroll.

BETWEEN THE DIGITS OF NUMBERS: 10,984. 234,617. 1,856,445. (The comma may be omitted in a number with only four digits unless the number occurs in a column containing numbers in which commas are used.)

The Semicolon

The semicolon is an intermediate mark, less emphatic than a period but more emphatic than a comma. There are many times when the rules would permit either a semicolon or a period, and a writer's choice must depend on his judgment about whether it would be better to continue the sentence or end it.

1. A semicolon is used sometimes between main clauses that are not joined by any connective.

> Privately endowed schools must not be underestimated; they fill a genuine educational need.

2. A semicolon is used between main clauses connected by a conjunctive adverb rather than by a coordinating conjunction. (Conjunctive adverbs are such words as *also, accordingly, consequently, furthermore, hence, however, indeed, moreover, nevertheless, otherwise, still, then, therefore, thus*.)

> He had shown fine managerial ability; consequently his promotion was rapid.

3. A semicolon is used between main clauses when the second clause begins with an explanatory term such as *in fact, for example, that is*.

> All the costs have increased; for example, the cost of raw material has increased by 15 per cent.

Note: Rules 1, 2, and 3 might be summarized: A semicolon is normally the proper mark to use between independent clauses occurring in a single sentence except when the clauses are connected by a coordinating conjunction.

4. Even if independent clauses are connected by a coordinating conjunction, a semicolon may be used between them if it is desirable to set them apart more sharply than usual—for example, to set off one clause from two or more others to which it stands in contrast.

> Its paint was damaged, its lights were broken, and its fenders were a complete loss; but the motor was in good condition.

5. Coordinate elements of any type, clauses or otherwise, are often separated by semicolons if any of them contain commas.

> Some economies, perhaps, may be possible; but however hard we try to hold down expenses, a considerable increase will be unavoidable.

> The inspection was made by William Smith, representing the company; Walter Brosser, president of the union; and Boyd Anderson, inspector for the Bureau of Mines.

The Question Mark

1. A question mark is used at the end of a direct question.

> Is the price level rising or falling?

2. A question mark may be used to show that any expression is intended as a question, whether the form is interrogatory or not. (The use of a noninterrogative form to ask a question is seldom seen in any writing except reproduction of conversation.)

> You claim the records have been altered?

3. A question mark is replaced by a period at the end of a "courtesy question," which is actually a request though it may be interrogatory in form.

> Will you please send us this information as soon as possible.

4. A question mark, enclosed in parentheses, is used to express doubt.

> Thomas Hooker, a founder of Connecticut, lived from 1586 (?) to 1647.

The Exclamation Point

An exclamation point is used after a word, phrase, or sentence to indicate intense feeling or forceful utterance. There are few occasions, however, to use an exclamation point in technical writing.

> Ridiculous! The signature is forged!

The Colon

1. A colon is used before a long direct quotation that is being introduced formally.

> John Stuart Mill expressed his doubts as follows:

2. A colon is used to introduce a formal enumeration—especially after *follows* or *the following*.

Bids were offered by the following contractors: Wilson and Taylor Construction Company, Toledo; Central Builders, Incorporated, Akron; Herman L. White and Company, Cleveland.

3. A colon is used between two phrases or clauses when the second is actually the equivalent of the first. In this use it conveys a meaning similar to that of *namely* or *that is.*

The method that they used had one unique advantage: it could be used by personnel who had received only one week of special training.

The Dash

1. A dash can be used before introductory words such as *namely, in fact,* and *that is,* and before abbreviations such as *i.e.* and *viz.,* to introduce an enumeration. (See also Semicolon, Rule 3.)

It is superior in three respects—namely, economy of operation, safety, and comfort.

2. A dash can be used to set off an informal enumeration or a list of examples that are separated by commas.

Some of the accessories—the heater, the fog lights, and the bumper— are really necessities.

3. A dash is used after a list that is followed by a summarizing expression.

Colds, influenza, sore throats—all the winter ailments were prevalent.

4. A pair of dashes may be used to set off interpolated material. In this use, dashes create sharper separation than commas but less sharp than parentheses.

Most of the additional cost—approximately 90 per cent—was passed on to the consumers.

5. A dash may be used to indicate incomplete or interrupted thought. (This use of the dash would be unlikely in technical writing.)

The reasons for our decision—but no, I'll not bore you with them.

Note: The dash is a mark to use when clear-cut rules make it correct. It should not be used haphazardly, merely because one is uncertain what mark would be appropriate. Unless one is writing dialogue or writing very informally, the use of dashes to show interruption of thought indicates lack of smoothness and continuity.

Note: In typewritten material, a dash is indicated by a double hyphen, or by a single hyphen preceded and followed by a single space.

Quotation Marks

1. Quotation marks are used to enclose direct quotations.

"The modern automobile," he pointed out, "sells at about the same price per pound that is charged for beefsteak."

Note: If a quotation is more than one paragraph long, opening quotation marks are used at the beginning of each paragraph but closing quotation marks are not used until the end of the quotation.

Note: Quotation marks are not used when the material quoted is set in smaller type or when it has wider margins than those of the regular text.

Note: Quotation marks are not used to enclose widely known proverbs, such as *Honesty is the best policy,* or other well-known quotations that the reader will recognize as quotations without assistance.

2. Quotation marks are used to enclose titles of short poems, articles, short stories—in general, the titles of writings that are not printed as independent publications.

The statistics come from an article entitled "Science and Public Relations."

3. Quotation marks are sometimes used to enclose the names of ships, trains, airplanes, etc., and to enclose words used as words. (Italics are used more frequently.)

He had secured reservations on "The Portland Rose."
In the fourth paragraph, the word "unique" is used incorrectly.

4. Quotation marks may be used to indicate that a word or phrase is used to convey the meaning it has acquired in some special field. For example, in writing addressed to readers in general, quotation marks might be placed around *pickle* as used in the metals industry, *flip flop* as used in connection with computers, or *mark sense* as used in connection with IBM cards.

This use of quotation marks should be held to a minimum, for it is obtrusive if it occurs very often. In writing addressed to readers who are familiar with special vocabulary of a field, quotation marks are not needed around the terms in question. In writing addressed to readers who lack that familiarity, it is better to use standard English if it will convey the meaning efficiently. If frequent use of such terms is unavoidable, it is better to omit the quotation marks and insert a parenthetical explanation of each term the first time you use it.

5. A quotation within a quotation is indicated by single quotation marks.

The instructions say, "You are to write 'Rejected' on the top of every imperfect copy."

Quotation Marks in Relation to Other Punctuation

1. A period or a comma ordinarily precedes closing quotation marks, even though it might logically belong outside.

One of his poems, "Fuzzy Wuzzy," was especially popular.

2. A colon or a semicolon ordinarily follows closing quotation marks.

3. A question mark or exclamation point is placed inside the closing quotation marks if it applies to the quotation, but outside if it applies to the sentence as a whole.

His exact words were, "Why was the gun concealed?"
Had he ever read "The Third Ingredient"?

The Apostrophe

1. An apostrophe is used to form the possessive case of nouns and indefinite pronouns. (Indefinite pronouns include such words as *one, everybody, everyone, nobody,* etc.)

(a) Singular or plural words that do not end with the sound of *s* form the possessive by adding *apostrophe* plus *s.*

the company's property	everybody's business
one's conscience	the men's wages

(b) Singular words ending with the sound of *s* also form the possessive by adding *apostrophe* plus *s.*

Mr. Jones's desk	the horse's age
the boss's office	

EXCEPTION: If the form created by following this rule would be difficult to pronounce, it is permissible to add only the apostrophe, especially if the word in question is a person's name.

Moses' people (not Moses's people)   Mr. Jones' desk
Dickens' novels

(c) Plural words ending with the sound of *s* form the possessive by adding only an apostrophe.

the companies' policies   the workers' houses

2. An apostrophe is never used to form the possessive case of a personal or relative pronoun. (The possessive of *it* is *its*, not *it's*. The possessive of *who* is *whose*, not *who's*. *It's* means *it is; who's* means *who is.*)

3. The apostrophe to show the possessive case is often omitted in a formal title. In using any title, the form to follow is the form that has official sanction.

The Teachers Retirement Act   The Farmers Co-operative

4. A compound term such as *director of information* or *everybody else* is made possessive by adding the *apostrophe* plus *s* (or *apostrophe* only, if appropriate) to the last word.

Director of Information's statement   his father in law's tool chest

5. Joint possession is indicated by a change in the ending of only the last of two or more nouns.

Fred and Henry's office (Joint possession.)
Fred's and Henry's offices (Each has a separate office.)

6. An apostrophe is used to indicate the omission of one or more letters in a contraction.

can't	o'clock	they'll
isn't	it's (it is)	I'll
you're	who's (who is)	

7. An *apostrophe* plus *s* is used to form the plural of words used as words, letters as letters, figures as figures, etc.

The sentence contains too many *and's*.
The *e's* could not be distinguished from the *i's*.
The *8's* were blurred and looked like *3's*.

Note: There is a growing tendency to omit this apostrophe when clearness would not be reduced. It would be clear, for example, to write Bs, Cs, 8s. Note, however, that omitting it before adding *s* to *A*, to *U*, or to *I* would result in *As*, *Us*, and *Is*.

Parentheses

1. Parentheses are used to set off a word, phrase, or clause that constitutes a definite interruption in continuity.

The store used "loss leaders" (articles priced below cost to attract customers) only on exceptional occasions.

Note: If material in parentheses is inserted into a sentence, no other punctuation precedes the opening of the parentheses, but the closing of the parentheses should be followed by whatever punctuation would have been used if the parenthetical material had not been inserted. If the parenthetical material is itself a sentence and is inserted at the end of a sentence, a period is used in the normal manner at the end of the sentence preceding the parentheses, and a period is placed inside the parentheses at the end of the parenthetical sentence.

Brackets

1. Brackets are used to mark off material that is inserted into a quotation but not quoted.

"This year [1949] the outlook is less favorable."
"It is definitely established that he [Mr. Schenley] signed the contract."

CAPITALIZATION

1. The first word of a sentence or of a line of poetry is capitalized.

The air was smoky.

"A voice by the cedar tree
In the meadow, under the hill."

2. The first word of a quotation is ordinarily capitalized, but a capital letter is not used when the quotation merges into the structure of the enclosing sentence.

His exact words were, "The request is refused."
He objected to "the capitalization of unrealized anticipations."

3. Proper nouns, their derivatives, and common nouns used as proper nouns are capitalized.

(a) Capitalize personal and geographical names, names of races, nations, languages, etc.

Henry A. Collins	American
English	France
Negro	Hudson River
King County	Lake Erie
The National Biscuit Company	Reed College

Note: Such words as lake and bay are always capitalized when they precede the word that indicates the specific bay or lake. Some magazines and most newspapers, however, do not capitalize them when they follow the word that indicates the specific name (for example, *Payette lake, Hudson bay*). Many other such words—for example *mountain, street,* and *railroad*—are similarly treated.

Note: When the terms discussed above are preceded by two proper nouns, they are never capitalized.

The Mississippi and Missouri rivers.

(b) Capitalize the names of organizations, businesses, governmental bodies, etc.

Veterans of Foreign Wars   The Builders Supply Company
The Federal Communications Commission

(c) Capitalize the days of the week, months, holidays.

Monday   June   Memorial Day

(d) Capitalize titles of books, magazines, articles, and other written materials. (The first word and each important word thereafter are capitalized. Such unimportant words as *a, an, the,* and most conjunctions or prepositions shorter than five letters are not capitalized. The word *The* is capitalized when it is the first word in the title of a book, but is not capitalized at the beginning of the title of a newspaper or magazine.)

Essentials of Microwaves	the Saturday Review
The World Almanac	Science and Public Relations

(e) Capitalize the title of a person if it precedes his name, but do not capitalize a title that follows a name unless it is a title of distinction.

Professor Page	Sergeant Keppler
Judge William E. White	Dr. Springer
President Johnson	

Lyndon B. Johnson, President of the United States
Byron R. White, Associate Justice of the United States
   Supreme Court

but

Norman Page, professor of chemistry
William E. White, police judge
John Moore, president of the Rotary Club

Note: The illustrations above indicate capitalization in ordinary text. In the address of a letter or in most display printing, most titles would be capitalized.

(f) Capitalize words that are derived from the names of persons, places, or other proper names.

The crew lived in a Quonset hut.
The Plimsoll mark was visible.

Note: Eventually, such capitalization is usually discontinued, as in *sandwich* and *boycott*. Since the discontinuation is gradual, there will always, at any given time, be many terms in which usage differs in different publications. A dictionary will give guidance, but dictionaries necessarily lag behind technical books and magazines.

4. Nouns and pronouns referring to the Deity, and numerous other words with sacred significance are capitalized.

"Earth changes, but thy soul and God stand sure."
"So take and use Thy work."

5. The pronoun *I* and the interjection *O* are capitalized, but *oh* is not capitalized except at the beginning of a sentence or quotation.

6. In ordinary text, capitalization merely as a means of emphasis is poor form. Inexperienced writers tend to capitalize too frequently. The following precautions, especially, should be observed:

(a) North, south, east, and west are capitalized only when they are used as proper nouns, that is, as the names of specific geographical regions. When these words indicate mere direction, they are not capitalized.

> He lived in the South.
> He lived south of the tracks.

(b) Such words as chemistry, psychology, and history are not capitalized except when they occur as part of a title—for example, the title of a specific university course.

> Being interested in physics, he decided to take The Physics of Sound.

ITALICS

Italics (indicated in typing or longhand by an underline) show that words are used in some special manner and hence should be set off from the rest of the material.

1. Italics are used for the titles of books, magazines, newspapers, bulletins, or other separately issued publications.

> *Basic Engineering Metallurgy*   *The American College Dictionary*
> the *Chicago Tribune*   *Webster's Seventh New Collegiate*
> the *Farm Science Reporter*   *Dictionary*
> *The Business Letter in Modern Form*

Note: If the word *A, An,* or *The* is the first word of the title of a book, it is italicized; at the beginning of the title of a periodical, it is not italicized.

2. Italics are used for the names on titles of ships, trains, airplanes, works of art, etc. Some authorities, however, place such material in quotation marks.

> the *Lusitania*   El Greco's *Cleansing of the Temple*
> the *Twentieth Century Limited*

3. Italics are used for words considered as words, phrases considered as phrases, and letters or numbers considered as letters or numbers. (Quotation Marks are sometimes used for the same purpose. See Rule 3 under *Quotation Marks.*)

> The writer used *effect* incorrectly.
> The phrase *in case of* is overworked.
> The *i* looks like an *e,* and the 8 is so dim it looks like 3.

Note: A letter used to indicate shape, as in "V-shaped" or "I-beam," is not italicized.

4. Foreign words or phrases are italicized, whether written out or

abbreviated. (This rule covers Latin scientific names.) To determine whether some words are considered foreign or are accepted as English, it may be necessary to consult a dictionary.

coup d'etat   *ipso facto*   *de facto*

5. Italics are used to indicate special emphasis, but their use for this purpose should be limited to occasions when the emphasis is abnormal or when special emphasis is really necessary to make sure that the reader grasps the intended meaning.

> Do you mean to tell me that you met *the* Walter Huston?
> He definitely gave instructions that the deduction should *not* be made.

ABBREVIATIONS

The following rules for abbreviation apply to ordinary writing only. The additional abbreviations needed for technical style, and the use of abbreviations in footnotes, bibliography, and technical parts of letters, are discussed with those particular topics.

In ordinary writing, abbreviations should be used sparingly. Unless one of the following rules clearly calls for abbreviation, a word should be written out.

1. The abbreviations A.M., P.M., A.D., and B.C. are always used in place of the terms for which they stand.

2. The abbreviations *e.g.* (for example), *i.e.* (that is), and *viz.* (namely) may be used when informality is appropriate. At any other time, their English equivalents are preferable.

3. The abbreviation *etc.* is so extremely informal that it should usually be avoided in regular text that is offered as finished writing. It is acceptable, however, in a series of brief rules—as you see it used, for example, in Rule 2 of *Italics*, above.

4. In recent years many abbreviations such as NATO, TVA, and FBI have come to be used as if they were actual names. Their acceptance results from the length of the names that they stand for. When the readers addressed are sure to understand their meanings, they are acceptable except on occasions so formal that nothing except full, official names would be appropriate.

5. Such abbreviations as *Jr., M.A., Ph.D.,* and *C.P.A.,* when following names, are preferred to the full words or phrases. Three abbreviations for titles—*Mr., Mrs.,* and *Dr.,* are used before names. In ordinary text, however, all other titles are in better form if written out whether they precede or follow a name. Examples of these titles are *Professor, Captain, President, Senator, Governor, Major.* Like these titles, terms of re-

spect such as *reverend* and the *honorable* (these are not titles) should be written out.

6. Such words as *figure* and *number* preceding a number may be abbreviated: *Fig. 3; No. 7.*

7. Abbreviations are not used for the names of persons: *James, William, Robert,* not *Jas., Wm., Robt.*

8. Abbreviations are not used in ordinary text for the names of states or similar terms (except for *D.C.* and sometimes *N.Y.*); nor are they used in text for words such as *street, avenue, company, volume,* and *chapter.*

SPELLING

Among all the possible errors in English there are few that are so damaging as errors in spelling. Mistakes in spelling are noticed and found annoying by readers who pass over all but the most glaring errors. No person who expects to do technical professional work can afford to shrug his shoulders and say "I never could learn to spell."

The first necessity in overcoming weakness in spelling is the development of an adult attitude, a determination not to go through life handicapped by a juvenile weakness. Once such an attitude is acquired, improvement may not be easy, but it is hardly so formidable a task as might be anticipated. Even a weak speller, if he keeps a list of the words that he misses, is usually surprised at its shortness. The frequency of his errors does not ordinarily result from his misspelling a great number of words, but from his repeatedly misspelling certain words that he uses frequently. He can often eliminate most of his errors by learning to spell no more than 40 or 50 words.

If you are weak in spelling, you should be able to make steady improvement if you will carry out the following instructions:

First: Check your work carefully for the express purpose of correcting the errors that result from sheer carelessness rather than from ignorance.

Second: Keep a list of every word you miss, and have that list in front of you when you write. Your individual list will be more valuable than a list taken from a book. You will soon come to recognize any word on the list when you start to write it, and can check the way you spell it without taking time to consult a dictionary.

Third: Learn just a few rules—the ones that are violated most frequently.

Fourth: Give special attention to certain words that are misspelled because of sloppy pronunciation, and to pairs of words that are confused because of their similarity.

The Rules

The following rules do not cover everything; they represent an attempt to eliminate as much as possible, so that the rules that are most helpful will not be buried in the mass of rules and exceptions that would be necessary for completeness.

1. *ie* and *ei:*

When the pronunciation is long *e*, use *i* before *e* except after *c*, and use *e* before *i* after *c*. (When the pronunciation is not long *e*, the spelling is usually *ei;* but few words except those where the pronunciation is long *e* cause trouble.)

believe	receive	weigh
chief	conceit	neighbor
field	ceiling	foreign

EXCEPTIONS: either, neither, seize, leisure, weird, financier, species.

2. The effect of prefixes:

When a prefix is placed before a word, the spelling of the word itself remains unchanged. (This rule will solve many troublesome questions about double letters.)

dis + appoint = disappoint	un + worried = unworried
dis + appear = disappear	un + noticed = unnoticed
dis + satisfied = dissatisfied	grand + daughter = granddaughter

3. Treatment of final silent *e* when a suffix is added:

(a) When a suffix beginning with a consonant is added to a word ending in silent *e*, the *e* is retained.

hope + ful = hopeful	shame + less = shameless
move + ment = movement	like + ly = likely

EXCEPTIONS: *duly, truly, argument, awful.* Also, dropping the *e* is preferred to retaining it in the spelling of such words as *judgment, acknowledgment,* and *abridgment.*

(b) When a suffix beginning with a vowel is added to a word ending in silent *e*, the *e* is dropped. (This covers the spelling of hundreds of words to which *ing* may be added.)

hope + ing = hoping	quote + able = quotable
move + ing = moving	promote + ion = promotion
locate + ion = location	change + ing = changing

EXCEPTION: The letters *c* and *g* always have a hard pronunciation before *o* and *a* (*cat, coat, gave, go*). Hence a final silent *e* must sometimes be retained to keep the pronunciation of *c* or *g* soft.

enforce + able = enforceable	courage + ous = courageous
change + able = changeable	

EXCEPTIONS: *Mileage, saleable,* and *useable* are exceptions to the rule for dropping the silent *e*. (*Milage* is an error. *Salable* and *saleable* are equally correct. *Useable* is acceptable, but *usable* is preferred.) Also, there are a few words such as *singeing* or *dyeing* in which the *e* is retained to prevent confusion with other words (*singing, dying*).

4. Doubling a final consonant:

When a suffix beginning with a vowel is added to a word ending in a consonant, the final consonant of the word is doubled under the following condition: (a) The word must end in only one consonant, preceded by only one vowel, and (b) the word must be accented on the last syllable. (This would include all one-syllable words.)

Final Consonant Doubled

occur + ed = occurred	stop + ed = stopped
refer + ed = referred	drag + ed = dragged
begin + ing = beginning	lag + ing = lagging

EXCEPTIONS: gas + es = gases   gas + eous = gaseous

Final Consonant Not Doubled

rent + ing = renting	(Word ends in two consonants.)
read + ing = reading	(Two vowels precede the consonant.)
offer + ed = offered	(Accent not on last syllable.)
refer + ence = reference	(Accent shifted back to an earlier syllable.)

Note: Though the rule just discussed seems somewhat complicated, its application may be greatly simplified, for the misspellings that may be corrected by applying the rule are almost exclusively the result of overlooking the portion of the rule referring to accent. Characteristic errors are *occured, begining, refered*. For purely functional purposes, the rule could be simplified to read: *If you are in doubt as to whether to double a final consonant when you add a suffix, notice where the accent lies. If it lies on the last syllable* (this obviously covers all words of one syllable) *double the final consonant. If it is not on the last syllable, do not double the final consonant.*

The cases where this would not apply will not cause trouble. Even the weakest spellers would spell words such as *needed* or *spending* correctly without even considering the question of doubling a final consonant.

5. Adding a suffix to a word ending in *y:*

(a) When a suffix is added to a word that ends in *y* preceded by a *consonant*, the *y* is changed to *i* unless the result would be double *i*.

worry + ed = worried	mercy + ful = merciful
accompany + ment = accompaniment	hurry + ed = hurried
pity + able = pitiable	worry + ing = worrying

EXCEPTIONS: There are several exceptions, including words such as *shyness, citylike, secretaryship.* None of the exceptions is likely to be misspelled, or even to occasion doubt. Hence the rule may be applied, in case of doubt, without danger of causing an error in spelling.

(b) When a suffix is added to a word that ends in *y* preceded by a *vowel,* the *y* remains unchanged.

joy + ful = joyful   assay + ed = assayed
annoy + ance = annoyance   employ + ment = employment

EXCEPTIONS: *laid* (from lay + ed); *said* (from say + ed); *daily* (from day + ly).

Note: The most valuable fact to remember about errors resulting from addition of suffixes to words ending in *y* is that practically all these errors result from a single cause: failure to change *y* to *i* when it should be changed. The section of the rule expressed in (a) should receive major attention.

6. Words ending in *ede* or *eed:*

Among the troublesome words ending in *ede* or *eed,* only three end in *eed,* namely *exceed, succeed,* and *proceed.* All the others end in *ede*—for example, *concede, recede, precede, supersede.* It is further worth noting, if one is doubtful whether *c* or *s* precedes the *ede,* that only one word, *supersede,* ends in *sede.*

7. For rules that concern the apostrophe, consult the discussion of punctuation.

Pairs of Words That May Be Confused

Many misspellings result from confusion between the word desired and some other word that resembles it in spelling or pronunciation. Some of the words commonly confused are as follows:

accept, except   eminent, imminent
advice, advise   formally, formerly
affect, effect   forth, fourth
all ready, already   incidence, incidents
all together, altogether   its, it's
born, borne   lead, led
brake, break   lightening, lightning
breath, breathe   loose, lose
capital, capitol   manufacturers, manufactures
choose, chose   passed, past
cite, sight, site   perform, preform
coarse, course   personal, personnel
complement, compliment   precedence, precedents
dual, duel   presence, presents
dyeing, dying   principal, principle
emigration, immigration   prophecy, prophesy

stationary, stationery
their, there, they're
to, too, two

whose, who's
your, you're

Words Misspelled Because of Pronunciation

Many words give trouble in spelling because they are mispronounced or pronounced carelessly. If the correct pronunciation of these words can be learned, the errors in spelling will be corrected automatically. Some of the most troublesome words of this sort are listed below:

accidentally (not accidently)
arctic (not artic)
athletics (not atheletics)
boundary (not boundry)
disastrous (not disasterous)
drought (not drougth)
foundry (not foundary)
height (not heighth)
hindrance (not hinderance)
incidentally (not incidently)
irrelevant (not irrelevant)
laboratory (not labratory)

mathematics (not mathmatics)
miniature (not minature)
mischievous (not mischeevious)
performance (not preformance)
perseverance (not perserverance)
prescription (not perscription)
quantity (not quanity)
similar (not similiar)
sophomore (not sophmore)
temperament (not temperment)
temperature (not temperture)

Miscellaneous Spelling List

absence
accept
accidentally
accommodate
accumulate
acquaint
across
address
advice
aggravate
allotted
all right
already
amateur
analyze
annual
appearance
appropriate
argument
auxiliary
beginning
believe
beneficial
calendar
ceiling
changeable
coarse
committee

comparative
comparison
competent
completely
conscience
conscious
continuous
controlled
convenience
course
criticism
criticize
curriculum
cylinder
deferred
definite
dependent
description
desperate
develop
disappear
disappoint
dormitories
dual
duel
embarrass
emphasize
employees

environment
equipped
especially
exaggerate
exceed
excellent
except
exercise
exhaust
existence
familiar
feasible
finally
fluorescent
foreign
foremost
forth
forty
fourth
gases
gauge
government
grievous
guarantee
height
hindrance
hypocrisy
immediately

inconvenience
independence
indispensable
interest
its
it's
laboratory
lead
led
leisure
liable
lightning
loose
lose
maintenance
manufacturer
mathematics
mileage
miniature
missile
nineteen
ninety
ninth
noticeable

occasion
occurred
occurrence
omitted
optimistic
parallel
particle
partner
perform
permissible
perseverance
personal
personnel
plain
plane
practically
precede
preferred
prejudice
principal
principle
procedure
proceed
quantity

quiet
quite
receipt
receive
recognizable
recommend
repetition
representative
reservoir
schedule
seize
separate
similar
sincerely
soluble
sponsor
studying
therefore
thorough
transferred
unnecessary
wherever

GLOSSARY OF USAGE

The following list includes many but far from all of the words and phrases that persistently trouble a great number of writers.

The term *colloquial* is used with the liberal meaning *informal* rather than being restricted to its original meaning of *conversational*.

Accept, Except. *Accept* means *to receive willingly*. If you use *except* with that meaning, you are in error.

Affect, Effect. *Affect*, as a verb, means *to influence*. *Effect* as a verb means *to achieve or accomplish*. *Affect* is never correct as a noun (except in one highly technical usage in psychology). *Effect* as a noun means *result* and is essentially the noun form suggested by *affect* as a verb.

> The weather *affected* their plans.
> The attorneys *effected* a settlement of the suit.
> The weather had no *effect* on their plans.

Already, All ready. *Already* means *previously*. *All ready* means *entirely prepared*.

Among, Between. *Among* is used in reference to more than two persons or objects. *Between* is used in reference to two only.

The profits were divided *among* the employees.
The profits were divided *between* the two partners.
The profits were divided *between* the company and the employees.

Amount, Number. *Amount* refers to quantity. *Number* refers to objects that can be counted.

The *amount* of beef in storage was increasing.
The *number* of cattle on the range was increasing.

And/or. Useful though this expression seems, it is frowned on by most authorities. Never use it in ordinary text if you can avoid it.

UNDESIRABLE: It had been colored by the use of ammonium carbonate, and/or ammonium chloride.
BETTER: It had been colored by the use of ammonium carbonate, ammonium chloride, or both.

As. Often ambiguous when used to introduce a clause that might be introduced by *because* or *since*.

AMBIGUOUS: *As* the time of departure was drawing near, he became very nervous.
CLEAR: *Since* (or *because*) the time of departure was drawing near, he became very nervous.
CLEAR: *When* the time of departure came he grew very nervous.

As per. A bit of commercial jargon undesirable, in normal use, as a substitute for *in accordance with*.

UNDESIRABLE: The work was done as per instructions.
BETTER: The work was done in accordance with the instructions.

Bad, Badly. See *Adjectives and Adverbs*, pages 354-6.

Balance. The word *balance*, except in connection with bookkeeping or accounting, should not be used for *remainder*.

WRONG: We will do the *balance* of the work next week.
CORRECT: Our *balance* in the bank account had decreased.

Because. Do not misuse *because* for *for*. *Because* should be used to introduce a clause that tells the cause of some result rather than a clause that merely tells the reason for a belief or knowledge.

WRONG: He has not been here today, *because* his tools are still in his locker.
CORRECT: He has not been here today, *for* his tools are still in his locker.
CORRECT: He stayed away *because* he was ill.

Beside, Besides. *Beside* means *by the side of*. *Besides* means *in addition to, except, moreover*.

WRONG: *Beside* the reason mentioned, there are other reasons.
CORRECT: *Besides* the reason mentioned, there are other reasons.

But what, But that. The word *but* in these expressions is meaningless, has no grammatical function, and should be omitted in formal writing.

> WRONG: We had no doubt *but what* (or *that*) he would be acquitted.
> CORRECT: We had no doubt *that* he would be acquitted.

Can, May. *Can* indicates ability. *May* indicates permission. In recent years, however, the objections to using *can* for *may* have grown less vigorous.

Can't hardly, Can't scarcely. These terms are illogical just as a double negative is illogical. Taken literally, either of them would cause a statement to mean the exact oposite of what it was intended to mean.

> WRONG: We *can't hardly* see it from here.
> CORRECT: We *can hardly* see it from here.

Can't help but. This expression cannot be defended from the grammatical standpoint and is avoided by careful writers except in extremely informal use. It is a distortion of the extremely formal expression, *cannot but.*

> WRONG: I *can't help but* agree with him.
> CORRECT: I *can't help* agreeing with him.
> CORRECT, BUT EXCESSIVELY FORMAL: I *cannot but* agree with him.

Come. Use of *come* for *came*, as in "We *come* here ten days ago," is highly illiterate. It persists in the oral language of many people who would not write it.

Considerable. *Considerable* is an adjective. It should not be used as a noun or adverb. As a noun it is colloquial; as an adverb, illiterate.

> WRONG: The company lost *considerable* during the first year.
> WRONG: We were influenced *considerable* by what he said.
> CORRECT: The company lost a *considerable amount* of money during the first year.
> CORRECT: We were influenced *considerably* by what he said.

Continual, Continuous. *Continual* means *constantly recurring* (as in *continual* interruptions). *Continuous* means *without cessation* (as in the *continuous* increase in pressure).

Could of, Would of, Should of, etc. In all such expressions, *of* is misused for *have* as the result of careless pronunciation in speech. The wrongness of these expressions is apparent when one realizes that they are comparable to "I *of* gone."

Data, Phenomena, Strata. These forms are all plurals. Their singulars are *datum, phenomenon, stratum.* There is some tendency, recently, to use *data* as a singular when referring to a mass of facts considered as a whole; but most careful writers still restrict it to use as a plural.

Different from, Different than. *Different from* is preferred.

Differ from, Differ with. *Differ from* means *to be dissimilar. Differ with* means *to disagree.*

> Apple trees *differ from* pines in appearance.
> The manager *differed with* the president as to who should be promoted.

Enable. *Enable* means *to make able, to give ability to.* It should not be used in such a sentence as, "This appropriation *enables* the road to be paved," for the road is not given any new ability. It would be preferable to say, "This appropriation *enables* the highway department to pave the road."

Farther, Further. Careful writers prefer *farther* in reference to actual distance and *further* in reference to quantity or degree.

Fewer, Less. *Fewer* should be used when numbers are referred to; *less,* when quantity is referred to.

> CORRECT: *Less* wheat was harvested this year than last; consequently *fewer* (not *less*) freight cars will be needed.

Good, Well. See *Adjectives and Adverbs,* pages 354-6.

Had of. The *of* is meaningless, unnecessary, and wrong. *Had* is sufficient.

> WRONG: I wish I *had of* learned the news earlier.
> CORRECT: I wish I *had* learned the news earlier.

Had ought. This is an undesirable form, mistakenly substituted for *ought* or *should.*

> WRONG: *He'd* (he had) *ought* to resign.
> CORRECT: He *should* resign.
> CORRECT: He *ought to* resign.

Hardly. See *Can't hardly.*

Have got. A redundant way of saying *have,* and an undesirable substitute for *must* or *have to* except on occasions of extreme informality.

> REDUNDANT: We *have got* many things to be thankful for.
> UNDESIRABLE: *We've got* to reach the town before morning.
> CORRECT: We *have* many things to be thankful for.
> CORRECT: We *have* to reach the town before morning.
> CORRECT: We *must* reach the town before morning.

If. *If* is ambiguous when used in place of *whether* because it does not imply *or not* with sufficient emphasis.

> AMBIGUOUS: Let me know *if* you expect to visit us.
> CLEAR: Let me know *whether* you expect to visit us.

Imply, Infer. A speaker or writer implies. A listener or reader infers. It is inaccurate to say, "I *implied,* as I read your letter, that. . . ." Similarly, it is wrong to say, "Did you mean to *infer,* by your remarks, that. . . ." The same distinction applies to *implication* and *inference.*

Is when, Is where, Is because. These phrases are often misused, as seen in the following sentences.

> WRONG: Insolvency *is where* one cannot pay one's debts.
> WRONG: Bankruptcy *is when* one's property is administered for the benefit of one's creditors.
> WRONG: The reason for his absence *is because* he is ill.
> CORRECT: Insolvency is a lack of funds to make payments that are due.
> CORRECT: Bankruptcy is a state *in which* one's property is administered for the benefit of one's creditors.
> CORRECT: The cause of his absence is *that* he is ill. (or *is illness*)

Lie, Lay. *Lie* is an intransitive verb meaning *recline. Lay* is a transitive verb meaning to *place,* or *cause to lie.*

> Principal parts: lie, lay, have lain
> lay, laid, have laid

> CORRECT: He lies on the bed. (present)
> CORRECT: He lay on the bed. (past)
> CORRECT: He *has lain* on the bed all afternoon.
> CORRECT: He *lays* the newspaper on the bed.
> CORRECT: He *has laid* the newspaper on the bed.
> WRONG: He *lays* on the bed.
> WRONG: He *laid* (or *has laid*) on the bed all afternoon.

Note: The confusion results primarily because the past tense of *lie* is identical with the present tense of *lay.* Some errors also result from the use of *laid* as the past tense or past participle of *lie.*

Like, As if. Careful writers do not use *like* as a conjunction, preferring *as if* or *as though. Like* is correct, however, as a preposition. In conversation, *like* as a conjunction slips into the language even of many literate people.

> CORRECT: He looked *like* a man of forty.
> CORRECT: He spoke *as if* (or *as though*) he had a cold.

Note: Being a preposition, *like* cannot introduce a clause; and the usual sign that the construction is a clause is the presence of the subject and verb. An easier way to avoid misuse of *like* is to try *as if* in its place, and use it if it sounds right. You may be sure that when *as if* is wrong it will sound wrong.

Most, Almost. These are two distinct words, with different meanings. Sometimes, however, *most* is used colloquially for *almost* as in "He made an error in *most* every copy." The simplest way to avoid this error is to remember that *most* is never correct when *almost* would convey the desired meaning.

> CORRECT: He made errors on *most* of the copies.
> CORRECT: It was a *most* unfortunate statement.
> COLLOQUIAL OR WRONG: Most everyone in the crowd saw the incident.

Of. Do not use *of* for *have* as in "He must *of* gone," for "He must *have* gone." Other examples of this error are *could of, should of,* and *might of.* The error is a carry-over from careless pronunciation.

Percent. This term should not be loosely used for *portion* or *part.* Ordinarily, it should be used only following a number. It should not be used for *percentage,* though to save space many writers disregard this distinction in tables and figures.

> CORRECT: The company earned a 10 *percent* profit.
> CORRECT: The *percentage* (not *percent*) of profit increased.
> WRONG: A large *percent* of the profit resulted from sales abroad.

Practicable, Practical. *Practicable* is used to indicate that a method *can* be used or that a result *can* or *could* be accomplished. *Practical* goes further; it indicates that whatever is being considered not only is a possibility but would actually give results that would justify action. For example, building a steam-powered automobile is *practicable* but has not proved to be *practical.* In most sentences either word makes sense, but they convey different meanings to well-informed readers.

Principal, Principle. *Principal* as an adjective means *main* or *chief,* and as a noun means *the main* or *controlling person,* as the *principal* of a school or one of the *principals* in a lawsuit. *Principle,* always a noun, means *fundamental truth, basic law.*

> CORRECT: The *principal* reason for its failure was defective workmanship.
> CORRECT: The *principles* of democracy must be preserved.

Rise, Raise. The distinction between *rise* and *raise* is essentially the same as the distinction between *lie* and *lay. Rise* is an intransitive verb, *raise* is transitive.

> Principal parts: rise, rose, have risen
> raise, raised, have raised
>
> CORRECT: The prices *rise* when the supply becomes scarce.
> CORRECT: The dealers *raise* the prices when the supply becomes scarce.
> WRONG: The prices *raised* when the supply became scarce.
> CORRECT: The prices *rose* when the supply became scarce.

Seldom ever. Redundant; the full meaning is expressed by *seldom* alone.

Shall, Will. The careful discrimination between *shall* and *will* is not so common as in past times, and even literate writers frequently use *will* on some occasions when *shall* is called for by the rules. The main points to remember in order to make the traditional discriminations are as follows:

(a) To indicate simple future or expectation, *shall* is correct in the first person and *will* in the second and third persons.

> I *shall* be a senior next year.
> He *will* spend August in Omaha.

(b) *Will* is correct in the first person, and *shall* in the second and third persons, to indicate determination or command.

> I *will* do it in spite of your objections.
> You *shall* change your itinerary.
> They *shall* not pass.

(c) *Will* is used in all persons to express willingness.

> I *will* go if no one else *will*.

Should, Would. Basically, the difference between *should* and *would* is the same as that between *shall* and *will*. That is, if we are meticulous we say, "I *should* enjoy reading the book," and "He *would* enjoy reading the book." Each of the two words has special uses, however, as the following comments show.

Should is used in all persons in the sense of *ought to* or in a conditional clause—which is usually a clause beginning with *if*.

> I *should* give him credit for working overtime.
> He *should* give me credit for working overtime.
> If I *should* refuse, no one could blame me.
> If he *should* refuse, no one could blame him.

Similarly, *would* is used in all persons to indicate customary action. It is also used whenever *should* would be misleading in that it might suggest *ought to*.

> CUSTOMARY ACTION: Long before closing time, I would begin preparing to go home.
> AVOIDANCE OF THE MEANING OF OUGHT TO: Under the circumstances, I would have refused.

Sit, Set. The distinction between *sit* and *set* is essentially the same as the distinction between *rise* and *raise*, and *lie* and *lay*. *Sit* is an intransitive verb; *set* is transitive.

> Principal parts: sit, sat, have sat
> set, set, have set

CORRECT: He *sits* at my desk, where he *sat* yesterday, and where he *has sat* so many days before.

CORRECT: He *sets* the case on the desk, where yesterday he *set* it down so carelessly. He *has set* it there every time he has come in the office.

Some, Somewhat. *Some* should not be used as an adverb with the meaning of *a little*. The correct word for this use is *somewhat*.

WRONG: I was feeling *some* better.

CORRECT: I was feeling *somewhat* better.

These kind. This expression is wrong. The plural *these* should not modify the singular *kind*.

Try and. This expression should not be substituted for *try to*. *Try and* is just as illogical as "*I am able and*" for "*I am able to*."

WRONG: I will *try and* go.

CORRECT: I will *try to* go.

Type. The common tendency among technical writers to use *type* as an adjective does not conform with the rules of good use. *Type* is a noun or verb, not an adjective. It should not directly modify a noun unless, in a hyphenated term, it becomes part of a compound adjective.

WRONG: We installed the new *type* machinery.

CORRECT: We installed the new *type of* machinery.

CORRECT: The design calls for an *injector-type* condenser.

Very. It is not good idiom to use *very* to modify a past participle. Some word such as *much* or *well* should be used between *very* and the participle. It is a poor style to overwork *very* as an intensifier. In a phrase such as *very nauseating*, *very* is superfluous.

WRONG: The customers were *very pleased*.

CORRECT: The customers were *very much* (or *very well*) *pleased*.

While. Care must be taken to prevent *while* from being ambiguous when it is used in the sense of *although;* its use with this meaning is often regarded as improper.

AMBIGUOUS: *While* his work was heavy, he did it well.

AMBIGUOUS: The first floor was neat, *while* the second floor was cluttered.

CORRECT: *Although* his work was heavy, he did it well. (or: *As long as* his work was heavy, he did it well.)

CORRECT: The first floor was neat, *but* the second floor was cluttered.

With. *With* should not be loosely used to establish some vague, undefined thought relationship.

WRONG: *With* the plans completed, the president of the company went on a vacation.

CORRECT: The plans having been completed, (or, When the plans had been completed,) the president of the company went on a vacation.

WRONG: The production was increasing, *with* the prices holding steady.

CORRECT: The production was increasing, *and* the prices were holding steady (or, *but* the prices were holding steady).

EXPLANATION OF GRAMMATICAL TERMS

Absolute. An expression that is not grammatically connected with the sentence where it occurs; sometimes called a "nominative absolute."

The job being completed, the crew was laid off.

Adjective. One of the parts of speech. A class of words used to modify (describe or limit) nouns or pronouns.

rough road; *this* year; *reasonable* profits

Adjective clause. A clause used as an adjective to modify a noun or pronoun.

The tire *that blew out* was defective. (The clause *that blew out* modifies the noun *tire.*)
Everyone *who came* enjoyed himself. (The clause *who came* modifies the pronoun *everyone.*)

Adverb. One of the parts of speech. A class of words used to modify verbs, adjectives, or other adverbs.

He drove *cautiously.* (*Cautiously* modifies the verb *drove.*)
The problem is *very* hard. (*Very* modifies the adjective *hard.*)
The frame was *very* strongly built. (*Very* modifies the adverb *strongly.*)

Adverb clause. A clause used as an adverb to modify any part of speech that an adverb might modify, usually a verb. Such a clause often tells how, when, or where.

If the cost is excessive, we shall cancel the project. (The italicized clause modifies the verb *shall cancel.*)
They will burn the slashing *when the weather grows damper.* (The clause modifies the verb *will burn.*)

Agreement. The necessary correspondence between a subject and verb in person and number; between a pronoun and its antecedent in person, number, and gender; and between a demonstrative adjective (*this, these*) and the noun that it modifies, in number. (See pages 350-4.)

Antecedent. The noun or the other pronoun to which a pronoun refers.

After reading the *report* he returned *it.* (*Report* is the antecedent of *it.*)

Appositive. A noun or other substantive placed next to some other noun, used in the same way grammatically, and referring to the same thing or person.

> The main plant, *a four-story building*, stood at the edge of town.
> It was discovered by the watchman, *a reliable employee.*

Article. Any of three words—*a, an,* or *the.*

Auxiliary. A word used as part of a verb to assist in indicating the tense, voice, mood, etc. of the main verb.

> *are* working; *have* answered; *must have* heard; *shall* or *will* arrive

Clause. A grammatical unit containing a subject and a finite verb. At least one independent clause is necessary in any complete sentence. (Sometimes part of the clause may be implied rather than expressed, in which case it is called an elliptical clause.)

A main or independent clause is one that makes an independent assertion.

A subordinate or dependent clause is one that is not self-sufficient and does not of itself make an assertion, but is used as part of a main clause. It is always used as if it were a single word—a noun, adjective, or adverb.

> INDEPENDENT CLAUSE: The sky is blue.
> SUBORDINATE CLAUSE USED AS A NOUN: We heard *that the request was refused.*
> SUBORDINATE CLAUSE USED AS AN ADJECTIVE: I know of a hotel *that will be satisfactory.*
> SUBORDINATE CLAUSE USED AS AN ADVERB: Please close the door *when you leave.*

Comparison. The change of form in an adjective or adverb, indicative of change of degree, as in *good, better, best; long, longer, longest; easily, more easily, most easily.*

Complement. An element that ordinarily follows a verb and completes the assertion made by the verb about the subject. Types of complements are shown in the following examples:

> DIRECT OBJECT: The farmer raised *wheat.*
> INDIRECT OBJECT: The manager gave *him* a check.
> PREDICATE ADJECTIVE AS SUBJECTIVE COMPLEMENT: The tractor is *old.*
> PREDICATE ADJECTIVE AS OBJECTIVE COMPLEMENT: The news made him *happy.*
> PREDICATE NOUN AS SUBJECTIVE COMPLEMENT: The tree is an *oak.*
> PREDICATE NOUN AS OBJECTIVE COMPLEMENT: The president made John Jones the *manager.*

Complex sentence. See *Sentence.*

Compound sentence. See *Sentence.*

Compound-complex sentence. See *Sentence.*

Conjunction. One of the parts of speech. A word used to connect words, phrases, or clauses. Coordinating conjunctions connect elements that are equal in grammatical rank. Subordinating conjunctions are used to connect subordinate clauses to main clauses.

Coordinating conjunctions: and, but, or, nor, for; sometimes *yet* and *so.* See also *Correlative Conjunctions.*

Subordinating conjunctions: after, as, because, since, when, where, etc. For example, in the sentence "He did not come because he was ill," *because* makes the clause it introduces subordinate.

Conjunctive adverb. An adverb that functions also as a conjunction to join main clauses (*also, however, moreover, consequently, furthermore,* etc.). Ability to discriminate between conjunctive adverbs and coordinating conjunctions is important as a means of avoiding the serious error known as the "comma splice." (See pages 358-9.)

Correlative conjunctions. Conjunctions used in pairs to join elements of equal rank.

> either . . . or; neither . . . nor; not only . . . but also; both . . . and

Ellipsis. The omission of words that are necessary for the grammatical completeness of the sentence, the words omitted being implied by what is expressed.

> While (I was) working out of doors, I gained weight.
> The new model is sturdier than the old (model is).
> (You) Send me the answer promptly.

The subject of an imperative sentence is practically always *you,* implied. Hence an imperative sentence is almost always elliptical.

Expletive. A word that bears no real meaning but is used to fill out a sentence. An expletive at the beginning of a sentence is sometimes necessary, but sometimes causes postponement of the word that should be the subject.

> *It* is certain that production will increase.
> *It* is snowing.
> *It* is nine o'clock.

Gender. The status of a noun or pronoun as masculine (*man, waiter, he*), feminine (*woman, she, waitress*), neuter (*tree, house, it*), or common (*mouse, person, you*).

Gerund. A verb form used as a noun. A gerund plus its object is a gerund phrase.

> GERUND: *Walking* is good exercise.

GERUND PHRASE: *Pruning a tree* demands judgment.

Idiom. An expression that is accepted as correct even though it may not be in accordance with the normal patterns of the language, and that often conveys a meaning that would not be conveyed by the literal meaning of its component words.

The more the merrier is a typical idiom. It conveys more meaning than can be accounted for by the words and is acceptable as a sentence even though it does not have the elements a sentence calls for. *Make off with* is an idiomatic expression meaning *take away. Of yours* (as in "that car *of yours*") is idiomatic, for it is acceptable even though the object of a preposition is in the possessive case. *Many a person is* is an idiom for it is accepted as correct even though *many,* a plural, modifies a singular word and though a subject with a plural meaning takes a singular verb.

When we refer to the *idiom of a language,* we refer to its particular manner of using words to convey ideas—a manner that cannot be entirely accounted for by rules or by the meaning of individual words. The use and meaning of prepositions, especially, depend upon the idiom of the language. When some expression in your speech or writing is corrected on the grounds that it is not idiomatic of the language, it is usually impossible to justify the correction by citing rules.

Infinitive. The form of a verb that is used after *to,* though sometimes the *to* is implied rather than expressed. (He hoped *to be* present. He can *go.*) When it is part of the verb phrase, as in the examples above, an infinitive is called a complementary infinitive because it completes the verb.

An infinitive can also be used as a noun, an adjective, or an adverb.

> INFINITIVE AS A NOUN: *To err* is human. (*To err* is used as the subject of the verb *is.*)
> INFINITIVE AS AN ADJECTIVE: I have a confession *to make.* (*To make* modifies the noun *confession.*)
> INFINITIVE AS AN ADVERB: They were eager *to accept.* (*To accept* modifies the adjective *eager.*)

Inflection. Variation in the form of words to indicate change of number, gender, person, tense, or mood. Inflection of nouns is referred to as declension; inflection of verbs as conjugation; inflection of adjectives and adverbs as comparison.

Interjection. One of the parts of speech. A type of word placed at the beginning of a sentence or inserted into the sentence (whence *interjection—thrown in*) but not connected with the grammatical structure. Words such as *oh, alas,* and *well* (as an exclamation) are interjections.

Linking verb. A verb that expresses neither action nor condition, but merely establishes a connection between its subject and a noun, pronoun, or adjective in the predicate. A noun or pronoun following a linking verb is in the nominative case. The commonest linking verb is the verb *to be*. Other characteristic linking verbs are *become, appear, seem, smell* (in the sense of "possess an odor"), *taste* (in the sense of "possess a flavor"), and *feel* (in the sense of "experience a sensation").

> The seed *is* pure.
> The price *seems* right.
> The warmth *feels* good.

Modifier. A word is a modifier when it is used to limit or change the meaning of some other word, or of a phrase or clause. A phrase or a clause, as well as a word, can be a modifier.

> WORD AS A MODIFIER: His *slightly* embarrassed manner was amusing. (*Slightly*, an adverb, modifies *embarrassed*, a participial adjective, which in turn modifies the noun *manner*.)
> PHRASES AND CLAUSES AS MODIFIERS: Construction *of the bridge* will be postponed *until the weather is warmer*. (*Of the bridge*, an adjective phrase, modifies *construction*. *Until . . . warmer*, an adverb clause, modifies the verb *will be postponed*.)

Mood. The form, in a verb, that indicates how the action or condition expressed by the verb is conceived by the writer or speaker. In the statement of a fact or the asking of a question, the indicative mood is used. In giving a command, the imperative mood is used. In expressing doubt, wish, or condition contrary to fact, the subjunctive mood is used.

> INDICATIVE: The rock *is* heavy. *Can* you *lift* it?
> IMPERATIVE: *Examine* the surface carefully.
> SUBJUNCTIVE: If I *were* you, I *should accept* the offer.
> I wish he *were* not so young.

Nonrestrictive modifier. A modifier that merely gives information about the term modified rather than limiting or identifying it.

> The roof, *which was very old,* was damaged by the wind.
> His oldest son, *who was more experienced,* handled the case efficiently.

Noun. One of the parts of speech. A word used to name a person, place, thing, quality, etc.

> *John; Aristotle; engineer; Atlanta; wood; courage*

Many words can be used, of course, as more than one part of speech. Such words cannot be classified until they are actually used. For example, *green* is a noun in the sentence, "Green is its natural color" but an adjective in "The green grass is attractive."

Noun clause. A subordinate clause used as a noun.

I know *what you mean.* (Noun clause used as object of the verb *know.*)

How he had escaped was a puzzling question. (Noun clause used as subject of the verb *was.*)

Object. The word, phrase, or clause identifying the person or thing that receives the action indicated by a transitive verb, or the substantive referred to by a preposition.

DIRECT OBJECT OF A VERB: The company installed a *lathe.* (*Lathe* is the direct object of *installed.*)

INDIRECT OBJECT OF A VERB: He offered *me* a bribe. (*Me* is the indirect object of *offered,* for it indicates the person to whom the offer is made. *Bribe,* like *lathe* in the preceding example, is a direct object.)

OBJECT OF A PREPOSITION: He worked on a *farm.* (*Farm* is the object of *on.*)

Participle. The form of a verb ending in *ing* (though this form may also be a gerund) or the form used after *have.* A participle may be used as the main element in a verb phrase or as an adjective.

PARTICIPLES AS VERBS: I am *following* the route I have *followed* before.

PARTICIPLES AS ADJECTIVES: *Running* water purifies itself. The *rejected* casting was returned. The guard was *tired.*

Parts of speech. The classifications under which all words are classified. The eight parts of speech are nouns, pronouns, verbs, adjectives, adverbs, prepositions, conjunctions, and interjections. Each of these terms is defined in its proper alphabetical place in this Glossary.

A word qualifies as one or another part of speech only on the basis of its use in a sentence or phrase; it is possible for the same word to be used as more than one part of speech. Good usage, however, limits the *permissible* uses of most words. To determine whether it is correct to use a word as a certain part of speech, it is sometimes necessary to consult a dictionary.

Person. Some pronouns and most verbs vary in form to indicate whether they refer to the person speaking or writing (first person), the person addressed (second person), or the person spoken or written about (third person).

First Person	Second Person	Third Person
I come	you come	he comes
I have	you have	he has
I shall find	you will find	he will find
We shall find	you will find	they will find
I am	you are	he is
I can	you can	he can

Phrase. A group of related words that does not include a subject and predicate and that is usually used as a single part of speech—adjective, adverb, verb, or noun. Phrases may be prepositional, participial, gerund, infinitive, or verb.

> PREPOSITIONAL PHRASE: He discovered the address *of the owner.* (Adjective phrase, modifying the noun *address.*)
> PREPOSITIONAL PHRASE: The road will be closed *in December.* (Adverbial phrase, modifying the verb *will be closed.*)
> PARTICIPIAL PHRASES: *Entering the room,* I noticed that the fan *standing in the corner* was noisy. (Adjective phrases, modifying, respectively, *I* and *fan.*)
> GERUND PHRASE: *Pitching hay* is strenuous work. (Noun.)
> INFINITIVE PHRASE: *To predict the results* is impossible. (Noun.)
> VERB PHRASE: The method *has been found* successful.

Predicate. The portion of a clause consisting of the verb, its complements, and the modifiers of both. Except for interjections and absolute phrases, neither of which appears frequently, the predicate consists of everything in a clause or sentence except the subject.

Preposition. One of the parts of speech. A word used to introduce a noun or pronoun and establish its relationship to the sentence.

> He will come *in* the morning *on* the plane *from* Chicago.

Principal parts. The three forms of a verb from which, by help of auxiliary verbs, the various tenses are derived. These forms are the present infinitive, the past tense, and the past participle. (The past participle is the form used after *have.*)

Present Infinitive	Past Tense	Past Participle
work	worked	worked
sing	sang	sung
begin	began	begun
catch	caught	caught

Pronoun. One of the parts of speech. A word used in place of a noun.

> PERSONAL PRONOUNS: *I, you, he, she, it we, they*
> INTERROGATIVE PRONOUNS: *who, which, what*
> RELATIVE PRONOUNS: *who, which, what, that*
> DEMONSTRATIVE PRONOUNS: *this, that, these, those*
> INDEFINITE PRONOUNS: *each, either, neither, any, anyone, some, someone, one, no one, few, all, none*
> RECIPROCAL PRONOUNS: *each other, one another*
> REFLEXIVE PRONOUNS: *myself, yourself, himself*
> INTENSIVE PRONOUNS: *myself, yourself, himself*

Relative clause. A clause, always dependent, introduced by a relative pronoun. The clauses used as restrictive modifiers below are examples.

Restrictive modifier. A modifier that narrows, and thus restricts, the meaning of whatever it modifies.

All persons *who drive recklessly* should be arrested.
The cases *that were damaged* have been returned.

Sentence. A group of words expressing a thought and containing, either actually or by implication, a subject and a finite verb (predicate). Grammarians have never defined the term *sentence* to their own complete satisfaction, but this definition will serve our purpose. In grammatical form a sentence may be simple, compound, complex, or compound-complex.

A simple sentence consists of a single independent clause, though as indicated by the second example below, its subject, its verb, or both may be compound.

> SIMPLE SENTENCE: The building is old.
> SIMPLE SENTENCE: Both industry and labor support the new ruling and oppose the old.

A compound sentence consists of two or more independent clauses.

> COMPOUND SENTENCE: Sales were falling off, and inventories were increasing.

A complex sentence contains a single independent clause and one or more dependent clauses.

> COMPLEX SENTENCE: The police recovered the property that had been lost.

A compound-complex sentence contains at least two independent clauses, hence being compound, and at least one dependent clause, hence being complex.

> COMPOUND-COMPLEX SENTENCE: The wind was rising and the sky had clouded over when we finally reached the shelter.

Subject. The substantive that a verb or verbal makes an assertion about, asks a question about, or gives an order to.

> SUBJECT OF A SENTENCE: *Birds* fly south in the winter.
> SUBJECT OF AN INFINITIVE PHRASE (A VERBAL): I know *him* to be honest. (*Him* is the subject of *to be.*)

Substantive. A noun, or any word or group of words used as a noun. Any of the following, in addition to a noun, may be a substantive: pronoun, infinitive phrase, gerund, or noun clause. (See separate listing for each of these terms.)

Tense. The distinctive form in a verb that indicates time.

> PRESENT TENSE: It *runs* well.
> PAST TENSE: It *ran* well.
> FUTURE TENSE: It *will run* well.
> PRESENT PERFECT TENSE: It *has run* well.
> PAST PERFECT TENSE: It *had run* well.

FUTURE PERFECT TENSE: It *will have run* well.

Tenses appear in the progressive and emphatic forms of verbs, as well as in the simple forms.

PRESENT PROGRESSIVE: I *am reading*.
PRESENT EMPHATIC: I *do read*.

Verb. One of the parts of speech. A word or phrase that indicates action, being, or state of being. In a declarative sentence the verb is the word or phrase that actually makes the assertion.

A transitive verb takes an object.

He *bought* the *house*.

An intransitive verb cannot take an object.

The sun *rises* in the east.

Some verbs may be either transitive or intransitive.

TRANSITIVE: I *read* the letter.
INTRANSITIVE: I *was reading*.

Verbal. A word or phrase derived from a verb but not making an assertion. Infinitives, gerunds, and participles (participles used either in participial phrases or as adjectives) are the three types of verbals. Each is listed as a separate entry.

Voice. The form of a verb that shows whether the subject of a verb or verbal performs the action indicated (active voice) or has the action performed upon it (passive voice). Only transitive verbs can be in passive voice.

ACTIVE VOICE: The government *collected* the taxes.
PASSIVE VOICE: The taxes *were collected* by the government.

APPENDIX

ABBREVIATIONS FOR SCIENTIFIC AND ENGINEERING TERMS

The number of abbreviations in current use is so great and is expanding so rapidly that in a book like this only a small fraction of them can be listed. For those in positions that make it necessary for them to use long and highly specialized lists, such lists are usually available. Also it is worth noting that both collegiate and unabridged dictionaries provide abbreviations for hundreds of technical terms.

Since minor differences persist in actual use, the abbreviations in different lists are not always the same in form, but those in the list that follows are supported by well-regarded authorities.

As you use the list you will observe that some terms are abbreviated in one way when they appear alone and otherwise when they appear in the abbreviation for a phrase, especially if the phrase contains *per* or a diagonal line (/) standing for *per*. For example, *ft* is the abbreviation for *foot* or *feet* and *sec* for *second;* but *feet per second,* which includes both words, may be shortened to *fps.* Other examples of abbreviations that are used as combining forms are: *m* for *miles* and *h* for *hour* in *miles per hour* (*miles* standing alone is not abbreviated and *hour* is abbreviated as *hr* or *h*); *g* for *gallons* and *m* for *minute* in *gallons per minute* (the ordinary abbreviations for *gallons* and *minute* are *gal* and *min*); and *rf* for *radio frequency* (*radio* is not abbreviated standing alone, and *frequency* is abbreviated as *freq*). Even in abbreviating a phrase, however, it is better not to use the combining forms if there is any doubt about their being easily understood by the readers. For example, *ft per sec* is sometimes better than *fps.*

The abbreviations in this book do not include arbitrary signs and symbols. (Such signs and symbols are not actually abbreviations and should rarely be used in ordinary text.) They comply, so far as facts permit, with the sound generalization that capital letters are ordinarily used in abbreviations only when the terms for which the letters stand would be capitalized if written out. Periods are omitted except when omitting them might cause the abbreviation to be mistaken for a regular word, or when the term is abbreviated in general as well as in technical writing. You should not hesitate to use periods, however, if personal observation convinces you that it is customary to use them in the field that includes your subject.

abampere . . . . .abamp
absolute . . . . .abs
acoustic . . . . .acst
acre . . . . (spell out)
acre-foot . . . . .acre-ft
air horsepower . . . . . . .ahp
air position indicator . . .api
air speed indicator . . . .asi
alternating-current (adj.) a-c
American Standard . . . .Amer Std
American Wire Gage . .AWG
ammeter . . . . .am.
ampere . . . . .amp
ampere-hour . . . . .amp hr
amplitude modulation . .am.
angstrom . . . . .A
approximate . . . . .approx
atmosphere . . . . .atm
atomic weight . . . . .at wt
audio frequency . . . . . .a-f
auxiliary . . . . .aux
azimuth . . . . .az

barometer . . . . .bar
barrel . . . . .bbl
Baumé . . . . .Bé
billion electron volts . .bev
biochemical oxygen
    demand . . . . .bod
board feet . . . . .fbm
boiler horsepower . . . .bhp
brake horsepower . . . . .bhp
brake horsepower-hour bhp-hr
Brinell hardness . . . . . .Bh
Brinell hardness
    number . . . . .Bhn
British thermal unit . . . .Btu

calorie . . . . .cal
candle-hour . . . . .c-hr
candlepower . . . . .cp
carrier wave . . . . .cw
cathode ray . . . . .cr
Celsus C

centigrade C
centimeter . . . . .cm
chemically pure . . . . . .cp
circumference . . . . .circ
cologarithm . . . . .colog
continuous wave . . . . . .cw
counts per minute . . . .cpm
cubic . . . . .cu
cubic centimeter cc
cubic feet per minute . .cfm
cubic feet per second . .cfs
cubic foot . . . . .cu ft
cubic inch . . . . .cu in.
cubic yard . . . . .cu yd
cycles per minute . . . . .cpm
cycles per second . . . .cps

decibel . . . . .db
decimeter . . . . .dm
degree . . . . .deg °
dew point . . . . .dp
direct-connected . . . . . .dir-conn
direct-current (adj.) . .dc or d-c
distilled water . . . . .dw
dry bulb . . . . .db

effective horsepower . . .ehp
efficiency . . . . .eff
electromagnetic units . .emu
electromotive force . . . emf
electron volts . . . . .ev
elevation . . . . .el
equation . . . . .eq
extremely high fre-
    quency . . . . .ehf

Fahrenheit (or degrees
    Fahrenheit) . . . . . . .F
farad . . . . .f
feet board measure
    (board feet) . . . . . .fbm
feet per minute . . . . . .fpm
feet per second . . . . . .fps
fluid . . . . .fl

° The symbol (°) is sometimes used in text as an abbreviation for degrees of latitude, longitude, or angles, but should not be used in place of the regular abbreviation for degrees of temperature. Since it is permissible, however, to use F, C, and K respectively for *degrees* Fahrenheit, Centigrade, and Kelvin, there is a strong tendency to do so and to omit *deg*.

fluid ounce . . . . .fl oz
foot . . . . .ft
foot candle . . . . .fc
foot per minute . . . . . .fpm
foot pound . . . . .fp
fractional horsepower . .fhp
free on board . . . . .fob
frequency . . . . .freq.
frequency modulation . .fm
fusion point . . . . .fp

gallon . . . . .gal
gallons per day . . . . . . .gpd
gallons per hour . . . . . .gph
gallons per minute . . . .gpm
gallons per second . . . . .gps
gram . . . . .gr
gravities (acceleration
    of gravity) . . . . .g
ground position in-
    dicator . . . . .gpi

hectogram . . . . .hg
henry . . . . .h
high explosive . . . . . .he
high frequency . . . . . . .hf
high frequency current .hfc
high-potential test . . . . .hipot
horsepower . . . . .hp
horsepower hour . . . . . .hphr
hour . . . . .hr or h
hundredweight . . . . . . .cwt

inch . . . . .in.
inch-pound . . . . .in-lb
inside diameter . . . . . .id
inside dimension . . . . .id
intermediate frequency .i.f.
International Critical
    Tables . . . . .ICT
international unit . . . . .iu

jet propulsion . . . . .jp
joule . . . . .j

Kelvin (or degree
    Kelvin) . . . . .K
kilo . . . . .k
kilovolt . . . . .kv

kilovolt-ampere . . . . . .kva
kilowatt . . . . .kw
kilowatt-hour . . . . .kwh
kinetic energy . . . . . . .ke

lambert L
latitude . . . . .lat
linear . . . . .lin
linear foot . . . . .lin ft
liquid . . . . .lq
liquefied petroleum gas .lpg
liter l
logarithm (common) .log
logarithm (natural) . . .ln
longitude . . . . .long.
low frequency . . . . . . .lf
lumen . . . . .lm
lumen hour . . . . .lhr
lumens per watt . . . . . .lpw

man hour . . . . .man hr
maximum . . . . .max
meter . . . . .m
miles per gallon . . . . . .mpg
miles per hour . . . . . . .mph
millimeter . . . . .mm
minute . . . . .min
modulator . . . . .mod
modulus . . . . .mod
molecular weight . . . . . .mol wt
motor-generator . . . . . .mg

National Aircraft
    Standards . . . . .NAS
National Bureau of
    Standards . . . . .NBS
National Electrical
    Safety Code . . . . . . .NESC
National Electric Code
    Standards . . . . .NEC
negative . . . . .neg
net weight . . . . .nt wt
nickel-silver . . . . .ni-sil
normal temperature
    and pressure . . . . . . .ntp
number . . . . .no.

octane . . . . .oct
optical . . . . .opt.

optimum working fre-
quency . . . . .owf
oscillate . . . . .osc
ounce . . . . .oz
outside diameter . . . . . .od

parts per billion . . . . . . .ppb
parts per million . . . . . .ppm
permeability . . . . .perm
perpendicular . . . . .perp
phase . . . . .ph
phase modulation . . . . .pm
polar . . . . .pol
potentiometer . . . . .pot.
pound . . . . .lb
pound-foot . . . . .lb-ft
pounds per cubic foot . .pcf
pounds per square foot .psf
pounds per square inch .psi
power amplifier . . . . . . .pa
probable error . . . . .pe
pulse-amplitude modu-
lation . . . . .pam

qualitative . . . . .qual
quality . . . . .qual

radio direction finder . .rdf
radio frequency . . . . . . .rf
Rankine . . . . .R
Réaumur . . . . .Ré
reference line . . . . .ref l
revolutions per minute .rpm
revolutions per second .rps
rheostat . . . . .rheo
Rockwell hardness . . . .Rh
roentgen . . . . .r

scleroscope hardness . . .sh
second . . . . .sec
second-foot . . . . .sec-ft
shaft horsepower . . . . . .shp
short wave . . . . .sw

signal-to-noise ratio . . . .snr or s/n
solenoid . . . . .sol
specific gravity . . . . . . .sp gr
spherical candlepower . .scp
square . . . . .sq
square meter . . . . .sq m
square mile . . . . .sq mi

tachometer . . . . .tach
tangent . . . . .tan
temperature . . . . .temp
template . . . . .temp
tensile strength . . . . . . .ts
tension . . . . .tens.
thermal . . . . .thrm
thermocouple . . . . .tc
thermometer . . . . .therm.
thousand . . . . .m or M
thousand cubic feet . . . .mcf
tolerance . . . . .tol
transceiver . . . . .xvr

ultrahigh frequency . . . .uhf
United States Standard .USS

vacuum . . . . .vac
vacuum tube . . . . .vt
variable . . . . .var
variable-frequency oscil-
lator . . . . .vfo
very high frequency . . .vhf
video frequency . . . . . . .vdf
volt v
volt-ampere . . . . .va

watt . . . . .w
watt-hour . . . . .wh or whr
wavelength . . . . .wl
wet bulb . . . . .wb

yard . . . . .yd
year . . . . .yr
yield point . . . . .yp
yield strength . . . . .ys

HELPFUL PUBLICATIONS FOR TECHNICAL WRITERS

Technical Writing and Reports

Blickle, Margaret D., and Kenneth W. Houp, *Reports for Science and Industry.* New York: Holt, Rinehart & Winston, Inc., 1958.

Brinton, Willard Cope, *Graphic Presentation.* New York: Brinton Associates, 1939.

Comer, David B., and Ralph R. Spillman, *Modern Technical and Industrial Reports.* New York: G. P. Putnam's Sons, 1962.

Giesecke, Frederick E., Alva Mitchell, and Henry Cecil Spencer, *Technical Drawing,* 4th ed. New York: The Macmillan Company, 1958.

Graves, Harold F., and Lyne S. S. Hoffman, *Report Writing,* 4th ed. Englewood Cliffs, N.J.: Prentice-Hall, Inc., 1965.

Harwell, George C., *Technical Communication.* New York: The Macmillan Company, 1960.

Jordan, Richard C., and Marion J. Edwards, *Aids to Technical Writing.* Minneapolis: University of Minnesota Engineering Experiment Station, 1944.

Kapp, Reginald O., *The Presentation of Technical Information.* New York: The Macmillan Company, 1957.

Kerekes, Frank, and Robley Winfrey, *Report Preparation,* 2nd ed. Ames, Iowa: Iowa State College Press, 1951.

Luzadder, Warren J., *Basic Graphics,* 2nd ed. Englewood Cliffs, N.J.: Prentice-Hall, Inc., 1962.

Menzel, Donald H., Howard Mumford Jones, and Lyle G. Boyd, *Writing a Technical Paper.* New York: McGraw-Hill Book Company, 1961.

Mills, Gordon H., and John A. Walter, *Technical Writing,* rev. ed. New York: Holt, Rinehart & Winston, Inc., 1962.

Racker, Joseph W., *Technical Writing Techniques for Engineers.* Englewood Cliffs, N.J.: Prentice-Hall, Inc., 1960.

Schmid, Calvin F., *Handbook of Graphic Presentation.* New York: The Ronald Press Company, 1954.

Souther, James W., *Technical Report Writing.* New York: John Wiley & Sons, Inc., 1957.

Sypherd, W. O., Alvin M. Fountain, and V. E. Gibbens, *Manual of Technical Writing.* Chicago: Scott, Foresman & Company, 1957.

Ulman, Joseph N., and Jay R. Gould, *Technical Reporting,* rev. ed. New York: Holt, Rinehart & Winston, Inc., 1959.

Zall, Paul M., *Elements of Technical Report Writing.* New York: Harper & Row, Publishers, 1962.

Zetler, Robert L., and Robert George Crouch, *Successful Communication in Science and Industry.* New York: McGraw-Hill Book Company, 1961.

General English

Dean, Howard H., and Kenneth D. Bryson, *Effective Communication,* 2nd ed. Englewood Cliffs, N.J.: Prentice-Hall, Inc., 1961.

Kierzek, John M., and Walker Gibson, *The Macmillan Handbook of English,* 4th ed. New York: The Macmillan Company, 1960.

Leggett, Glenn, C. David Mead, and William Charvat, *Prentice-Hall Handbook for Writers,* 4th ed. Englewood Cliffs, N.J.: Prentice-Hall, Inc., 1965.

A Manual of Style, 11th rev. ed. Chicago: University of Chicago Press, 1949.

Perrin, Porter Gale, and Karl W. Dykema, *Writer's Guide and Index to English,* 3rd ed. Chicago: Scott, Foresman & Company, 1959.

U.S. Government Printing Office Style Manual. Washington, D.C., 1959.

Indexes

The Biological and Agricultural Index
Applied Science and Technology Index (1958-   )
Bibliography of Scientific and Industrial Reports
The Engineering Index
The Industrial Arts Index
International Index to Periodicals
The New York Times Index
Readers' Guide to Periodical Literature

Sources of General or Special Information

The Census Volumes (Department of Commerce, Bureau of Census)
    Agriculture
    Construction Industry
    Drainage of Agricultural Lands
    Irrigation of Agricultural Lands
    Manufacturers
    Retail Distributors
    Unemployment
    Wholesale Distribution
Encyclopedia Americana
Encyclopaedia Britannica
Minerals Yearbook (Department of the Interior, Bureau of Mines)
The Statesman's Yearbook
Technical Book Review Digest
U.S. Government Publications Monthly Catalog
Van Nostrand's Scientific Encyclopedia
The World Almanac

INDEX